Y0-BYZ-528

EX LIBRIS

THE ROMANCE TREASURY ASSOCIATION

TORONTO · NEW YORK · LONDON
AMSTERDAM · PARIS · SYDNEY · HAMBURG
STOCKHOLM · ATHENS · TOKYO · MILAN

These stories were originally published as follows:

DON'T CALL IT LOVE
Copyright © 1984 by Lindsay Armstrong
First published by Mills & Boon Limited in 1984

A FOOL TO SAY YES
Copyright © 1986 by Sandra Clark
First published by Mills & Boon Limited in 1986

THE LAST BARRIER
Copyright © 1986 by Edwina Shore
First published by Mills & Boon Limited in 1986

ROMANCE TREASURY is published by
The Romance Treasury Association

Story Illustrations by Muriel Hughes
Book Design by Charles Kadin
Printed and bound by Arcata Graphics
Kingsport, Tennessee U.S.A.

ISBN 0-373-04199-3

Printed in U.S.A.   A199

CONTENTS

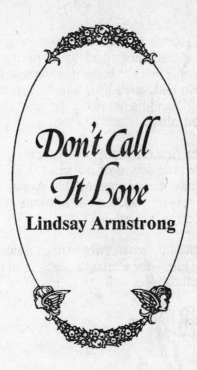

Don't Call It Love

Lindsay Armstrong

Anna Horton was a sane, down-to-earth kind of person and not normally given to wild excesses. Then she became governess to Richard Gillespie's little daughter, Chrissy, at their Yandilla home off the coast of Australia.

For the first time in Anna's life, love secretly touched the depths of her heart. But Richard was under the impression that Anna, with good reason, was as contemptuous of love's illusions as he was.

So he saw no reason why Anna couldn't marry him—for Chrissy's sake—and not be disillusioned.

CHAPTER ONE

ANNA HORTON picked herself up from the dusty roadway and brandished a clenched fist at the rear of a huge semi-trailer that was laboriously and noisily gathering speed as it moved away from her.

She had just climbed down from the cab of the same vehicle, seething with anger and distaste at what the driver had proposed to her, had had her bag pushed out after her, and had landed on the road in an undignified heap.

But what she didn't realise, as she stood in the middle of the road giving vent to her feelings, was that the driver of the semi-trailer, high up in his cab, had noticed a car approaching in his rear-view mirror that Anna was unaware of for several reasons—a bend in the road which she had her back to in any case and the noise of the giant engine of the semi-trailer itself being the two main reasons.

In fact the first intimation she had of the approaching car came when she lowered her fist, grimaced at the cloud of dust enveloping her and walked a few steps towards her bag. Then everything happened so quickly she had no time to take evasive action. The car swerved and she found herself unwittingly right in the path of that swerve. The next few minutes were a nightmare of squealing tyres, an even thicker cloud of dust and the heart-stopping conviction that she was going to be killed.

That she wasn't had to be a miracle, she knew not much later when an unnatural quiet descended and the boiling dust sank a little and she could see the car with its bonnet only inches from her and smell the burning rubber of the tyres as the body rocked on tortured springs.

She lifted her hands to her face and began to sink to her knees from sheer, shocked reaction, but the driver of the car took matters into his own hands then. He climbed out swiftly, strode up to her, jerked her upright by her shoulders and attempted to shake the life out of her.

'You bloody idiot!' he swore. 'I could have killed you!'

'I…I didn't see you,' she faltered, staring up into a pair of scorching grey-green eyes and receiving a confused impression of a tall, powerful presence and an arrogantly moulded face beneath thick, fairish hair.

'I'm not surprised!' the man blazed at her. 'You weren't damn well looking!'

'B-but you must have seen me,' she stammered.

'I came round that bend to see a swirl of dust and when I swerved you stepped out of it right under my wheels!'

'Perhaps you shouldn't drive so fast,' she countered, a faint spirit of rebellion coming over her. 'You…' But she stopped and gasped as he shook her again, so hard that her head flew back painfully. *'Don't!'* she pleaded. 'You're hurting me!'

He let her go abruptly and she reeled back against the bonnet of the car.

'Perhaps you'll think the next time you're tempted to dally in the middle of the road,' he said savagely.

He looked around then as if expecting to see something, but all his eyes alighted on was her bag lying almost under his wheels and his angry gaze came back to rest on her white, dust-streaked face.

'Just what the hell are you doing here anyway?' he demanded with an all-encompassing gesture that took in the virgin bush stretching limitlessly to the horizon on either side of the road. But almost immediately his face changed and she felt shrivelled by the look of withering scorn he cast her as he said contemptuously, 'Oh, don't tell me! You hitched a ride on that semi-trailer I was catching up on, didn't you?'

'I . . .' Anna bit her lip.

'So what went wrong, sweetheart?' he queried derisively. 'Was the price of the lift becoming a bit more than you thought you should pay? You know, you should always be strictly businesslike about these things, then these little misunderstandings wouldn't occur. Why don't you get a price list printed? Say, something like—up to a hundred miles, a kiss or two permitted; up to two hundred miles, some fondling allowed . . .'

'You . . . !' Anna snapped furiously, and slapped his face.

But no sooner had she done it than she found herself regretting it, for the retaliation that came was swift and brutal and humiliating. He jerked her into his arms and sought her lips unerringly with his own and kissed her mercilessly.

And when he'd done the job thoroughly, her lips were bruised and swollen and her legs shakier if anything, than they had been several minutes earlier, so that she had to bear the added humiliation of finding herself clinging to him helplessly as she stared up at him shocked and wide-eyed and breathless.

'Let that be a lesson to you to pick someone your own fighting weight next time, my friend,' he said softly but with so much mockery that a flood of colour came to her cheeks and she pushed herself away from him angrily.

He laughed then and she tensed anew, but something warned her not to cross swords with this man again, so with a toss of her head and her lips set defiantly, she lifted her bag off the road and walked away as steadily as she was able to. Which was none too steadily, unfortunately, and she stumbled almost immediately and felt his hand on her arm.

'Let go of me,' she said coldly.

'Then get in the car.'

'No! If you *think* . . .'

'I think, yes,' he interrupted, and swung her round.

Anna swallowed and said tightly, 'If you think I'd go anywhere with you, you're wrong! After having the gall to say to me what you did and then . . . and *then* . . .'

'Kissing you?' he supplied with one eyebrow raised quizzically.

'Yes!' she said hotly. 'I'd rather walk to Cape York!'

'Oh well,' he stepped back and for the first time there was a glint of genuine amusement in his eyes, 'it's up to you. I don't think you'll find yourself walking to Cape York, but you might have to walk to Innisfail. You see, what you might not know is that my car was the last one to cross the river on the ferry back there. It's now closed until tomorrow morning.'

Anna had been in the act of turning away again, but she stopped abruptly. 'So . . . I mean . . .' She trailed off uncertainly.

He nodded.

'But there'll be local traffic on the road, surely?' she said somewhat desperately.

'I doubt it. I know this road pretty well. There's no habitation on it for the next fifty miles, roughly.'

'Fifty miles?' she echoed faintly, and looked around. It would be dark soon, she knew. The swift velvet darkness of the tropics.

'And you'll be coming into cane country soon,' he added casually. 'That has its disadvantages for pedestri-

ans. Cane is notorious for unpleasant things like snakes
and rats.'

Anna closed her eyes briefly. 'How—how far is it to Innisfail?'

'It will take me a bit over two hours. I don't think you
have much choice, my dear,' he said indifferently. 'Nor do
I have all the time in the world to stand here while you deliberate,' he murmured coolly.

Anna licked her lips and gazed at her would-be rescuer,
taking him in properly for the first time. He was tall with
a body that was powerful, as she now well knew, but it was
also elegantly streamlined and the khaki bush shirt and
trousers he wore didn't hide it. But his face was what she
concentrated on, and she thought he didn't look like a
would-be rapist or seducer. I mean, she amended to herself, can you tell by just looking at someone? Yet that
man's face was intelligent and his mouth well cut. Other
things about him pierced her consciousness too—the fact
that he had an air of confidence, that his car was powerful and foreign and obviously expensive as was the watch
he wore. She stared at the watch and noticed absently the
fine golden hairs on his arm and that his hands were slender yet powerful-looking too and faintly freckled on the
backs.

Not a man, she thought with a sudden, curious awareness that made her skin prickle, not a man who would need
to take anything by force, probably.

'Have you quite finished?' the object of her inspection
drawled. He leant back against the car and glanced at his
watch. 'You have two minutes,' he said evenly.

Anna's eyes narrowed. 'I'm sorry to keep bringing this
up,' she said gently, 'but considering your earlier sentiments on the subject of hitch-hiking, I'm a little surprised
that you should object to me weighing the odds.' She

shrugged. 'After all, what are a few snakes—I'm told they're shy creatures anyway—compared to a fate worse than death?' she added.

There was a tense little silence during which his eyes roamed over her and left her in no doubt that he was mentally undressing her. And she began to regret her words and her impulsive nature which not infrequently led her into awkward situations.

Then he straightened up. 'Actually, I've revised my opinions,' he observed. 'Perhaps I was a little harsh on you.'

'What do you mean?' she asked after a moment. 'Because I prefer the thought of snakes and rats, have I suddenly become more respectable?'

'Oh, it's not that.' He smiled slightly. 'It's the fact that upon consideration, you kiss like a proper novice, my dear. Thus, you can banish all thoughts you might have been nurturing that I would try to take advantage of you in the way our late, unlamented semi-trailer driver did. So are you coming or not?' he finished impatiently.

Anna was so angry at the moment, she found she couldn't speak. And he took advantage of it to prise her bag from her fingers and sling it into the back seat of the car. Then he got in himself and leaned across to open the front passenger door for her.

She clenched her fists and thought of her brave words about snakes and rats. And she thought of trudging fifty miles in the dark and the fact that she was hungry and tired and filthy and considerably shaken up one way or another. The options seemed to be wildly overloaded.

'All right,' she said tautly as she slid into the car and looked at him, her face still pale with strain beneath its coating of dust, 'all right, you win—this time. But there are people expecting me in Innisfail so...'

'What other times are there likely to be?' he interrupted as he set the car in motion. 'Once we get to Innisfail we will part company most properly and I have no doubt you will go upon your merry way, hitch-hiking around Australia.'

'I—how did you know?' she asked, sinking back into the beautifully sprung seat.

'The signs are unmistakable,' he said. 'Even covered in dust you have a sort of—clean-cut, college girl air about you. Besides, the other kind of girl doesn't usually get herself turfed out on to a deserted stretch of roadway as you did.' He turned his head and their eyes clashed. 'I'm right, aren't I? You grew up in suburbia and you've saved for this ever since you left school? It's been the big dream of your life?'

Anna leant her head back and considered his words. 'You're more or less right. Although I'm working my way around rather than hitch-hiking, but I have hitched now and then. If you could work it all out, though, why were you so angry?'

'Perhaps because I don't often come so close to running someone down and splattering them on the roadway,' he said dryly.

'Well, I can understand that, and I'm sorry,' she said after a moment. 'But you were just as angry because I'd hitched a ride.'

'If I was,' he conceded grimly, 'it was because it's become an increasingly dangerous thing to do. You only have to read the papers to know that.'

Anna stirred. 'As a matter of fact I don't make a habit of it. But sometimes there are circumstances which...'

'Did you explain that to your semi driver?' His voice was taunting.

'Yes!' She sat up. 'I told him the whole sad story—how I'd been working on a station out from Georgetown and that I'd come into town to catch the bus to Innisfail, to find that it was their annual picnic race day,' she said bitterly. 'Which, to cut a long story short, I discovered to my cost is also their annual pickpockets' day. I was—relieved of all my money.'

'Go on,' he said tautly.

'I should have thought the rest was obvious,' she said shortly. 'I tracked down the lone policeman the town boasts, only to find him dead drunk because he'd backed the winner of the Cup for the first time in twenty years. There seemed to be no solution other than to hitch a ride to Innisfail where there's a branch of the bank I patronise in a small way. Do you know,' she grimaced, 'that driver was fifty if he was a day and he kept telling me about his grandchildren! He even showed me their pictures,' she added aggrievedly. 'To think that I deliberately bypassed several younger, more—well, virile-looking truck drivers and picked on a fatherly, homely-looking man, only to find...'

She stopped suddenly and turned her head. 'Which all goes to prove your point, doesn't it?' She smiled ruefully. 'I stand convicted,' she said quietly.

There was a brief silence. Then he smiled back at her and she caught her breath unexpectedly, because it was an amazingly attractive smile that lit his eyes with amusement and she found herself wondering, curiously, how old he was. Probably in his mid-thirties, she decided.

And as they drove on through the fast gathering dusk in an oddly companionable silence, she found herself thinking, rather strangely, of all the men she had dated since leaving college. All of them nice enough in their own way, she mused, but in comparison to this man...well, boys, not men would be an apt description, she thought, although they would be horrified to have me say so. Then again, they were all round about my age, and I'm only twenty-three—just, so perhaps I'm being unfair...

Her eyelids drooped at this point and although she strove valiantly to keep them propped open, the fact that the headlights were now picking up an everlasting, serried sea of cane on either side of the road didn't help. Nor, probably, did the fact that it had been a totally traumatic day, and she fell asleep.

SHE WOKE with a jerk and sat up to stare round confusedly. The car had stopped.

'We're here,' her companion said a shade dryly.

Anna turned to him and blinked. 'Innisfail? How...I...' She trailed off awkwardly and peered out through the windows. But there was no doubt they were in the sugar town of Innisfail. She could see a sign to Johnson River bridge and also the tracks in the road for the cane trains. 'I'm sorry,' she said uncomfortably, 'I must have been asleep for ages! Not the most entertaining companion in return for...but thank you very...'

'Hang on,' he said, as she reached over to get her bag. 'You mentioned something about people expecting you. I'll take you there.'

'Oh no! No, this is fine, honestly. And you did say you didn't have much time...'

He regarded her thoughtfully for a moment before remarking, 'Another half hour won't make much difference. And having brought you this far I might as well complete the job.'

Anna winced and went faintly pink. 'That wasn't true, actually—what I said about people expecting me. I said it to...to...'

His lips twitched and then he started to laugh at her confusion. 'Did you really think that of me?' he asked finally and with a wicked glint in his green-flecked eyes.

She breathed deeply. 'How was I to know what to think?' she said stiffly. 'And you yourself...'

'Got hoist with my own petard,' he agreed, looking still amused. Then he sobered. 'But what will you do? You said you had no money, and the banks won't be open.'

'That's no problem,' she said hastily. 'A couple of months ago I worked at a hotel here—in fact it's only a block or so away,' she pointed down the road, 'so they know me and I'll have no trouble getting a room and a meal. And tomorrow I'll get to the bank.'

'Then I guess this is farewell, Miss Hitch-hiker, reformed,' he said gravely.

'Definitely reformed,' she agreed wryly.

'I'm glad to hear you say that,' he said softly, and she looked across at him, trying to formulate the correct words of gratitude, and was suddenly arrested by what she saw in his eyes—a mixture of devilish irony and something else that made her heart start to pound in a curious way.

'W-what do you mean?' she stammered.

'I suppose you could put it this way,' he drawled. 'It wouldn't take much on my part to start wondering how you'd look once you got rid of that layer of dirt. But I think I could guess. In fact I can just see you stepping out of a shower now.' He stared at her consideringly, 'Yes, dark hair, blue eyes and a faintly olive skin, an unusual combination but quite delightful, I'd say. And that smooth skin would gleam like satin and be damp and cool, and that figure you've rather unsuccessfully tried to hide under a man's shirt and jeans would catch the light in some places and be deliciously shadowed in others. I think it would be a thing of grace and beauty and lovely, curving symmetry, your body, and not at all hard to picture lying naked beside me.'

Anna stared at him, mesmerised, for a long moment, until he said, 'Perhaps you can visualise it too?'

Then she came out of her trance and was visited by a tremendous gust of anger. 'Oh . . . you . . . !' she breathed, but found she couldn't go on so she yanked her bag off the back seat, stumbled out of the car and slammed the door shut as violently as she could. But she heard his laughter all the same, and if she'd had a rock or a brick to hand, she would have thrown it at the car as it pulled away from the kerb smoothly and he had the gall to toot his horn in farewell. Then he turned a corner and was gone from sight.

'Of all the . . . !' She couldn't think of a suitable epithet and had to be content with venting her rage on an inanimate kerbstone with her boot, which hurt her more than the stone. 'I could die of mortification!'

A COUPLE of hours later she was not dead though considerably cleaner, but not in any better frame of mind. Because in spite of herself, she had paused after stepping out of the bath. There were no showers in the rather antiquated hotel she was lodged in, in fact there was only one bathroom on each floor. All the same, she stepped out of the old-fashioned bath with its claw feet and found herself gazing into the uneven, mildewed mirror with her towel held in both hands in front of her.

The wavering reflection that stared back at her held no immediate surprises. Just a fairly tall girl with very dark, heavy hair which she usually wore brushed back loosely from her face to reveal a perfect widow's peak, and pinned behind her ears to fall in a smooth curve to her shoulders—well defined eyebrows, thick lashes and blue eyes that could look grey or bluer depending on what she wore, and a curving mouth that, although she didn't know it, revealed her generous, sometimes impulsive nature. And what she privately thought was her best feature, very clear smooth skin that was not precisely olive, as the man in the car had called it, but more like warm ivory that tanned easily.

But, as her hands hovered for a moment, it was not her face she was thinking of, nor her face that she studied as she dropped the towel to the floor. Nor was it that she had never thought about her body because she had wondered what it would be like to lie naked beside a man and she had received several offers to do it, two from men she had liked very much but not enough, it had seemed, on reflection, to take them up. She had also often been conscious of a feeling of gratitude that she had a slender waist, firm breasts that were neither too big nor too small, a trimly curved bottom and long shapely legs, because it was the kind of figure that was easy to dress and looked good in inexpensive clothes that she could make herself and not only save money—a thing she *had* been doing since she left school—but also give some rein to her own sense of style.

It was none of those things that she thought of as she stared at her reflection—at least, it seemed like something very different to her as she heard those words again in her mind—a thing of lovely, curving symmetry, and saw a faint tinge of colour stain her cheeks, and felt again the undeniable magnetism that had kept her rooted to her seat for those moments. Only it got worse. For a fleeting instant her imagination took wings and with a sharply indrawn breath she found herself picturing her rescuer-cum-tormentor naked too, his long, streamlined body beside hers in some dim shadowy place, his hands on her...

She shivered and closed her eyes suddenly, and wondered how it could be that a man she barely knew and didn't even like should have had this effect on her. But almost immediately she got angry all over again and snatched the towel up and began to dry herself vigorously, resolving severely at the same time never to think of him again.

It was only later, when she was in bed, that she was finally able to relax and even laugh at herself a little in the darkness.

'I'm never liable to meet him again, thank goodness,' she told herself. 'But why couldn't I have thought of something cool and cutting to say to him? And why couldn't I have slid casually out of the car and waved to him after I'd verbally demolished him? Why do I always think of the right things to say two hours too late?'

But it occurred to her that in this instance, she still hadn't thought of anything cool and cutting she could have said, and she rolled over with a wry smile, punched her pillow and vowed to put the whole traumatic day out of her mind.

Two DAYS later she was taking tea with Mrs Robertson who owned the Hotel Louis, on a side verandah. Mrs Robertson was a lively, elderly widow who was something of an institution in Innisfail, as was the equally elderly Hotel Louis. It was only ten-thirty in the morning, but already a heat haze was shimmering across the rooftops of the houses nearby and Bob Wetherby, the hotel yardman, was raking and watering the gravel paths around the building which he did twice a day to cool them. The air was already heavy with humidity—an enervating fact of life about northern, coastal Queensland where, in summer, any activity after about eight o'clock in the morning left one drenched in sweat.

'Well, Anna love,' said Mrs Robertson, 'you know I'd only be too happy to have you back if you need a job.'

Anna glanced at her affectionately over the top of her cup.

She said, 'That's very kind of you, Mrs Robertson . . .' and hesitated.

'But you want to move on? Of course you do,' Mrs Robertson said briskly. 'So would I if I was your age. Just thought, having had all that money stolen, you might need a bit of a job to tide you over. Know what I mean?' She tilted her head with its crown of rigid curls to one side like a bright-eyed, enquiring bird.

'Yes, and I love you for it,' Anna said sincerely. 'But in fact I'm not broke. It's just that I was going to use the money that was stolen to give myself a little treat. I was going to take a proper holiday—just a week, seeing places like Bingal Bay and Mission Beach and all those romantic-sounding islands like Dunk and Hinchinbrook. But now,' she shrugged, 'I think I'll head for either Cairns or Cooktown and look for work there. Which isn't exactly a penance. They say it's lovely up there too.'

'Yes,' Mrs Robertson said slowly, 'it is. Still, it's a pity to miss out on Mission Beach and so on, because I doubt if even Cairns or Cooktown could beat it . . . Now what am I thinking?' she asked herself, and screwed up her eyes. 'That's it!' she cried suddenly. 'Yandilla! It would be perfect, and it's right there,' she added triumphantly, and went on to explain to Anna's look of enquiry, 'Mrs Lawson, my bowls partner, was telling me that Mrs Gillespie from Yandilla was in town only the other day, looking for someone to help her with the child. Not quite sure how old the child is now—round eight I think. Well, she didn't find anyone who suited and she said she was going to advertise in the Brisbane papers, see, for a governess. That's what you are, isn't it?' She looked at Anna expectantly. 'I mean, you're a qualified teacher, and that's what you were doing up round Georgetown, weren't you?'

'Yes,' said Anna, and thought of the job she had just left. It had been no easy task trying to governess five lusty boys on a truly outback property who would definitely have preferred to spend all their time on horseback anyway, and she'd thought sympathetically of their permanent governess who'd been taking well-earned, no doubt, leave. But if this was only one child...

'You said it was right there. Do you mean on that part of the coast? How would one get there?' Because if I'd have to hitch a ride, it's out, she added, but to herself.

'You'd take a bus and then a boat,' said Mrs Robertson.

Anna stared. 'A boat?'

'Yes. It's an island. Haven't you ever heard of Yandilla? It's somewhere near Dunk, off Mission Beach, but it's privately owned. The Gillespie family have owned it ever since I can remember—they have some enormous cane farms on the mainland.' Mrs Robertson sprang up energetically. 'Now why didn't I think of this earlier? Bob!' she called to her long-suffering yardman. 'It'd be as easy as falling off a log to get to Yandilla from here, wouldn't it?'

'I wouldn't say that,' Bob replied from over the verandah railing. He rested his broom and spat out a piece of matchstick. 'Who wants to go?'

'Anna here, and of course it's easy,' Mrs Robertson said crossly. 'All she'd have to do is take a coach from here to Mission Beach and then get on one of those boats that take day trippers round the islands. I know they stop at Yandilla if necessary, because Cynthia Lawson was telling me that's how they get their supplies and mail. Now you run over the road and find out when the next coach leaves, Bob Wetherby,' she commanded. 'And don't take your time about it!' she added.

Bob departed mumbling under his breath, and Anna blinked.

Mrs Robertson turned back to her. 'Don't think I'm trying to rush you, Anna, but this is a marvellous opportunity. They've got scads of money, the Gillespies, and they tell me the island is like a tropical paradise. And it's right in the heart of the Great Barrier Reef—have you ever seen the reef? No—well, it's incredible. And I'll tell you something else—once Mrs Gillespie advertises in the southern papers, there'll be a mort of city slickers applying for the job!'

Anna laughed. 'I was one of those myself not so long ago.'

'If you ever were, you got the worst of it out of your system before you hit here, love. And you'd be perfect for the job. What do you think?' Mrs Robertson asked excitedly.

Anna frowned faintly. But it was hard not to be affected by such enthusiasm. 'It sounds almost too good to be true,' she confessed. 'But just to turn up? Shouldn't I...?'

'Can't do any harm to be on the spot, can it? And you can mention Cynthia Lawson's name—I'll square it with her. See, she and Mrs Gillespie went to school together. Also, I'll write you a reference. There aren't many people in these parts who don't know my name—and respect it, what's more!'

Anna didn't doubt this, but still she hesitated.

'The other thing is,' Mrs Robertson said persuasively, 'in the unlikely event that they don't take to you, there'd be the opportunity for other jobs in the area. People come from all over the world to see the Reef, you know. And there's the resort on Dunk and motels on the mainland, boats to work on... What time did you say, Bob?' she called as Bob approached the verandah railing.

'I didn't yet,' he replied dourly. 'You never give me half a chance to get a word in edgeways. But she'll have to sprint,' he jerked a thumb at Anna, 'because it goes in half an hour, and it's the last one today.'

CHAPTER TWO

'... IF MRS Gillespie of Yandilla went to school with Mrs Lawson, who's a friend of Mrs Robertson's, wouldn't she be a little old to have an eight-year-old child?'

Anna shook her head as she stared out of the window of a large tourist coach and found she was still a bit dazed by the speed with which events had occurred. Mind you, she mused, there's no saying how old Mrs Lawson is, because Mrs Robertson has friends of all shapes and sizes and ages. Look how she's befriended me! And they do say bowls is appealing more and more to younger people. But what if they want a permanent governess? For all that Yandilla might be a tropical paradise, I don't want to be tied down for ever. As it is, it's taken me nearly nine months to get this far, and I'm not even out of Queensland yet. Maybe two years is just not long enough to work your way around Australia!

She sighed lightly and decided that the deed was done now and there could be no harm in having a look at Yandilla, at least.

And it wasn't hard to turn her attention elsewhere after a while, as the coach threaded its way through the spectacular scenery between Innisfail and Mission Beach and they drove through glorious rain forest and the abundant fertility of an area that had the highest rainfall in Australia.

'They don't talk about how many inches of rain they had last night in this part of the world, folks,' the driver of the coach said into his microphone. 'Here the rain falls in feet. No, I'm not joking either,' he added as a surprised murmur ran down the length of the bus.

But none of the lush scenery they passed through prepared her for the beauty of Mission Beach. To the north, the high cliffs of Bingal Bay swept down to the beach and then the land flattened and the beautiful white sands curved away to the south almost as far as the eye could see, richly fringed with a variety of tropical vegetation—banana trees and coconut palms and many that she didn't know. Dunk Island dominated the sea, looking rocky and faintly forbidding but enticing at the same time. Other, smaller islands were visible and far away to the south, looking violet and insubstantial in the distance, lay Hinchinbrook Island, the largest of them all and separated from the mainland by a narrow strip of water known as the Hinchinbrook Channel.

Anna savoured all these names as she stood and drank in the sheer beauty of it all, and she wondered which island was Yandilla. And decided there was only one way to find out.

'YANDILLA?' THE captain of the pleasure boat, the *Lotus Lady,* said. 'Sure. We've got a cruise leaving in ten minutes and it'd be no sweat to stop off at Yandilla. You...uh...expected?' He looked her over thoroughly.

Anna smiled inwardly. The captain of the *Lotus Lady* looked to be in his late twenties and he had bright brown eyes in a pleasantly open face so it was hard to be insulted by that all-encompassing look.

'No, I'm not,' she said gravely. 'But I've heard they're thinking of engaging a governess and I thought I'd apply in person.' She stopped abruptly at a sudden thought. 'But perhaps you can't just go to Yandilla? Perhaps you need a pass or an invitation? Would you know?' she asked.

He shrugged. 'I take all their stuff over and if there's an embargo on people, no one's ever told me about it. So you're a governess?'

'Well, I'm a qualified teacher. Same thing, more or less.'

He grinned suddenly, an appealing grin that made his eyes twinkle. 'Maybe. All I can say is, things have changed since I was at school. Teachers didn't come put together quite the way you are, ma'am, if you don't mind me saying so, in those days.'

'Thank you,' Anna said politely, and was struck by another thought. She frowned faintly. 'I . . . I was just wondering how I could get off Yandilla. You see, they might not like me, and it would be awkward to be stuck there. Do you . . . does the cruise come back that way, by any chance?'

'Can do! But there'd be worse places to be stuck than Yandilla. So they're engaging a governess now for Chrissy, eh?' he said thoughtfully. 'Seems only yesterday that she was a baby.' A shadow seemed to cross his face, then it was gone, and he straightened up from the post he had been leaning against. 'Time flies,' he said. 'I'm Mike Carmody, by the way. Do you have a handle, or are you just there to be looked at?'

Anna, having now had some experience with the jargon and customs of the north, interpreted his meaning correctly. In a subtle yet at the same time direct way, he was trying to establish whether she was available for, or averse to, being 'chatted up', as the time-honoured saying went. She had also established her own formula for dealing with this approach.

She put out her hand and said very seriously, 'I'm Anna Horton.'

They shook hands. And after a moment, Mike Carmody said with an amused look of resignation, 'Pleased to meet you, Anna Horton. You're still a sight for sore eyes, if you don't mind me saying so.'

Anna smiled at him, content that all communications had been received and decoded correctly.

But she had to admit a little later, as the *Lotus Lady* ploughed majestically through the quiet, inner reef waters with its happy load of tourists, that while Mike Carmody might have read everything loud and clear, there was something in the way his eyes lingered on her now and then which led her to think that he might not altogether have discarded the idea of slower approach.

Then someone mentioned Yandilla and she forgot everything else. Viewed from the sea, Yandilla wasn't very big. In fact all you could see of it was a white, elliptical beach topped by a fuzz of coconut palms and the only sign that it was inhabited was a long white wooden jetty upon which, presently, she found herself standing and accepting her bags from Mike Carmody and, at the same time, his assurances that he would be back three hours later to pick her up if necessary. Then the *Lotus Lady* pulled away with a powerful thrust of her engines and she lifted a hand to wave, but dropped it almost immediately as it tooted a deep, asthmatic-sounding horn.

'That's twice,' she murmured out loud. 'In three days I've been tooted at by two men!'

She thought of the other man who had saluted her in like manner and shivered for no reason at all—except, perhaps, that despite her resolution it hadn't been that easy to put him out of her mind, and she had even once thought suddenly, *hazel*—that's what you'd call those green-flecked eyes. Light hazel . . .

She stared out over the sea. 'Follow the path from the jetty, Mike Carmody said. It'll lead you to the homestead.' She sighed as she watched the *Lotus Lady* getting smaller. 'I can't help wishing I was still aboard you. This *is* a strange way to arrive! I wonder if I should have allowed myself to be stampeded into it?' She sighed again. Anyway, I'm here now, she thought as she bent to pick up her two bags, one of which Mrs Robertson had kept for her while she was up country. And how does the saying go? Nothing ventured, nothing gained!

She took a deep breath and turned resolutely to start the long walk up the jetty, and immediately narrowed her eyes.

Because a wind-surfboard had suddenly appeared, complete with colourful sail, in the waters beside the jetty, and as she watched it skim across the water away from the beach, the small form clinging to it let out a faint cry of alarm which the playful breeze picked up. Then, quite suddenly, the breeze died and the sail went limp, and the would-be surfer let go of the bar and toppled into the water.

Anna dropped her bags and stared anxiously across the water to see the small figure—it had to be only a child, she thought—bob up beside the board, only to get solidly clouted on the head by it.

She didn't stop to think then. She pulled off her sandals and dived into the deep, clear water.

It was a tiring swim because the distance between the jetty and the board had been deceptive and she had to keep stopping to check her direction. But at least she could still see the bedraggled sail lying on the water and a blob of orange beside it. And when she finally made it, it was to realise that the blob of orange was a life-jacket, and she breathed a sigh of relief as she gathered the small limp form wearing it into her arms and flipped on to her back and changed strokes to a lifesaver's crawl.

The bump on the head must have knocked him—her, more likely, with such long hair—out, she thought breathlessly. If she hadn't swallowed too much water...oh, please God, she prayed, let her be all right!

Then her thoughts took a different turn as she realised she was nearly at the end of her strength and there was no sign of shallow water yet. The skirt she was wearing wasn't helping either, and she found herself grimly trying to remember all the life-saving techniques she'd ever learnt. Not to panic, that's it—golden rule number one. And I must be getting pretty close to the beach by now.

Yet it seemed like an intolerable age before her feet struck sand, and when it happened she barely had the strength to wade through the water and she found she had to crawl clear of the water mark, dragging the small, still lifeless body along.

Then she thought she must be dreaming or hallucinating, because out of nowhere, it seemed, a confused babble of voices surrounded her and many hands seemed to be tending her and the child. But it was no dream, she realised, as someone kept asking her urgently if she was all right, and finally she found the breath to say yes, she was, and not to worry about her, just to concentrate on the little girl—and she tried to explain about the bump on the head.

From that point on things became ever more confused, and all she could remember afterwards was seeing two dark people working on the child and then feeling herself being lifted into a pair of strong arms, and it wasn't until she felt herself being deposited on to something soft that the world began to make some sense again.

She sat up and realised she was on a broad, well-padded cane lounger on the verandah of a strange house and that there was an almost tangible air of urgency about the place. She looked around slowly, taking in the cool white walls and the stone floor of the wide verandah and the comfortably luxurious cane furniture with its bright lime-green cushions, and realised that the air of urgency was probably induced by the sound of fleet footsteps moving around inside and someone saying harshly, 'What the hell's going on?'

A confused murmur of several voices answered this query, but Anna couldn't make out what was said, and she gripped her hands in her sodden lap and found she was praying again.

Then, she didn't know how long afterwards it was, she heard a woman's voice saying distractedly, '*All* I know is, Chrissy was doing a jigsaw puzzle and I left her for a few minutes, only to find she'd *gone* when I got back. So I sent everyone off to look for her, and they all converged at Jetty Beach just in time to see a complete stranger dragging Chrissy out of the sea. The...*your* windsurfer was out in the water, capsized, and it seems Chrissy must have been on it...'

The person the woman was talking to swore then and it was obvious it was a man. Anna frowned.

'Quite so,' the woman said. 'But be that as it may, either we've been harbouring a stowaway or some phenomenon delivered a perfectly strange young woman on the scene, and she undoubtedly saved Chrissy's life.'

'If it's a strange young woman,' the man's voice said, 'you can bet your life she's a trespasser. It's happened before,' he added grimly. 'Where is she?'

'She's on the verandah,' the woman said agitatedly. 'I don't think she came to any harm, but she was quite ex-

hausted, and even if she is one of *those,* you mustn't...
after all...oh, come!'

Anna had tensed violently during this conversation. I
must be imagining this, she thought dazedly. It couldn't
be! No...

She turned jerkily as a screen door opened and she stood
up steadily with her lips formed to ask how the child was.
But her mouth dropped open and her eyes widened incredulously, and she said foolishly instead, 'It *is* you! W-
what are you doing here?'

A pair of hard, angry grey-green eyes swept over her—
and narrowed. Then the man who only two days ago had
so nearly knocked her over, rescued her from the consequences of her own folly and then propositioned her, said
coolly, 'I happen to live here, Miss Hitch-hiker. More to
the point, what are *you* doing here?'

'Richard!' The woman beside him looked shocked and
anxious and harassed.

'I...I...' Anna began helplessly. 'Actually I...' She
swallowed and found it amazingly hard to speak. But it
didn't occur to her that her confusion would be taken for
anything else than what it was—the shock of seeing him
coming on top of her recent ordeal, until he ended the
strangely tense little silence himself.

'Did you perhaps decide you weren't quite so averse to
my thoughts on a certain subject?' he said meaningfully.
'I wonder what made you change your mind? Was it finding out who I was or, more importantly, what I repre-
sented that did it?'

'I...I had no idea who you were!' Anna stammered.
'How could I?'

He raised his eyebrows sardonically and shrugged. 'For
one thing, my car is the only one of its kind in these parts.
And I've long since realised that anything to do with Yan-

dilla is not only a common source of gossip from here to Cairns, but it's also a rather powerful attraction to members of your sex. Is that why you're here?'

Anna stared up at him aghast. She tried to speak, but again found it impossible.

'Well, Miss Hitch-hiker, I'm waiting,' he drawled, and when she still couldn't produce anything intelligible, he laughed and remarked, 'You should have come better prepared, my dear.'

The woman beside him stared up at him open-mouthed and then glanced at Anna's white face. 'Richard!' she burst out. 'I don't believe what I'm hearing. You...whatever...you're still talking to the person who saved Chrissy's life—your own *daughter's* life!'

'Oh, I'm very grateful for that,' Richard Gillespie said coolly. 'And she'll be suitably rewarded. Most suitably. In fact, Samson can take her across to the mainland right now and he can see that she gets some medical attention in case she needs it. And I'll pay for her to spend a week wherever she chooses to...recuperate. Now don't argue, Phil,' he commanded. 'I can do no less.'

'You'll do no such thing!' the woman called Phil exclaimed in outraged tones. 'And don't for one minute think you're fooling me with this so-called...generosity!'

Oh, God, Anna thought distractedly as the two of them stared at each other belligerently. And she sank back because her legs would no longer support her and burst into tears—a thing she hadn't done for years.

Her bout of weeping proved unexpectedly difficult to bring under control. It must be reaction—to everything, she thought dimly, as she tried desperately to master the sobs that racked her body. And the fact that the two people with her on the verandah were still arguing fiercely over her head didn't seem to help.

Then Richard Gillespie said distinctly, 'Very well! No, I'll do it. You'd better get back to Chrissy.'

Anna found herself powerless to resist as she was again lifted into a strong pair of arms and carried a short way into the house, to be deposited on to a bed. For some reason, this filled her with a strange sense of fear and she struggled to sit upright, but was immediately pressed back against the pillows.

'Don't fight me,' Richard Gillespie said curtly. 'And stay there until I get back.'

Anna stayed, but only because she was quite sure her legs still wouldn't support her.

He reappeared a minute or two later with a glass in his hand and sat down on the bed beside her. 'Here, drink this,' he said briefly. 'It's brandy.'

But all she could do was stare up at him, her face tear-streaked and flushed now and her damp hair clinging to her temples.

He made an impatient sound and slid an arm around her to lift her up a little, and put the glass to her lips as if she was a child. 'Drink it. And don't look like that, I'm not going to eat you.'

Anna drank some of the brandy and choked as it slid fierily down her throat. She tried to turn her head away but he made her take another mouthful. Then he put the glass down on the bedside table and let her lie back.

'I'm sorry,' he said abruptly. 'Phil's right—that was no way to repay you for an act of extreme bravery under... any circumstances. And there's no question of you leaving until you're fully recovered.'

Anna licked her lips and found herself saying huskily, 'That's all right.'

His lips quirked in a way she remembered. 'Is it? I guess if our positions were reversed, I'd think that a very tame apology.'

'Well,' she hesitated, 'when you get a shock like that— seeing someone you love half-drowned, you react strangely. I remember once when I was a child and I fell out of a tree and broke my arm my father, who loved me dearly, shouted at me first and then turned on my mother, although it was no fault of hers I was up the tree in the first place...' She trailed off uncertainly and wondered incredulously why she should be defending this arrogant, insufferable man to himself.

He said dryly, 'You have a point, although I haven't yet got stuck into Chrissy, but the urge was there.'

'How is she?' Anna asked quickly.

'She's fine. She came round almost as soon as they got her up here. She's got a bump on her head and may have some concussion, but she doesn't appear to have shipped any water. In fact, she's sitting up now and chatting, and I don't for one minute believe that this experience will keep her out of mischief for any longer than it takes for the bump to subside,' he added with a wry bitterness. 'How do you feel now, though? From what we've been able to piece together now, you must have seen her from the end of the jetty, which is a considerable distance to swim to where you both ended up on the beach.'

'I—I'm quite a good swimmer,' Anna confessed. 'At least, I used to get medals for it at school. I'm also still very wet,' she added wryly, 'and making a mess of this bed.' She fingered the pristine white cotton bed cover.

'Don't worry about it. How would you like to have a shower or a bath,' something in his eyes flickered, 'and to get into something dry and then have a long sleep? You look as if you could do with it.'

Anna stared up at him and felt her nerves tighten and her fleeting sense of good will towards him drain away. Because that look in his eyes at the mention of showering had not escaped her, and it had looked very much like sardonic amusement to her. And although she felt wearier than she had thought possible, it suddenly seemed supremely important to let him know just how much she disliked him.

'The last thing I'd want to do in any house of yours is take a shower, thank you all the same,' she said deliberately and dispassionately. 'If I could just have my bags brought up from the jetty so I could change into dry clothes and . . . and have a rest somewhere until the *Lotus Lady* calls back for me, I'll be fine.'

The silence was complete for about a minute while she met his meditative gaze coolly and disdainfully and refused to look away.

'Your bags are already here,' he said finally. He stood up. 'And there's no question of you going back on the *Lotus Lady* today, so I'll send a message down when she comes in. Er . . . further to the question of you relieving yourself of the liberal amount of sand you've acquired, if you thought I was offering to help you get rid of it personally, you were mistaken.' He smiled slightly. 'I find the half-formulated urge I once had to see you without your clothes has quite deserted me, Miss Hitch-hiker.'

Anna sat up and found herself speechless with anger.

Richard Gillespie waited for a moment, then shrugged and grinned. 'That upsets you too?' he said mildly. 'I can't win, can I? Would you have preferred it not to have had that assurance after all?'

'I . . . you . . .' she breathed.

He raised his eyebrows. 'You what?'

Anna's nostrils were pinched and white and her lips tight
and she looked longingly at the glass of brandy on the
bedside table because it was the only weapon to hand. But
her lashes flew up when he laughed and said dryly, 'You'd
be much better off finishing that, my dear, than throwing
it at me. I'll send someone in to give you a hand.' And he
strolled out of the room.

MANY HOURS later Anna swam up out of a deep sleep of
exhaustion and lay for a long time in the darkness, grappling with a frightening feeling of disorientation. Then it
all came back to her and she knew where she was and
sighed heavily, and reflected upon one of the stranger days
of her life.

I was so sure I'd never meet him again, she thought, and
how I wish I never had! But I still don't really understand
why he should have so automatically jumped to the conclusion that I'd...pursued him here! Even though I never
did get an opportunity to explain anything...

She frowned and her mind wandered back to the confused events after Richard Gillespie had walked out of the
room leaving her shivering with sheer, furious frustration.

The lady he had called Phil had arrived precipitously a
few moments later and been immediately consumed with
concern.

'My dear child!' she had exclaimed, anxiety again written all over her face which, although she looked to be in
her fifties, was still beautiful on account of the delicate
bone structure and luminous blue eyes. 'I'm so sorry to
have had to leave you alone when you're feeling so awful!
But it did seem at first as if Chrissy was the one we had to
worry about. Yet she seems to be quite fine and in the
manner of small children is actually lapping up all the at-

tention. She's in fact quite proud of herself, the naughty child! And I'm so glad to see her alive I haven't the heart to point out to her the error of her ways. But then Richard has always maintained that I indulge her too, too much. By the way, I'm Philadelphia Gillespie, Richard's aunt and Chrissy's great-aunt,' she had added. 'But everyone calls me Phil.'

Anna had blinked under this onslaught and been able to think of only one thing to say. 'How do you do? I'm Anna Horton...'

But her voice had trembled and of all things she had started to cry again. Not the awful sobs which had racked her earlier so much as a helpless welling of tears which had trickled slowly down her cheeks. She had wiped her nose on the back of her hand and said, 'You were right to concentrate on Chrissy. There's nothing wrong with me. I was just so afraid she'd...but she hasn't, has she? And I'm so very glad...so...'

'You poor thing!' Philadelphia Gillespie had exclaimed, and crossed to the bed swiftly to take Anna into her arms. 'There, there, my dear, don't cry. I can't imagine what got into Richard earlier—well, I can, I suppose—but all the same, to carry on like that! I'm not surprised you feel dreadful, coming as it did on top of everything else. There are times when I quite despair of him, and so I shall tell him! The only excuse I can offer is that it came as an awful shock to *all* of us, but more so to him, I suppose, to see her...to think she'd drowned too. Then, when she sat up and said brightly, "But I was wearing a life-jacket"—well, you know how it is...'

'Yes, I do,' Anna had sobbed. 'I do! I told him...'

'Come, sweetheart,' another voice had interjected, and Anna had looked up to see a broad brown face with very white teeth grinning down at her. 'I got you a bath runned,

pet. You'll feel one helluva lot better with all that sand
washed off. Come with me and Phil.'

'Letty's right,' Philadelphia Gillespie had said. 'There's
no way you could be comfortable like that. And unless you
make a habit of swimming a couple of miles a day you
might end up very stiff.'

'I put some herbs in the bath water,' the woman called
Letty had said, and Anna had seen hazily that she was almost as broad as she was tall and that she had grizzled grey
hair and a round face with not a wrinkle on it and the
laughingest eyes she had ever seen. Then, between the two
of them, they had undressed her as if she was a child and
tenderly helped her into the bath and commanded her to
lie for a while. After which they had helped her out, put on
one of her nightgowns and put her back into the freshly
made bed.

'Letty will stay with you until you fall asleep,' Phil had
said. 'And we shall look in on you every so often, but if
you wake up and don't know where you are . . .'

But the warm bath or the herbs or something had done
the trick, and she had fallen asleep.

Now, LYING in the darkness, she thought—stiff, and
moved warily. Only a little, she conceded, and wondered
what herbs Letty had used. She also wondered what the
time was. Her room was in darkness, but there was a faint
glimmer of light coming through the partly open doorway
as if a dim night light was on somewhere. This, and the
fact that the house was very silent made her think it was
very late.

Her thoughts moved on as she lay quietly in the com-
fortable bed, and it struck her that she had met Chrissy
Gillespie's father, her great-aunt, and someone called
Letty, but not her mother. Was she away? she wondered.

Perhaps she was down south interviewing prospective governesses? She smiled a little grimly. Unless...unless Philadelphia Gillespie was the Mrs Gillespie of Mrs Lawson's acquaintance?

Almost immediately something else niggled at the back of Anna's mind. Something Phil had said...to think she'd drowned too...yes, that was it. She frowned. Had someone actually drowned at Yandilla? she wondered.

Two things disturbed her thoughts. Some faintly heard birdsong which made her wonder incredulously if she had slept from mid-afternoon to dawn; and a movement beside the bed which nearly made her die of fright.

CHAPTER THREE

'WHO'S THERE?' Anna whispered after a moment, with her heart still pounding uncomfortably.

'It's me,' a whisper came back. 'Chrissy Gillespie. Did I wake you? Can I put the lamp on? I'm *dying* to see you because Aunt Phil and Letty and everyone says you saved my life!'

'Well...oh!' Anna blinked as a soft rosy glow flooded the room and she found herself staring into a dark lashed pair of grey-green eyes in a pointed little face, that were regarding her with the utmost solemnity. 'Hello, Chrissy,' she said gravely. 'I'm very happy to meet you.'

'Me too,' the child answered, and flung her arms around Anna's neck in a sudden movement that took Anna completely by surprise. 'I'm very, very grateful to you, Anna— may I call you Anna? Aunt Phil said that was your name. And seeing as you saved my life, I'm yours to command for ever,' Chrissy Gillespie added dramatically, and went on, 'I read that in a book once and thought it sounded awfully silly, but now I see that it's not. Er...would you mind if I slipped in with you? You see,' she pulled a face, 'I'm not supposed to be out of bed on pain of death. But I wouldn't actually be out of bed if I was in bed with you, would I?'

'Well,' Anna temporised, 'technically no. I suspect you were not meant to get *up* in the first place. But seeing that you're already up, we'll waive the small print. Hop in,' she invited, and moved over.

Chrissy needed no second invitation. She hopped in and settled down beside Anna with a contented sigh. 'Shall I turn the lamp off?' she asked. 'There's something about talking in the dark that makes it special, don't you think?' She reached out and switched off the light. 'See what I mean?'

Anna smiled in the darkness. 'I do. What shall we talk about?'

There was a short, pregnant silence, then Chrissy said, 'Could we talk about you? Because there seems to be a bit of a mystery about you. I think you must be the new governess, only I can't ask because ... well, I can't.'

Anna started to speak, but was struck by the coincidence of this artless revelation and changed tack. 'Why can't you ask? And what makes you think that anyway, Chrissy?'

'I heard Daddy and Aunt Phil talking about getting a governess for me a few days ago, but they didn't know I was listening,' Chrissy confessed. 'You'd think they'd at least discuss it with me, though, wouldn't you? After all, I'm the one directly involved. But Daddy's like that. Much as I love him, he can be exasperating sometimes. Aunt Phil says it runs in the family,' she added in a quaintly unconscious but perfect imitation of her great-aunt's intonations.

'I see. Chrissy...'

But Chrissy chatted on, 'Did you know my great-great-grandfather bought Yandilla for fifty guineas and we Gillespies have lived here ever since?' she said proudly. 'We made all our money out of sugar—still do,' she added matter-of-factly. 'Only Letty says the family's running out now, because I'm the only one in my generation and I'm a girl. She didn't know I was listening when she said that,' she said hastily. 'But it's sad, don't you think?'

'But you might one day have a brother or a sister,' Anna suggested.

'No.' Chrissy sighed heavily. 'My mother's dead, you see. She died when I was nearly two. I can just remember her—she was very beautiful. She was drowned—that's why they were all in such a tizz yesterday. It would have been ghastly if I'd been drowned too, you have to admit.'

Anna was silent for a moment, suddenly seeing things more clearly. She said finally, 'Yes. But why did you do what you did then?'

'I...I'm not quite sure,' Chrissy Gillespie answered honestly. 'Sometimes you just do things you know you shouldn't. Don't you ever?'

'Sometimes,' Anna admitted wryly.

'Of course, if I had a governess I probably wouldn't... well, not so often.'

'Have you never had one?' Anna asked curiously.

Chrissy sighed dolefully. 'No. Not a proper one. But I've had dozens of nannies.'

'Really?' Anna queried sceptically.

The little girl shrugged. 'Four, actually. But they never stayed long. And I haven't had anyone for ages.'

'Why was that? I mean why didn't they stay long?'

Chrissy sighed again and said in a voice heavy with drama, 'They all fell in love with Daddy and he had to send them away.'

Anna stirred and nobly refrained from laughing at the thought of a succession of nannies falling in love with Richard Gillespie. Surely not all four? she thought with an inward grin. She said gently, 'I think you're having me on, Chrissy.'

'No!' Chrissy sat up indignantly. 'They did! And two of them were really nice—they'd have made super mums and I even told them so, but he just didn't fall in love back. I don't think he understands how much I want a mother, otherwise...' She trailed off, then turned to Anna urgently. 'Did you have a mother?'

'... Yes.'

'Then how would you have felt if she'd died when you were just a baby?'

Anna was silent for a minute, because despite a certain unreality about this conversation, she couldn't help feeling unwittingly touched by the ring of desperation in the child's voice.

'I wouldn't have liked it much,' she said eventually. 'But sometimes these things happen, and finding a new mother isn't such a simple matter. She'd have to be a special person for both you and your father.'

'I know that,' Chrissy said broodingly. 'It means he'd have to fall in love with her. That's the big problem—at least it is for him,' she added almost accusingly.

'Well,' Anna thought for a moment, 'you see, falling in love is a strange thing. It's not something you can... tell yourself to do. It just happens.'

'I know that too,' Chrissy said despondently. 'I heard Miss Sawyers—she was the last one—say to Aunt Phil, that she hadn't wanted it to happen. That's what she said and she was crying and angry. What I don't understand is, why it's so easy for them and not for him? Why does he find it so hard to fall in love back? Have you ever been in love, Anna? You sound as if you know something about it.'

Anna grimaced and felt some pity for whoever it was who did end up as Chrissy Gillespie's governess—for more reasons than one, she thought.

She said, 'No. I've never been in love. But there's probably more written about it than any other subject and as you grow up, you see it in other people.'

'Then, seeing as you're grown up, Anna, why do you think my father's so hard to please?'

Anna bit her lip and wondered if she was imagining this conversation.

'Anna...?'

'Honey, I barely know your father so it would be impossible to say.' She grimaced in the darkness and thought, actually not hard at all, Chrissy. From what I've seen of your father so far, he's an arrogant, overbearing bastard who'd find it hard to fall in love with anyone but himself. How he managed to have such an appealing child is...

Then something occurred to her and she turned to the child and said gently, 'Chrissy, there's another thing. When someone you love dies, it can take time before you can even begin to think of loving someone else in the same way.'

There was a long silence until Chrissy said, 'It's been nearly six years now. And I think he's really lonely sometimes, you know.'

Anna moved and put her arm round the child. 'But he's got you. And you've got him. I... in a way, you're luckier than I am. Because although I had a mother and father all the time I was growing up, they were both killed in a car crash three years ago, so...'

Chrissy sucked in a breath and turned to embrace Anna fervently. 'Oh, you poor thing!' she whispered. 'How terrible you must feel! Why didn't you say so before, then I wouldn't have carried on like that. How do you manage on your own?'

Anna couldn't help feeling warmed. 'I've got...more used to it now. And I've got my job and I'm at present...'

'What do you do?' Chrissy interrupted.

'I...I'm a teacher, but...'

'Well, now you're here,' Chrissy interrupted again, and patted Anna's face tenderly, 'I'll look after you. And so will Aunt Phil and Letty—you'll see! It'll be just like having a family again.'

'Chrissy,' Anna said urgently, 'I—thank you, you're very sweet, but...'

She stopped as Chrissy tensed and tensed herself as she heard someone moving about. 'Chrissy,' she said in a lower voice, 'I'm not...'

'Well, blame me!' Letty's voice wafted into the room quite distinctly. 'Drat that child! She gone again!'

'That's Letty,' Chrissy said unnecessarily. 'She was sleeping in my room...'

'Chrissy!'

But Chrissy wasn't listening as more voices became audible and footsteps came down the passageway, then there was the sound of doors opening and closing and Philadelphia Gillespie saying, 'She's not anywhere! I've looked in every room. Unless—no, surely not...'

Surely yes, Anna thought, and knew with a curious certainty what was going to happen. And it did. The bedroom door swung fully open and the room was flooded with light. And she found herself staring into three pairs of eyes, Aunt Phil's, Letty's and Richard Gillespie's.

Chrissy said, 'Don't be angry, Daddy. I just wanted to thank Anna for saving my life. And anyway, seeing she's going to be my new governess, the sooner I get to know her the better.'

Anna froze and could never remember when she'd felt more at a disadvantage than she did at that precise moment. Or more helpless, as Phil's mouth dropped open and Letty blinked incredulously.

No one said a word.

Then Richard Gillespie, who had neither gaped or blinked but merely narrowed his eyes as he took in the two of them lying side by side in the bed, sent Anna a look of such cold, murderous anger that she shivered involuntarily.

He said tersely, 'Back to your own bed, Chrissy. I'll talk to you later. As for you,' that he meant Anna was abundantly plain, 'I'll see you in my study in half an hour. In the meantime,' his lips twisted sardonically, 'can you fix up some breakfast for our guest, Phil? She's going to need it.' He turned on his heel and walked out.

'Oh dear,' Phil said nervously. 'I don't understand...anything!'

'Why is Daddy so angry?' Chrissy asked tearfully. 'What have I done that was so bad?'

Letty sprang to life. 'We didn't know where you'd gone, you naughty girl, that's all,' she scolded in such loving tones that Anna would have been moved to smile in any other circumstances. 'Now you come back to bed and Letty will make you comfortable.' And so saying she lifted the child from the bed and hurried out of the room with her.

Which left Anna and Philadelphia Gillespie confronting each other awkwardly.

'I...Chrissy just assumed that,' Anna stammered finally. 'I didn't...I...oh, what's the use!' she said wearily. 'Look, can I just get off this island as soon as possible? Please don't worry about breakfast, I *just* would like to leave. There must be some way—someone who could take me off.' Her voice had risen slightly and she fought to control the feeling of hysteria that was claiming her and was quite out of character for Anna Horton. But then Anna Horton has never had anything as insane as this ever happen to her, she thought grimly, and managed to say, equally grimly, 'And there must be some way that I don't ever have to see *him* again!'

Phil looked intensely embarrassed and twisted her thin, elegant hands. 'I'm afraid no one would take you off without Richard's permission.' She hesitated. 'Anyway, don't you think it would be better to have it out with him once and for all?' she went on.

'...Have what out?' Anna asked ominously. 'I can tell you categorically that Chrissy assumed I was the new governess because she'd overheard you and her father discussing hiring someone. As a matter of fact, you'd all probably be quite amazed at the number of things Chrissy overhears which she probably shouldn't. However, that's beside the point...'

'No, no,' Phil interrupted, looking troubled. 'I meant—well, it's obvious you and he have—' she took a breath, 'known each other,' she said in a rush, and smiled apologetically. 'Please don't think I'm being inquisitive or that I'm condemning you—I'm not, because I've known for years exactly the kind of effect Richard has on members of our sex. In fact I've occasionally thanked my lucky stars that I'm years too old for him and was very happily married to his uncle! But I still think,' she went on gently, 'you'd be better to...to have it out with him.'

Anna stared at her incredulously. 'I...it's not that way at all!'

'Then, forgive me, but why did you come to Yandilla?' Phil asked bewilderedly.

'I . . .' Oh hell, Anna thought hollowly, I knew I shouldn't have come here like this. Why did I let myself be stampeded into it?

'Although I for one will be eternally grateful to you,' Phil added, looking sympathetic as she observed Anna's confusion. 'My dear, men have a horrible habit of tying you in knots, don't they? But anyone with eyes in their heads could see that you're not the common run of sharp-clawed huntresses who have, I can't deny it, pursued him from time to time. And I sometimes think he treats all women as if they are, like some sort of . . . acid test! Which isn't right even if it is—perhaps understandable from his point of view. Look, I'll make some breakfast for you and some coffee, and that might make it easier for you. I don't know why it should be, but when your body's fortified, your soul seems to be too, have you noticed? Goodness me,' she glanced out of the window, 'the sun's come up! That's another thing that helps, I've found. Daylight always improves things. I'll leave you to get dressed,' she went on confidentially, 'and then when you've had some breakfast, you might feel like going in and telling Richard exactly what you think of him! You see if I'm not right,' she added over her shoulder, and actually winked.

Then she closed the door softly and Anna was left staring at it, quite bereft of any powers of speech.

FORTY-FIVE minutes later, nevertheless, she was sitting in Richard Gillespie's study.

She had breakfasted and she was dressed in a lemon-coloured crinkle cotton blouse, a full cream cotton skirt and yellow sandals. Her dark hair was loose and smooth, just brushing her shoulders. She wore no make-up other than a light moisturiser and some lip-gloss because when her skin was lightly tanned as it was now after six weeks in the outback, it had a silky bloom that needed no adornment.

Yet, despite having had breakfast and presumably fortified her soul, and despite the daylight and Aunt Phil's strangely fighting advice, she felt, as she sat with her hands lying loosely in her lap, that somehow her ire had lost its momentum. Or, put another way, that she didn't precisely feel like telling the tall, still coldly angry-looking man across the desk what she thought of him. I wonder why? she mused. Because he has a habit of always coming out on top? Perhaps, she thought. And perhaps I'm just a little afraid of him, but I don't know why. She looked down at her hands and then lifted her eyes to meet his green-grey gaze squarely, and to wince inwardly at the look of contempt she saw.

'So we meet yet again, Miss...'

'Just a minute,' Anna interrupted, knowing full well what he was going to call her and finding the thought of it returning the keener edge of her anger to her. 'My name is Anna Horton,' she said deliberately. 'And while we're on that subject, would you kindly inform your family—and everyone else—that we know so little about each other that you didn't, until now, even know my name.'

'Why the hell should I do that?' he asked after a moment.

'Because,' Anna said caustically, 'they're labouring under the delusion, at least your Aunt Phil is, that we have some... prior knowledge of each other.'

'But we do,' he drawled.

'No, we don't. Not the kind she's thinking of,' Anna retorted. 'She imagines we've had some kind of an affair, or something, and that's why I've mistakenly pursued you here. Perhaps you make a habit of abandoning your lovers or mistresses or whatever, which is why the thought naturally sprang to her mind?' She looked at him enquiringly.

'Or perhaps there just seemed to be no other explanation,' he remarked blandly. 'We don't seem to have got to the bottom of why you are here, do we?'

'I can tell you one thing,' Anna said softly, 'if you were the last man on earth, I'd die rather than pursue you even across this room. I don't think I've ever met a man I detested more—or, for that matter, a more presumptuous one,' she added with gritted teeth.

Richard Gillespie smiled, but it didn't reach his eyes. 'Brave words, lady,' he said casually. He sat back and folded his arms across his chest and studied her coolly. 'How old are you?' he asked abruptly, at last.

'Twenty-three. What's that got to do with it?' she demanded. 'Look, this is wasting my time just as much as it's wasting yours, so could we discuss something constructive for a change? For example, how I'm to get off this island.'

He raised his eyebrows. 'Certainly. As soon as you tell me why you came here in the first place and why Chrissy seems to think you're the new governess, we can discuss anything you like.'

Anna took a deep breath, and to give herself time to think, looked around the room.

She had thought it austere when she had first come in. Now, in spite of herself, she saw it was austerely beautiful like the other parts of the house she had seen. Built for the tropics, its ceilings were high and the walls thick and white-painted and the deep verandah ran right round the house, adding to the coolness. But the beauty lay too in the woodwork of the floors with only the occasional Persian rug to show up jewel-bright against the polished surfaces, and the carved doors with their brass handles. It was also an uncluttered house, as typified by this room which contained only the mahogany desk and two chairs, a built-in bookcase that took up one whole wall, an exquisite oval walnut table in the corner that bore a crystal vase of violet blue agapanthas, and one painting on the wall—an original Namatjira of the red, dusty heart of Australia. Across the room from where she sat, french windows opened on to the verandah and through them she could see in the still, early morning light, a sweep of green lawn that led to a gap in the coconut-palm-studded shrubbery and beyond, a tantalising glimpse of white beach and pale blue sea.

'Very well,' she said suddenly. 'You have a right to know, so I'll tell you why I came. You can believe it or not, that's up to you. But one thing you must believe,' she raised her eyes to his at last and stared at him levelly, 'is that I never led Chrissy to think I was the new governess. She *first* thought it because she'd heard you and her aunt talking about it some days ago. Then when I mentioned that I was a teacher—she, well I suppose it seemed to follow. That's the truth, and the fact that the rest is,' she shrugged, 'an amazing coincidence I suppose you could say, is not my fault excepting for one thing—I should have made an appointment to come here first. But I don't intend to go on defending myself about the rest of it.' Her gaze didn't falter and a stubborn light entered her blue eyes.

'Go on,' he drawled, his eyes never leaving hers. 'Tell me about this amazing coincidence.'

Anna did as best she could. And when she'd finished, she pulled Mrs Robertson's letter from her pocket and slid it across the desk to him. 'You're very welcome to check that out, by the way,' she said coolly. 'In fact I wish you would. Not because of the job, but because if you do, Mrs Robertson will be able to tell you that until she brought the subject up, I'd never heard of the Gillespies or Yandilla, or connected them with a certain person who gave me a lift into Innisfail, and one who I rather devoutly hoped I'd never meet again. You see,' she added dryly, 'I'm not in the least flattered by everyone's assumption, not the least *yours,* that I was so devastated by you personally, or what you represent, or both, that I came here on that account. And while I hope never to see you again after this, I'd just like to set the record straight.'

There was a curiously tension-laden silence as their eyes clashed. Then Richard Gillespie picked up the letter and opened it. 'I know of Mrs Robertson, as it happens,' he observed.

'Then you might find this quite believable after all.' Anna looked at him coldly.

'Mmm.' He scanned the letter briefly and as he did a wry grin twisted his lips. 'She has a way with words, Mrs Robertson. So,' he lay back in his chair and regarded her with a detached sort of interest, 'she recommends your character highly and, quote, thinks you'd make a fine governess, unquote. Would she know?'

Anna hesitated. 'No,' she said honestly. 'But she liked me and thought I was honest and trustworthy. And she knows I'm a qualified primary school teacher and that I've been governessing in fact I've just...oh!' She stood up and paced across the room. 'What are we getting into this for?' She threw him an irate look over her shoulder. 'There's no question of me being Chrissy's governess now, that's not the point, is it? All I'm trying to establish, in the hope that you might *some time* let me off Yandilla,' she said bitterly, 'is that I came here with a legitimate purpose! But I can assure you, if I'd had the least idea who you were, I'd never have allowed Mrs Robertson to talk me into it. And

I'll tell you something else,' she added tautly, 'if there's no other way, I'll swim off your precious island!'

He laughed softly. 'That reminds me of something else you once threatened me with. Something about walking to Cape York rather than go anywhere with me.'

Anna bit her lip unseen to him and castigated herself for letting her anger and indignation trap her into making wild statements.

'Mind you,' he went on pensively, 'it would probably have been less dangerous to walk to Cape York than to swim off Yandilla, so I wouldn't advise you to try it.' His voice was suddenly steely. Then he went on in more normal tones, 'But there's an alternative. I think you'd make an excellent governess for Chrissy.'

Anna stopped pacing as if she'd been shot and swung round. 'You don't mean that!' she said at last, taken utterly by surprise.

Richard Gillespie looked up at her thoughtfully. 'I said it. Don't you want the job now?'

Anna shook her head as if to clear it. 'No! I thought I made that clear. But I don't understand you! Why such an about-face? Ten—no, *two* minutes ago you were convinced I was a conniving adventuress or something worse. I'm afraid you go too fast for me, Mr Gillespie,' she said somewhat grimly, and sank down into her chair.

He looked amused. 'I thought the fact that I could revise my opinions would make you see me in a better light. But I've noticed before that you don't seem to appreciate this quality I have of being flexible. Would you rather I'd stubbornly refused to believe a word you've said?' he asked gently, tauntingly, his eyes alive with devilish amusement.

Anna's lips parted but no sound came and she found herself choking on her rage most ignominiously, while

Richard Gillespie grinned faintly, then offered politely to get her a glass of water.

She shook her head and thought to herself, that's it! That's the last time I cross swords with this detestable man. That's the last time I . . . even talk to him, she thought incoherently, and set her lips in a tight line and stared defiantly at him.

But he only shrugged and stood up and walked across to the french windows to gaze out over the garden. Then turned almost immediately and leant his wide shoulders against the frame.

And with a twinge of surprise Anna saw that all the mockery and amusement had gone from his eyes and what was left was complete, businesslike gravity.

'I apologise,' he said quietly. 'I haven't treated you very well and I'd like to be able to make amends. If you really want to leave, I'll arrange it immediately.' He paused, but she was too stunned to speak. He went on, 'However, I'd—we'd all be very happy for you to spend some time with us, as our guest. And while you did, you might like to reconsider the position of governess to Chrissy, but if you do spend some time with us please don't feel obligated to accept the post. The one's not contingent on the other in the least.'

Anna blinked and rubbed her brow. Is this some kind of extended dream? she wondered dazedly, and knew it was not. Then just how does one deal with a man like this? She gazed up at him blankly. In such a short space of time I've seen him violently angry, I've seen him coldly and cruelly angry, I've seen him sardonic and mocking and wickedly, cynically teasing at my expense. He's kissed me, propositioned me, all but denounced me to his family as the lowest of the low...and proved less than easy to get out of my mind. Not that I've had much time to do it, but now he's offering me a job or a holiday or both...

She licked her lips and thought, if I had any sense I'd get up out of this chair and run for my life. Which of course I will! At least, I'll say no—no, thank you to everything!

And all I did to get myself into this crazy situation, she marvelled, as she still gazed blankly up at him, was accept a lift from a lecherous semi-trailer driver, happen to be on hand when Mrs Robertson had a brainwave and rescue one small girl from drowning. Life's very odd...

'What are you thinking?'

Anna blinked again. 'I was thinking how strange life is,' she said huskily. 'I really didn't think I'd ever see you again, let alone in these peculiar circumstances.'

Richard Gillespie said nothing for a moment. The he smiled at her, genuinely and she saw with a sudden clarity what she had seen on the dusty roadside two days ago—a man to whom any woman would be attracted even without the knowledge of his wealth or Yandilla. Yes, it's all there, she thought, and wondered how best to sum it up. I suppose it's a combination of many things, an obvious though often cutting intelligence, a sort of worldliness and sophistication and a feeling that if you came up to his expectations as a woman it would be something to be proud of, and it would be heady and intoxicating and as if you were flying too high... Dear God, what am I thinking? she asked herself. A faint smile curved her lips at her next thought. Perhaps Chrissy was right after all—maybe they did all fall for him and have to be sent away lovelorn and desperate...

'I was thinking the same thing,' he said, cutting into her thoughts and with a curious inflection that she couldn't decipher. 'But you haven't given me an answer.'

Anna looked away and for no real reason felt a faint heat come to her cheeks. Be careful, she thought, don't let it happen to you...and almost immediately felt like laughing, for that would be crazier than anything else that had happened so far. She stood up and said with decision, 'Thank you very much, and I mean that, but I'd like to go as soon as possible.'

He regarded her silently until she began to feel unnerved again, although she was determined not to show it.

Then he said dryly, 'You haven't forgiven me, have you? And you're not prepared to let me make amends either.'

She rubbed her hands together awkwardly. 'There's nothing to forgive I...it was a misunderstanding. As for Chrissy, I'm only glad I was on the spot in spite of the...misunderstandings that came about.' She looked at him steadily.

He straightened up and said the most surprising thing. 'You so often speak with the maturity and good sense of someone much older. How come?'

Anna thought for a moment, very conscious that he was looking at her over assessingly but this time not in the least insolently. Yet she still found it strangely disturbing. She said finally, 'Twenty-three isn't so young really. And I've been on my own for a few years now, so perhaps that's why I sound older, if I do.' She smiled suddenly and added wryly, 'But then I often do things which...well, land me in trouble, very much like someone much younger—as you must know.'

His eyes narrowed. 'Do you mean you have no parents?'

'No.' She explained as she had to Chrissy.

'I see. Look,' he said abruptly, 'the more I get to know you, the more convinced I am that you'd be just what Chrissy needs. No,' he lifted a hand as she started to speak, 'please just let me explain. Chrissy lost her mother when she was nearly two—she no doubt told you?' He looked resigned as Anna nodded. 'She never loses an opportunity to tell people that. But anyway, since then she's had to make do with Phil and Letty who both adore her and spoil her rotten, and a succession of unsuitable nannies. Believe me, it's terribly hard to find someone, the right person for a motherless child. But I think you might be right for her. If—say if none of the...misunderstandings, as you call them, had occurred, would you have taken the job on?'

'I...maybe Chrissy doesn't need anyone. I mean anyone *employed*,' Anna said confusedly. 'Even if your aunt spoils her, and Letty, at least they love her and they're permanent.'

A fleeting hint of weariness touched Richard Gillespie's eyes. 'But she needs more. You see, Phil didn't have any children of her own and she treats Chrissy like an adult— which she readily admits, just as she admits that the child is becoming precocious because of it. Besides, Phil has her own career and she's not getting any younger. And Chrissy needs someone younger, not only to...balance the influences in her life but also someone who could cope with and channel all her energy more productively. That's why she's so everlastingly up to mischief.'

Anna swallowed. 'Chrissy...needs a mother,' she said quietly. 'I know,' she added as he moved impatiently, 'I know you can't produce one to order, but that's one reason why I'd be...very wary of taking on this job, why I'm not at all sure a governess, a young governess, is the answer for Chrissy. You see, she spilt her heart to me this morning. At first I thought she was romanticising, but I don't honestly think so.' She stopped and took a breath. 'You may not realise this, but every nanny she's ever had, she's weighed up as mother material, and two of them came through with flying colours, apparently. So much so, she let them know how she felt.'

Richard Gillespie frowned. 'What do you mean?'

'I mean she desperately wanted you to fall in love with them and marry them...'

'God!' he said reverently. 'Are you sure?'

'Well, she asked me why I thought you were so hard to please. She said they fell in love with you...' She stopped abruptly and coloured as his eyebrows shot up. 'Then she *was* making it up? They didn't...?'

'They...well...' he looked briefly uncomfortable, which Anna would have got some enjoyment out of in other circumstances but, oddly, didn't in these. 'Hell!' he muttered at last. 'I had no idea, believe me, that Chrissy was egging them on. I mean...' he sat down suddenly, 'can you imagine...it?'

They stared at each other and then both began to smile reluctantly and then to laugh.

'It's not funny, really,' Anna said at last.

'No,' he agreed. 'It must have been bloody unfunny for them,' he added, suddenly sombre. He looked at her. 'Does she really want a mother as badly as all that?'

Anna nodded. 'She...thinks you're lonely too, and that you need a wife. Also, that as a family the Gillespies are...running out...'

'Oh, Chrissy!' he sighed, and for a long time stared broodingly across the desk at nothing in particular. Then he looked up at Anna and smiled a twisted, self-mocking smile. 'I don't suppose you'd like to marry me, Anna Horton? No, don't answer that, but seeing that you've unwittingly become the recipient of all these confidences, Chrissy's and now mine, can you see a solution? I...she's terribly precious to me, for all that she drives me mad sometimes.'

Anna sat quiet for a few minutes, thinking and concentrating carefully. And she thought, after all, what have I got to lose? She said slowly, 'If—we were to make it very clear to her that it would be quite useless for her to entertain any dreams of matchmaking between us, I...would stay a while and be her governess. Although it wouldn't be the best arrangement, because I couldn't stay for ever. But then that's a risk you'd take with anyone, I suppose, and at least I understand...some things, and might be able to help after all.'

His eyes searched her face probingly. 'Thank you,' he said at last. 'I'm doubly grateful to you now.'

Anna bit her lip and found herself entertaining some second thoughts. It certainly wasn't what I meant to do, she reminded herself.

'Then you'll explain to her?' she said awkwardly.

'Of course. Unless you'd rather do it?'

'I...no. I've already tried to do a bit of explaining about love and how it happens and how it can't be engineered.' She smiled ruefully.

'No, it can't, can it? Have you ever been in love, Anna?'

'No. I thought I might be—you know how it is.' She grimaced. 'Now I've decided there are many variables, and perhaps the most important is not to go looking for it.'

'I'm surprised it hasn't come looking for you,' he commented. 'There must be plenty of young men who've been attracted to you.' He looked at her quizzically.

Anna frowned and found herself feeling curiously nettled. 'Some not so young too,' she replied. 'Although you can't always believe what they say—particularly when they have a habit of revising their opinions,' she added dryly.

He grinned at her appreciatively. 'Point taken,' he murmured meekly, but his eyes danced with devilry.

Anna stared at him frustratedly. 'But that is the point, isn't it? You have to learn to distinguish between that kind of thing and the real thing. Then, too, you have to consider that not everyone is cut out for a grand, hit-you-on-the-head kind of passion. Sometimes it's more like a slow sort of warmth that takes time to grow.' She smiled suddenly. 'I think that's what my parents had. It certainly took time to grow. They claimed they knew each other for ten years before they married and that their love grew out of a mutual interest in rats and mice—they were both biology teachers. I think that's how it might happen for me.'

'Because of the way it happened to them?'

She hesitated. 'Not necessarily. But, although you might not believe this, having somehow always contrived to catch me at a disadvantage, I'm really quite a sane, down-to-earth kind of person. And not—normally—given to wild excesses of any kind.'

His eyes travelled over her slowly and she felt her nerve ends flicker uncomfortably. 'Strange,' he said at last. 'You don't look to be a passive, stoical kind of person. You don't think it might only need the right man to come along for you to feel as wild and wanton as everything about you promises?'

A bright little flame of anger began to burn in Anna's eyes. 'I've no doubt that's a peculiarly male philosophy,' she retorted.

Richard Gillespie smiled slightly, a cool, faintly derisive twisting of his lips which angered Anna even more so that she tilted her chin defiantly. 'I've discovered that's not a very reliable guide either I'm afraid,' she added cuttingly.

'Oh? How?'

I've discovered you can feel that way, fleetingly, about someone you don't even know and don't even like... The words popped into her mind unbidden and for a horrified moment, she wondered if she'd said them and went hot and cold with relief that she hadn't. But she couldn't control the faint colour that came to her cheeks as she stared at him hostilely.

'How?' she said at last, suddenly uneasily conscious that his eyes had narrowed as he watched her. 'I...' She broke off and bit her lip.

'I'm sorry,' he said abruptly. 'I have no wish to pry into your personal life. Except to say that to sleep with a man in good faith isn't such a momentous thing to do these days, even if it doesn't end in wedding bells and all the trimmings. So, if you have any regrets, or feel you have good cause to distrust men who make you feel that way, I should try to put it all behind you.'

Anna's eyes widened. 'I...'

He waited, but the shock of what he had said, of what he had implied, made it impossible for her to think very coherently, let alone speak. And to make matters worse, the extreme discomfort she was displaying, she knew, could only be cementing his impressions. But at the same time, two things did occur to her—that to explain what she had in fact meant was not something she cared to get into particularly; and that he should have come to such a conclusion so easily—although I suppose I did lay myself open to it a little, but not *wittingly,* she thought—is insulting in the extreme.

At least enough, she discovered, to make her say finally and bitterly, 'I don't make a habit of it, so *if* ...'

'I didn't think you did,' he interrupted smoothly.

She eyes him angrily and thought, oh *hell!* What have I done now? Why don't you think before you speak, Anna?

Mind you, wouldn't it be more to the point to wonder why you accepted this insufferable man's job after all? And what does it matter—does it *really* matter if he thinks you're a virgin or not? It's not as if you're about to marry him... In fact, it might even get you off the hook! He might not think you're suitable any more...

She took a breath and hoped that none of what she was thinking was betrayed in her face as she said, 'I don't quite know how we got on to this in the first place, but if you'd like to change your mind on account of it, I'd understand.' She tried to look amused.

'It seems to be a topical subject in this house, I guess,' he murmured wryly, his eyes dwelling on her thoughtfully. Then he looked away and employed the same technique he had used earlier, so that when he looked back his expression was only businesslike. 'No,' he said definitely, 'I don't want to change my mind. However, if you'd care to reconsider, I'd understand, because I wouldn't want you to feel I'd played on your sympathy for Chrissy unfairly. It is, after all, not your problem.'

Oh, you clever, infuriating man, Anna thought acidly as she gazed at him. If I say no now, I'll look and feel a fool. She set her lips for a moment, then a stubborn light entered her blue eyes. 'I said I'd do it and I will. If *you're* sure?'

There was a little silence, then Richard Gillespie said briskly, 'Quite sure. And Chrissy will be thrilled, I've no doubt. By the way, welcome to Yandilla, Anna—may I call you that? We're quite informal around here, you'll find, and I'm sorry the welcome's a bit belated.' He grimaced slightly. 'My fault,' he apologised. 'Oh, one thing, I'm leaving for America tomorrow—I'll be gone for a few weeks, but you might appreciate that. It will give you a chance to get settled without me breathing down your neck.' He grinned at her just a touch maliciously, she thought.

And because on top of it, she was still feeling irritated and confused and altogether caught on the wrong foot, she was prompted to say sweetly—and unwisely, as it turned out, 'Ah! A holiday? How nice.'

He observed her speculatively for a moment before remarking dryly, 'If you're implying that I'm going away to waste my time in the manner of the idle rich, I'm not this time, as it happens. I'm attending a seminar on the Box Jellyfish which infests tropical waters and is a particular menace in this part of the world.'

'Oh,' she said feebly. 'Then you're a biologist?'

He nodded, his face quite grave but his eyes laughing wickedly. 'A marine biologist—in my spare time.'

'Oh...' was all Anna could find to say.

WELCOME TO Yandilla...

Anna grimaced drowsily many hours later. I ought to pinch myself to find out if I'm real, because here I am, back in the same bed again, only this time, contrary to all expectations and sworn vows and all that kind of thing, I'm here to say... for a time.

Well, not always in this bed, precisely, she mused, but to inhabit this pretty room, this house, this island for a time. How strange, how very curious, Anna. You have to admit that. You also have to admit you got outweighed this morning, overruled, outsmarted *and,* in the process, acquired a murky past! Quite a dubious achievement, wouldn't you say?

She sighed sleepily and her thoughts drifted back over the rest of the day. Chrissy Gillespie had been thrilled, of that there was no doubt. And Philadelphia Gillespie had been intensely relieved by the explanations her nephew had

given her—not that Anna had been privy to those explanations, but Phil's relief had been obvious when she had
said to Anna, 'I'm so very glad it was just a silly misunderstanding, my dear, and I do hope you'll forgive us.
Unfortunately, from time to time we do get trespassers on
Yandilla. And I'm afraid over the years—well, it hasn't
been unknown for girls to try and scrape an acquaintance
with Richard. It's one of the penalties of being wealthy,'
she had said humorously, but gone on immediately,
'though I didn't honestly think that about you, Anna.
Strange to say, I got the impression that Richard knew you
rather well! But then I often get things wrong… And
you've no idea how happy I am to have the question of a
governess for Chrissy settled so easily. So you could say we
were doubly blessed that you came to Yandilla!'

Then in the afternoon Chrissy had taken Anna on a tour
of the island instructing her knowledgeably as they went.

'Daddy's mad about the reef,' Chrissy had also confided to her. 'He loves it. Letty says even when he was a
little boy he was fascinated by it and everything to do with
it. She says she was always finding bottles hidden under his
bed with strange fish and things in them…'

An unexpected side to Daddy, Anna mused in the darkness, still smarting from the way her unruly tongue had led
her into discovering this side of Chrissy Gillespie's father.
But then all round, not quite the common run of daddy,
Chrissy… Or to put it better, not quite your common or
garden male of the species. More like a sleek dangerous
golden panther.

She thought of Richard Gillespie at dinner that night.
He had been friendly and seemingly unaware that she
wasn't quite at ease in his company. And she had found
herself watching him unobtrusively with a kind of irate
perplexity and thinking, it's strange that he hasn't mar-

ried again. Six years is a long time. Or is it? Perhaps not. Then again, he doesn't give the impression of being bereft. Not that it's any of my business . . .

'Exactly, Anna,' she muttered to herself, feeling rather wide awake now and correspondingly annoyed again. 'And for your information, Richard Gillespie, what I was trying to say when you somehow or other got me trapped into that peculiar . . . fiction, is that even while you may remind me of a Greek god, albeit a rather impatient, haughty, fallen kind of Greek god, I'm not so foolish as to imagine it meant anything more than a passing physical attraction, here today, gone tomorrow. Nor . . . oh, damn! For heaven's sake, just admit that you got carried away today, Anna! That you let one superior man taunt you into telling a lie—no, going along with it for the sake of pride or something. Just admit that, and get to sleep.'

CHAPTER FOUR

ANNA LOOKED up from the letter she was writing, and thought incredulously, I've only been here for three weeks now, yet some days it feels like three months. How the time's flown—and despite my misgivings, I can only say I've enjoyed it. Although, she grimaced wryly, that could be mostly due to the fact that my boss hasn't been here.

She put down her pen and stood up and wandered over to her bedroom window. It was that lovely hour between daylight and dark when normally the heat of the day was waning and the promise of cool breezes and dew on the grass was an intoxicating, reviving thought, although this particular day had been hotter than any day she'd spent on Yandilla so far, and she wondered idly if the evening breezes ever failed.

'And I've grown into the lifestyle here so very easily. At least, they've accepted me warmly—so warmly, all of them, I sometimes feel embarrassed. But at least they weren't suspicious of the way I arrived here, only touchingly grateful that I did.'

She winced as she thought back to that day, not sure why it still had the power to disturb her. She dropped her hand in a sudden restless movement. Probably because *he's* due home tonight, she thought ruefully. And I can't help wondering how that will change things.

A light knock interrupted her thoughts. 'You there, Anna?'

'Yes. Come in, Letty.''

'Your laundry,' said Letty as she advanced into the room. 'Didn't get a chance to bring it in earlier. Phew, it's pretty damn hot, isn't it?'

'You mustn't wait on me, Letty,' said Anna. 'I'm quite capable of collecting my own laundry.' She had said this before, but it hadn't taken long to discover that anything to do with the running of the house was something Letty preferred to do herself, and did magnificently, with the help of her young niece, who was called Sunshine.

'Remind me to tell you about Letty one day, Anna,' Phil had said to her not long after she had arrived. 'But one thing you'll soon find out for yourself—if Letty ever left us, Yandilla would fall apart.' And she had gone out to her studio looking vague and anxious, which was something Anna had now got used to, for one of the great surprises she had had on coming to Yandilla was to discover that Philadelphia Gillespie was none other than Eunice Thurby, whose detective stories were known and loved world-wide.

'There,' said Letty as she sorted Anna's washing into the drawers of her dressing table. She sank down on to the bed. 'Mind if I take a breather? Chrissy's safe in her bath, that's one place she is safe—she loves her bath. Mind you, since you've been here that child's pretty well reformed, and thank the Lord for it! I tell you, Chrissy Gillespie's put ten years on me, I reckon. Me and Phil both,' she added ruefully. 'How'd you do it?'

Anna grinned. 'I'm not sure. I think she looks on me as a sort of guardian angel after what happened.'

'That'd be right too. Every day I give thanks that you were there! Mr Richard should be home soon,' she added, apropos of nothing, and glanced at Anna keenly. 'You don't like him much, do you, Anna?'

Anna was caught totally off guard. 'I…' She bit her lip and remembered something else Phil had said about Letty—to the effect that Letty was devoted to Richard and Chrissy.

'You can tell me,' Letty said kindly.

'Well, I think we just rub each other up the wrong way. If…if it wasn't for Chrissy, I wouldn't be here,' Anna said quietly.

'Thought so,' Letty said wryly. 'But I reckon you oughta give him a chance. Sure, men get on your nerves sometimes! They act as if they're God, but he's not a bad man. I know, because I've known him since he was born. He's got a helluva temper sometimes—like his daddy, he is, but his mother used to cope—did you know I first came here to work for his mother?'

Anna shook her head.

'Yes,' Letty went on, 'I'm a Thursday Island girl—T.I., we call it up there in Torres Strait, and Mr Richard's mother was a teacher like you and she came up to T.I. when she was twenty—we were the same age. I didn't get a chance to go to school before that, but she didn't mind how old you were in her school. She stayed with us for two years and we got to be good friends. Then she met Mr Richard's father—swept her clean off her feet, he did! Letty smiled reminiscently and went on ruefully, 'All the same, when she found out about Yandilla and everything,' she waved an expressive hand, 'she said to me, I'm scared, Letty, they're very different people to what I'm used to. And I said to her, I'll come with you! You don't need to be scared of no one, but all the same I'll come with you if you want me to! I was a bit of a savage in those days, learnt a lot since, but she wanted me to come, so I did. And I brought my baby, Samson, and we've been here ever since. Oh, I go back once a year and check on the family and sometimes I bring one back with me, like Sunshine's here now, getting trained. But to get back to what I was saying, I've known Mr Richard all his life, and he's not a bad man.'

They gazed at each other and Anna was seized by an amazing thought. But she found herself rejecting it almost immediately. No, I'm really imagining this. Letty wouldn't be so foolish as to think I would be . . . mother material for Chrissy? No, she's only trying to ease a potentially awkward situation.

'You're right, Letty,' she said quietly. 'I took on the job because I couldn't resist Chrissy. And now that I've taken it on, it would be foolish to carry on a sort of silent feud with her father. But I . . . did feel . . . I'm sorry I made it so obvious I was a little tense about him coming home.'

'That's all right,' Letty said with a smile. 'And you didn't make it so obvious.—it's just that I'm a bit sensitive about anything to do with Mr Richard or Chrissy, I reckon. And that's why I took it upon myself to try and explain. You see, I'd do anything for them.' She hesitated. 'Something else—when something happens the way it did with Chrissy's mother, it can make you bitter and twisted about *everything*.' She looked at Anna searchingly. 'Even though it was a long time ago now. You . . . don't mind me butting in like this, do you, Anna?'

'No, of course not, Letty,' Anna said warmly. 'I only wish I had someone who cares for me the way you do for them. And I will try, I promise.'

Letty got up off the bed and hugged Anna. 'I knew you would,' she said. Then she looked up at her and grinned mischievously. 'All the same, you don't need to let him walk all over you. While I'm all for doing the right thing by a man if he does the right thing by you, it don't do any of 'em any good to think you've got no backbone. You gotta steer a middle course, but it helps if you understand some things. There now, I better go and see if Chrissy hasn't washed herself away...' And she took herself off.

Anna stared at the closed door for a minute or so, but again she rejected the strange thought that had occurred to her earlier. No... She shook her head impatiently and started to dress for dinner. And she found she felt oddly warmed, because although there was no doubt where Letty's devotion lay, at least she understood that her boss was not the easiest person to deal with. And she must like me enough to want to try and help, she mused.

BUT RICHARD Gillespie did not arrive as expected, and Chrissy grew fractious and tearful, and nothing Anna did helped much.

'She's worried about him,' Phil said quietly. 'She misses him when he's away. But I'm sure it's only a delayed flight, otherwise he'd have let us know. Also, it's turned so hot and muggy, hasn't it? Never improves people's tempers I've found.'

'It is hot,' Anna agreed, wiping her brow. 'Not that I can complain, it's the first really hot night I've had since coming here. It's usually so lovely and cool and breezy after dark.'

'It's bound to rain,' Phil said knowledgeably. 'It always does when the humidity gets this high. By the way, I've found the best thing for Chrissy when she gets this way is to put her to bed and read her a few stories until she falls asleep. But I must warn you, it can take quite a few!' she smiled ruefully.

Anna thought for a minute.

'You have a better idea?' Phil queried perceptively.

'I...no, not necessarily,' Anna said hastily. 'But I do have a little portable tape-recorder and a cassette of *Peter and the Wolf.* I've found most kids love it, but I usually keep it for special occasions. Then again, she might already know it?'

'No. What a good idea!'

As IT turned out, it was. Chrissy began to relax as they listened to *Peter and the Wolf* together and finally fell asleep trying to imitate the duck.

Anna pulled the sheet over her and smoothed her fair hair off her forehead, feeling her heart contract as she watched the child's face lose its tension in sleep and saw the absurdly long shadows her eyelashes cast on her cheeks. For in all honesty, she found that Chrissy Gillespie touched some deep, inner part of her heart that had never been touched before.

Maybe it's because I'm an orphan now and you're a part orphan, Chrissy, she mused with a half smile. Whatever it is, despite your reputation, you've treated me with so much care and consideration—just like you said you would—I'd have to have had a heart of stone not to be charmed and warmed...

She took a breath as Chrissy stirred, not wanting her to wake and worry about her father again. But she settled, and Anna stared down at her and thought, how sad for your mother to have missed out on you, Chrissy. No wonder...if I had a little girl I'd like her to be just like you, bright, sometimes impetuous, sometimes mischievous, a real tomboy sometimes, yet quaintly feminine other times...no wonder your father is bitter and twisted often! I think your mother might have been rather special too. I think that's what Letty was trying to tell me earlier. To—make allowances for him because he lost her...

THE LONG hot night felt as if it would never end. Anna twisted and turned uncomfortably and finally decided she wasn't going to sleep, so she climbed out of bed, slipped on her pale blue silk robe and slid noiselessly out on to the verandah on bare feet.

But it was just as hot and stifling outside—as if a great blanket impregnated with moisture lay overhead only waiting for some giant hand to squeeze it. And an eerie silence seemed to have the world in its grip. There were no cicadas trilling, no frogs croaking, not a sound. She decided to walk round the garden nonetheless, in the hope that it might make her sleepy. Then, when she was at the farthest garden boundary from the house, it started to rain. But it didn't begin with a few spots and gradually gain momentum—that wasn't how it happened in this part of the world, she recalled ruefully, as it simply started to pour and within moments she was drenched to the skin and gasping as the water ran off her in rivulets.

Yet it was such a relief from the hot, breathless stillness, and seeing she was drenched anyway, she stood there for an age, enjoying it. Then she turned regretfully to retrace her steps through the grey, strangely insulating downpour, and bumped heavily into something that bowled her right over.

She gasped again and lay winded and confused as she felt a pair of hands run over her and heard someone mutter something unintelligible. But the voice was recognisable even if the words were not, and she thought, oh no!

Then that voice swore briefly in an exclamation of surprise and Richard Gillespie said, 'Whoever the hell you are, would you mind telling me what you're doing in the middle of the lawn at this time of night just where I could trip over you?'

Anna sat up. 'You didn't trip over me! You bumped into me and *knocked* me over!'

There was a tiny silence, then he said wearily, 'Oh, not again! I should have known it would be you. Are you by any chance going to make it a habit to be where I can knock you down?' he demanded.

Anna bit back an angry retort and tried to scramble up and found she had to accept his help. 'No, of course not,' she said coolly, and as suddenly as it had started the rain stopped and a much overdue breeze got up playfully, the clouds parted overhead and a clear white moon shone down on them.

'Then what, Miss Anna Horton, are you doing out here, may I enquire?' he asked, taking in her sodden robe and the smear of mud on her legs. His eyes came back to rest on her face and they were as mocking as she'd ever seen them.

She stared at him, conscious of feeling the peculiar tension and irritability he seemed to be so adept at arousing in her. He was wearing a beautifully tailored grey suit that was damp too, although not quite in the soaked condition her clothes were in. 'I...nothing in particular,' she said haughtily, and almost immediately knew she had made a mistake as he raised his eyebrows.

'Oh, I see,' he drawled. 'Just another example of the sane, level-headed person you are, is that it?'

'No!' she said crossly.

'Then perhaps you came out to meet me?'

'Why would I do that? I didn't even...'

'You tell me,' he interrupted, and his eyes glinted challengingly at her, and she caught her breath because she had seen that look before and had felt before that he could hardly have undressed her more effectively with his hands.

But as she followed his gaze downwards, she flinched and bit her lip because the thin silk of her robe and the equally thin cotton of her nightgown beneath it had fused together wetly and were plastered to her body like a second skin, so that the curve of her breasts and the outline of her nipples were clearly visible and her hips and thighs were moulded unmistakably.

A torrent of colour poured into her cheeks and her hands clenched and unclenched as Richard Gillespie laughed softly and said, 'You're a funny girl, Anna. Sometimes you quite take me in and I'm convinced you're a little different from the great majority of the fair sex.' He lifted a hand and fiddled with a strand of her wet hair. 'All the same, I don't think I'm proof against this kind of an invitation.' His hand slid down her arm and crossed to the small of her back.

She moved jerkily and brought her hands up to push him away, but he smiled slightly and his other arm came up to encircle her shoulders. 'It's O.K., I get the picture,' he murmured. 'You don't want to appear *too* willing. That would never do, would it? So why don't you just stand there and let me do it all? Just to. . . preserve the illusion, shall we say?'

To say that his words stunned Anna was to put it mildly. She felt as if she was turned to stone, and it was only the feel of his lips on hers that brought her to life. She twisted her head away and fought dementedly, but she might just as well not have bothered, because he only laughed at her quietly and easily resisted all her efforts. Then when she lay panting with frustration in his arms, he started to kiss her again, not brutally as he had done once before but quite gently, and not her lips which she kept clamped shut but the corners of her mouth and her throat and the soft hollows where her neck met her shoulders, and she shivered suddenly and was conscious of the curious feeling of her bones melting and her skin tingling as if it was on fire where his lips had been.

He lifted his head at last and their eyes met, hers wide and shocked but with a different kind of shock registering now, and his dark and strangely sombre. And in the stark white moonlight and with the tantalizing fragrance of damp earth all about them, he said softly, 'I'm not going to hurt you, don't be afraid.' He bent his head again and this time he teased her lips apart—and what followed was something that Anna knew with a strange certainty she would never forget for the rest of her life.

For two reasons—because she offered no resistance, and because although she had been kissed before, it had never been like this, and she had never known it could be an experience so intensely intimate or so devastatingly sensuous, so that every other time she had been kissed faded by comparison almost as if it had never happened. In fact everything faded, the moonlight, the fact that the cicadas had come to life refreshed by the brief, heavy rain, and the frogs and all sorts of night creatures including two wallabies that hopped cautiously out into the open only feet from them and stood for a minute with ears twitching and nostrils quivering before bounding away into the bushes.

It all might not have been there, because the only thing she was burningly, achingly conscious of was Richard Gillespie and the feel of his tall, hard body against the softness of her own and the way she trembled at his touch as he moved his hands lingeringly, tracing the curve of her waist. And that to be kissed as he was kissing her was strangely and unbelievably intoxicating, and it made her heart beat heavily to think that she was surrendering to it willingly as if she had choice.

Then she moaned, a slight despairing sound, as much at
the beauty of it as at the sheer inexplicability of it, and his
lips left hers slowly and once again found herself clinging
helplessly to him, afraid that if he let her go, her legs
wouldn't support her.

But he didn't let her go. He held her loosely in his arms
and his grey-green gaze played over her quivering lips and
took in the shimmer of tears in her eyes. Then he said
quizzically, 'Whoever he was, either he didn't teach you
much or he didn't know much. You look just about as
shocked as someone who's never been kissed properly before.'

She took a ragged breath and coloured painfully.

'Anna?' His eyebrows were raised enquiringly.

'Perhaps it was the shock of... being taken advantage
of like that,' she said shakily, desperately trying to sum-
mon a sense of outrage into her voice. 'You shouldn't have
done it.' Her voice cracked unfairly, and a fresh wave of
colour crept into her cheeks.

He watched that tide of colour in the pitiless moonlight
and his lips twitched faintly. 'Perhaps not,' he said at last.
'But I wanted to.'

'W-why?' she stammered. 'You don't really believe I
came out here to waylay you, did you? I had no idea you'd
arrived! I only decided to walk in the garden because it was
so hot I couldn't sleep. And it could have rained any time
in the last few hours, it's been so muggy.'

He stared down at her consideringly. 'No,' he said
slowly. 'I think I might have wanted to, because of something we discussed once. You remarked that you weren't
given to—wild excesses, and—with a certain amount of
disdain—gave me to understand that you'd been turned
right off men... and this.' He touched her mouth gently.
'Which at the time made me wish I could be a fly on the

wall when some man cut through that so sane, no-
nonsense, slightly superior facade and kissed you into
submission so that you begged for more...'

Anna wrenched herself from his grasp and had no trouble in projecting a furiously, genuinely outraged image.

'Then you thought you'd appoint yourself to the task?
Well, you've miscalculated,' she spat at him. 'I'm certainly not going to beg you for more! And if you ever lay
a hand on me again... oh, *look!*' she said angrily. 'I can't
stay on here if you... if you... God knows why I agreed
to in the first place!' she stuttered.

'Not the first place,' Richard murmured. 'You knocked
me back the first time.' His eyes glinted in the moonlight.
'Perhaps, although you might not have admitted it to
yourself, because you were just a little afraid of the effect
we have on each other. I can understand why, now...'

'I...you...oh!' Anna gasped. 'You affect me like a hole
in the head!'

'So I noticed—just now,' he commented, and his lips
twitched again.

'If you laugh at me once more,' she said in a low, choking voice, 'I'll *hit* you, I swear. As for us affecting each
other, I think it would be fairer to say that for some in-
conceivable reason, you feel you have the right to kiss me
whenever you feel like it! And I can't help wondering if
you aren't a little disappointed that I didn't pursue you
here, after all!'

She stared up at him bitterly and was incensed to see him
take his time before answering.

'I have to admit,' he said at last, 'that in certain respects you leave the other...nannies we've had here for
dead.' He glanced fleetingly down the length of her and she
flinched visibly, and tried to drag her sodden robe into a
less revealing mould for her body.

'There should be a law about the kind of man you are, Mr Gillespie!' she snapped furiously, and bit her lip in silent but blazing frustration at the look of outright laughter she saw in his eyes. *All right,* she thought, all right, I'll just show you that I can be as cool about it as you can. She said coldly, 'Anyway, I thought we had an agreement about this kind of thing?'

'Chrissy and I have an agreement,' he said gravely.

The mention of Chrissy made Anna move restlessly. 'I...' She stopped abruptly, suddenly less sure of herself and conscious of a feeling of pain around her heart as she pictured Chrissy distraught and tearful as she had been during the evening. She sighed inwardly. 'Then if you want me to stay,' she said bleakly, 'you'll have to include me in that agreement.'

'If that's the way you want it,' he said after a moment, quite seriously, but she could see the amusement still lurking in his eyes.

'That's the way I want it,' Anna said flatly. 'Can you doubt it?' she added, suddenly hotly angry again despite her resolution. 'Do you really think I'd enjoy being,' her voice shook, 'treated like some sort of an experiment? Like someone in need of therapy, even *if* I...I mean,' she changed tack effortlessly, thinking swiftly, the principle's the same even if the circumstances are not! Take a man, it'll cure everything...'as if I was a stone statue that could be brought to life by any man? And say, just say I had begged for *more,* as you so insultingly phrased it, what would you have taunted me with then? Oh, you don't have to tell me,' she said ironically. 'Sooner or later, probably sooner, we'd have got back to that old question—why did I come here in the first place! And wasn't it after all to pursue you and your wealth and your p-precious island? But I can tell you, *either* I stay here as Chrissy's governess and *nothing* else, or I go.' She realised for the first time that she was crying and brushed the tears away impatiently.

'All right,' Richard said meditatively, 'I stand corrected, Miss Horton—as you once said to me. But I must add, in the interests of honesty, that while I did kiss you more or less,' he smiled suddenly, 'as an exercise in therapy—to see if I couldn't breath life again into a stone statue, I can't say I didn't enjoy the results. And when you've calmed down and all your natural indignation at being so shockingly treated subsides, you might find you don't feel so badly about these things now. You see, you're really so lovely, it's a crime to think of you all bitter and twisted about it. By the way,' he looked upwards and Anna followed his gaze to see that the moon was about to be eclipsed by a bank of lowering, threatening looking clouds, 'if you don't want to be drenched again, it might be an idea to get back to bed. See you in the morning.' He looked at her wryly.

'THE BOX Jellyfish,' Samson said measuredly, 'is a mean creature who don't pay no attention to the colour of your skin. He just wraps these'm long tentacles round you and if he gets holda enough of you, the pain's so bad you're dead in minutes.'

Chrissy shivered. 'Put it down, Samson,' she begged. 'Anyway, I've seen hundreds of them.'

Samson lowered the transparent, ghostly-looking 'creature' he was holding, into a tank. 'I got gloves on, Chrissy. Can't hurt me through them. And I thought Anna might be interested.'

Anna came back to the present at the mention of her name. 'Oh! Yes, I am, Samson.' She looked down at the round dome of the jellyfish and its frilly beard and long, delicate tentacles. 'A serpent in Paradise,' she murmured, and looked up.

'You could say so,' Samson answered, and she detected a ghost of a smile in his eyes. Letty's baby was in fact a tall sinewy man with none of his mother's roundness nor much evidence of her boundless good humour. Yet Anna had noticed before that his eyes smiled often, though not a trace of hilarity ever creased his face.

'You don't want to take any chances. Specially not now,' he said more to Anna than Chrissy, 'at this time of year when it gets really hot and we can get storms. That's when they seek out more sheltered waters like round Yandilla. Really, you shouldn't swim outside the enclosure now unless you wear pantyhose and a long-sleeved shirt.'

Anna grimaced, then had to smile. 'Sounds like taking a bath with your clothes on,' she said, and winced, thinking of last night.

'But it works,' Samson assured her.

'I will be careful,' she promised. 'Well, Chrissy, we've had a long break, what say we get back to lessons?'

Chrissy pouted. 'I don't really see why I have to do school work today. I think I should have a holiday because Daddy's back.'

'I think that's a good idea,' a voice said from behind them, and Chrissy spun round ecstatically and ran to her father.

Anna turned more slowly. So far, although it was only mid-morning, she'd managed to avoid Richard. She had deliberately stayed out of the way while he and Chrissy had been reunited and had been surprised to find that Letty had for once accepted her offer of help in the kitchen, and they had breakfasted out there together, while Phil and Chrissy could be heard discussing his trip animatedly with him in the dining room. But not long afterwards Chrissy had come to look for her, to show her the presents her father had brought home for her, and Richard had repaired to his study and closed the door. She had started lessons with Chrissy mostly because she could see the child was in a fever of impatience to be with him and becoming more disappointed by the minute as the study door remained firmly closed.

Now, she looked across the boatshed at the man who had taken such incredible liberties with her last night, and hoped that she didn't look as wan and heavy-eyed as she felt. For the truth of the matter was, she had found it even harder to get to sleep after her encounter in the rain with him than before, and no amount of sane, logical discussion with herself, nor any calling upon Letty's wisdom, which she had only remembered once back in the safety of her room, had helped to ease the turmoil of her mind.

Not anything, she had thought bitterly, not even the fact that *you are* bitter and twisted about life in general because you lost a wife you loved, is an excuse to treat me like that. In fact I don't believe that's got anything to do with it—sorry, Letty, she had found herself thinking torturously. I'm sure the real reason is that he's simply a male chauvinist of the highest order who thinks he can treat women as...mindless dolls, and I could *die* because for a little while that's rather how I felt...

'I...hello,' she said helplessly, knowing she was making heavy weather of hiding the conflict she felt but not able to do anything about it.

'Hello, Anna,' he said quietly, and slid his fingers absentmindedly through Chrissy's silky hair as he scanned Anna's face and took in the faint shadows beneath her troubled blue eyes. 'I'm sorry about what happened last night,' he added in the same quiet way.

Anna's lips parted with surprise.

'What happened last night?' Chrissy asked curiously.

Let him explain this, Anna thought fleetingly, and tensed anew. No, surely he won't... But then why bring it up in front of her...?

Richard looked down at Chrissy. 'I was rather rude to Anna last night. She was walking in the garden because she couldn't sleep when I got home, and we both got caught in the rain—in fact we bumped into each other and I knocked her over...'

'Told you you'd get soaked,' Samson interjected. 'Told you, if you waited a while after we got across from the mainland it might ease off. It did,' he said laconically.

'Remind me to take more notice of what you tell me, Samson,' Richard said wryly. 'But after a twenty-four-hour flight and a delay in Brisbane, and then having to drive up from Townsville, all I wanted to do was get to bed. Not,' he looked across at Anna, 'that *any* of that is an excuse for anything that happened last night.'

There was a strangely tense little silence and Chrissy looked from her father to Anna with wide eyes, and back again.

'But you're not still... cross, are you, Daddy?' she said with a slight break in her voice. 'Anna wouldn't...'

'Oh no,' he said to her, then smiled and put a finger to her lips. 'It's more a case of—is Anna still cross with me? Because I was the one who was in the wrong last night.'

Anna stared at him, not quite believing what she'd just heard and not in the least able, she found, to interpret it correctly. Either he's diabolically clever or... but what! 'I...' she said huskily, and stopped. Is Letty right after all? she wondered shakily. She must be, or why do I get the feeling this is a genuine apology, a genuine attempt to wipe the slate clean? But I've thought that before...

'Anna?' queried Chrissy, and her own turmoil was clearly visible.

Oh God, Anna thought, it isn't fair to bring her into this. 'No, sweetheart,' she said gently, 'I'm not cross.' She looked away and encountered Samson's gaze, of all things, which said as clearly as if he had mouthed words—you don't say! She caught her breath and blinked in astonishment, then looked back at Richard incredulously. He said immediately, 'Far be it for me to want to laugh again, Anna. But that no man is an island is particularly apt on Yandilla.' And his eyes *were* laughing but not at her so much as at her astonishment.

'That's true,' Samson remarked lugubriously. Then his expression brightened fractionally, but only so that he no longer looked as if he was going to meet a hangman's noose, just a life sentence instead, and he went on to say, 'The breeze is right, the cutter's all rigged up, and seeing as the boss has declared a public holiday, what say we head out for the reef? Ever seen the reef proper, Anna?'

'Oh, Daddy!' Chrissy exclaimed delightedly. 'Did you have this planned?'

'Not at all,' her father said.

'But...why, there's a picnic basket here!' she said, darting just outside the door. 'And my togs—and Anna's...you did, you did!' she accused lovingly as she danced back inside, her face alight with joy. 'I thought you'd forgotten all about me!'

'Not so honey—I've found that's very hard to do.' His eyes teased her. 'But I did have some overdue business to attend to this morning. Now that it's all out of the way, though, there's no reason why we shouldn't declare a week of holiday. What say you, Anna?'

He looked across at Anna and caught her off guard. She had been about to suggest that he and Chrissy might like to spend the day on their own, but something stopped her. She thought later it might have been the way Chrissy was looking at her, expectantly and happily, so that she knew she would only be putting a damper on her day if she opted out.

She said weakly, 'Sounds fine! No, I've never seen the reef proper, Samson.' But she thought, oddly, be careful, Anna. Don't get trapped...trapped? How could I do that?

CHAPTER FIVE

THE HOLIDAY week passed surprisingly quickly and pleasantly, in fact. So pleasantly that Anna found herself reviewing each day in some perplexity.

She even wondered once if she had imagined what had occurred in the rain-soaked garden the night Richard had come home from America. But of course not, she had assured herself immediately. And what he did was unforgivable. What's more, to be as he's been since, as if it had never happened, could be construed as unforgiveable too. Not that I'm complaining about that! Only . . . well, I suppose in all honesty I can't help feeling that to be kissed so passionately, and then to have that kiss dismissed as if it was a non-event, is just a little galling.

Now, Anna, she chided herself with a wry smile, what an utterly female way of thinking! You know very well you'd have hopped on your high horse if he'd given you so much as a questionable look in these past few days. Yes, I would, she agreed with herself. And if I'm a little piqued, I guess it's because I haven't been able to dismiss it so completely from my mind. But that's obviously because it's a surprisingly new experience for me—whereas for him—ah, I'd say not new, nor was his technique even a little rusty, she thought somewhat sardonically, for all that everyone around here thinks that you're an inconsolable widower, Mr Gillespie. At least if it was, I'd hate to think what you could do when you were 'in practice' again!

Then she sighed suddenly, conscious of feeling faintly bitchy and not liking it. I suppose I did ask for it in a way, she mused. And he wasn't to know I was being deliberately disdainful, was he, when I said what I did? Yet is it really any wonder I got on the defensive and tried to put him in his place, in the circumstances? Besides, when you're twenty-three, you're entitled to wonder if you're ever going to fall in love...but I've been through that before! I just wish I'd been able to act as anything other than...Galatea personified when he did kiss me!

She grimaced ruefully as she thought of the Ancient Greek legend, but had to smile almost immediately. 'I might have given a good impression of it at the time, though,' she murmured, and winced.

Then she set her teeth and thought, well, if he can do it, I certainly can!

And she carried this thought with her through the leisurely days that followed although something else began to niggle at her, for the most part subconsciously, and only crystallised in the vague thought that not all governesses were as fortunate as she was. For every time she tried to fade gracefully into the background so that Chrissy and her father wouldn't feel as if she was playing gooseberry, Chrissy objected strongly and Anna found herself included in every expedition they made, in fact everything they did virtually, which was plenty.

They made several trips to the 'reef proper', as Samson called it, where they fished and swam and Anna found herself being instructed on this phenomenon—the eighth wonder of the world, as some people called the Great Barrier Reef.

'Like all living things,' Richard said to her, 'it's vulnerable. A lot of people think of all coral as hard and dead, the kind you see in souvenir shops, and of course it dies like all living things. But that's not its natural state. And like most other living things on this planet, it needs to be conserved.'

'Is it in any danger?' Anna asked curiously. 'It's... there's so much of it.'

He hesitated, then grinned at her ruefully. 'That's a loaded question to ask me, lady. I'm surprised someone hasn't warned you about my pet hobbyhorse, because I tend to become a bit demented on that subject. But yes,' he said more seriously, 'it could be in danger from lack of *thought*. Some people would like to drill for oil out here, which could do untold damage. It also appears to have natural enemies, like the Crown of Thorns starfish. Then, a lot of people don't realise what a world-wide attraction it is and how many tourist dollars it earns for Queensland, but there are problems inherent in that too, people tramping on it, pollution problems from boats as well as humans... I could rave on.'

'Do you... you sound a little as if you'd like to bar everyone from it?' Anna looked at him questioningly.

He shrugged. 'Sometimes when I see the wilful acts of destruction that go on—yes, I do feel like that.'

'That wouldn't be very fair.'

'No.' He glinted a grey-green glance at her. 'But it's often hard not to be possessive about the things you care for.'

'I suppose so,' she said quietly.

'Do you... have anything you feel that way about?'

The question took her by surprise. The boat was anchored and they were sitting in the shade of the blue and white striped awning. Samson was fishing over the stern and Chrissy was curled up asleep on a cushion beside Anna, replete with a large lunch and the inevitable excitement of a trip to the reef. The sky was a limitless pale blue and there was no other craft in sight. 'I think I feel that way mostly towards people,' she said slowly. 'Not possessive so much, but I like to think—to feel that I've understood them. I like to... get through to them. I think that's more important to me than anything else. I mean, I agree with you that it would be awful to lose this,' she waved a hand, 'but I've not yet become burningly militant about it.'

'That's perhaps the tallest order of all,' he said. 'Human relations. By comparison, what I feel for this reef is so simple. I know what's good for it and what's not. I know that it will grow and flourish under certain conditions and wither under others. I can go in and fight for it without a qualm. Your... chosen sphere is much harder.'

'You make it sound as if you've given up human relations,' she said with a tinge of surprise. 'Yet if you go to battle for this reef it's people you have to do battle with.'

'That's true,' he said idly. 'And no, I haven't given up on people. I just find it hard to combat a natural cynicism, I suppose you could say.' He moved and clasped his hands behind his head. He was wearing only a navy blue pair of board shorts and his tall strong body was evenly and goldenly tanned. By comparison, Anna was more conservatively dressed—she had on a short white towelling dress over her swimming costume, and she had noted that although she was not normally shy or prudish about being seen in a bathing costume, it had become a habit to don this towelling dress whenever she got out of the water—whenever she was in Richard Gillespie's company. She also knew why she did this. Because she couldn't quite get out of her mind the awful embarrassment of that night when the rain had plastered her clothing to her body so that she might as well not have been wearing any. And something about the way he was lying sprawled back so easily made her think of it again, and she felt a slight prickle run along her nerve ends that could have been apprehension.

She said, to cover it, the first thing that came to mind. 'Mind you, I don't know how you'd do battle with the Crown of Thorns starfish. It might be hard to get through to them!'

Richard grinned. 'You're not wrong.'

For a time there was a companionable silence. Then Chrissy stirred and Anna quite naturally gathered her into her lap and smoothed her tangled hair. 'I'm here, poppet,' she murmured, and Chrissy relaxed.

She looked up to see that Richard was staring at her with a curious intentness. 'What is it?' she asked, feeling suddenly awkward. Maybe I'm exceeding my duties towards Chrissy—when he's around at least, she wondered. After all, he is her father. Perhaps he thinks he should be the one to comfort her...

'It's...no,' he said, and looked away. Then he shrugged slightly. 'I was just thinking that Chrissy is generally less highly-strung these days. Thanks to you.' His eyes came back to rest on her face. 'And indirectly, I suppose, I was thinking that you're right to stick to human relations, because you seemed to have a definite knack for it. You've proved it with her.'

'Oh, I think I might still be a sort of nine-day wonder with Chrissy,' Anna said uncomfortably.

'And Phil? And Letty and Samson?' he queried with a faint smile. 'They've gone overboard too, in case you hadn't noticed. And they've always been ... rather particular.'

'Which Chrissy hasn't?' The words were out before she could stop them.

'I didn't say that.'

She looked up to see if he was laughing at her, but he wasn't. Yet they both began to smile ruefully. 'Did...no,' said Anna, her grin fading and a faint colour coming to her cheeks.

'Did I explain to her about matchmaking?' he queried perceptively, his smile still lingering. 'Yes, I did. I told her to make the best of you while she had you and not to entertain any other foolish notions. In a simplified form.'

'Oh.'

'Has she...?'

'No,' Anna said hastily, 'she hasn't.' She took a breath. 'And yes, she does tend to be highly-strung at times. But she's also one of the brightest eight-year-olds I've encountered, and I've met a few. So I think, as you said once, if that intelligence can be properly channelled and...and she has a...' She stopped and bit her lip.

'Go on.'

'Well, stability is important to any child,' she said quietly.

'You don't think she has that?'

'Yes, she does.' She hesitated. 'Not the best form of it, perhaps, because amongst other things, not having a mother makes her more than normally anxious about you. I saw that the night you came home. When you were delayed, she was terribly worried and for the first time since I've been here, wouldn't let me soothe her. Although we did finally work something out.' She told him about *Peter and the Wolf*. 'But she does have Letty and Phil. She could be a lot worse off.'

'And now she has you,' he commented, and his gaze lingered sombrely and broodingly on the sleeping child.

'Yes,' Anna said uncertainly, 'but...'

'Wha-a-a!' Samson's voice interrupted and the boat lurched so that Chrissy woke up. 'Holy mackerel! That's the biggest damn fish that's ever got away from me. Holy Moses! That was a marlin, I reckon, and I tell you what! Just lucky I wasn't strapped into no chair, otherwise he'da towed the boat away!'

Saved by the bell, Anna thought later, and felt a further prickle of uneasiness. It's going to be hard to leave here... But then I did make that plain, that I couldn't stay for ever...

THE LAZY days of the week continued uneventfully. They sailed and swam and fished, went bush-walking and played Monopoly at night, Chrissy's favourite game. Sometimes Phil joined them when her book was going badly, but she could never be depended upon to stay, because whenever an idea seized her, she dashed off to her studio, which was separated from the main house, and anyone passing by could hear the typewriter keys being pounded furiously.

'Murder and mayhem—it never ceases to amaze me that Phil has a fascination for such gruesome subjects,' Richard said once when they had been arbitrarily deserted in the middle of a game of lawn croquet—another of Chrissy's favourite games.

But there was affection in his voice, and indeed, Anna couldn't help but realise that he was very fond of his aunt by marriage, and she of him. In fact they shared a bond of humour and understanding that it was hard not to envy. But then Richard Gillespie was surprisingly human, Anna discovered more and more. Human and amusing and stimulating, mentally, and very nice to be with—now. As for Philadelphia Gillespie, she mused once—well, you could only call her a honey. Genuinely unbelievably vague some days, but so sweet with it you could only chuckle at her. And she was always worrying about something. If it wasn't Richard or Chrissy or anyone on Yandilla, it was

the state of the world or nuclear disarmament, one of her
pet hobbyhorses. But one of the nicest things about Phil,
Anna thought, is how she's gone out of her way to make
me feel like one of the family. And I'd like to think it's not
only because I saved Chrissy's life.

THE HIGHLIGHT of the holiday week came on the last day
of it, in the form of a beach barbecue to which the occu-
pants of Yandilla's nearest neighbouring island, Bedrock,
were invited.

Bedrock was leased from its owners by a Colonel Jackson who, Anna discovered, had been a great friend of
Richard's father and who also ran three-monthly semi-
nars on the island for people interested in alternative lifestyles and an increased self-awareness.

'How—unusual,' Anna remarked to Phil.

'It's not really,' Phil replied. 'I mean, he's not into any
particular creed or philosophy, just his own conviction that
more and more people...are...how can I put it...are
interested in getting back to nature, being more independ-
ent and creative and that going back to the basics of life
can help to achieve this. They're entirely self-supporting
on Bedrock. They grow their food—everything's home-
made, buildings—the lot. The only form of entertainment
they have is what they themselves provide. They weave and
make carpets, paint, make pottery. And the amazing thing
is that when he first started this ten years ago, he only got
a trickle of people, but now there's a waiting list for each
course. And I think the beauty of them is that they attract
such widely different people. At any one time on Bedrock
of the twenty or so people in the seminar you can find
business executives, out-of-work plumbers—the cost of it's
not much more than what it would cost you to live for
three months anyway—airline pilots, grandmothers—it's

quite incredible. And they sing—I must warn you the Colonel's very strong on community singing!'

'What's the Colonel really like, Letty?' Anna asked curiously that afternoon as they put the final touches to the salads.

'Mad,' Letty said laconically. 'But nice,' she added affectionately.

'Like . . . Phil?'

'Exactly,' Letty replied, and snorted for no apparent reason.

However, as the barbecue progressed, Anna was able to judge for herself. And she decided that Colonel Jackson, who bore the indelible stamp of the British Army and was, she judged, in his late fifties, was really a honey too. Strangely shy when you considered he had the fiercest blue eyes, and with courtly, old-world manners. Really, the last person you would imagine to be into alternative lifestyles, she mused, and caught her breath unexpectedly as she saw the Colonel's eyes rest briefly, on Phil, who was looking flushed and attractive, and then move away with an expression of something like pain in them. He's in love with her, unless I'm imagining things? I wonder . . .

But she didn't get much chance to wonder further, because the barbecue got livelier and livelier. Someone brought out a guitar and they had a sing-song as the sun set, turning the sea from blue to a living rose pink. Then they ate, which Anna did in the company of the guitarist, who told her he had been a used-car dealer, but since coming to Bedrock he had discovered that the moon inspired him to write poetry, which gave him more satisfaction than he had ever believed possible.

And when he was called upon to play again so they could dance, Anna confessed to Phil that she had never seen food disappear so fast or with so much appreciation.

'It's the meat,' Phil said laughingly. 'A lot of them are trying to be vegetarians. Yes, thank you, Colonel, I'd like to dance,' she added gracefully, and went away with the Colonel without the least hesitation.

Doesn't look too good for the Colonel, Anna mused. That's a pity—I think. With no children of her own…but then she's got Chrissy, and it's not for me to wonder why. And she joined in the gaiety and was much in demand as a dancing partner as the night wore on.

IT WAS inevitable that after a week off, it took some doing to get back to a working routine. But Chrissy did settle down after a few days.

As for Richard, he and Anna didn't have a great deal to do with each other, but what they did passed peacefully enough. In fact Anna even began to think that she was approaching the kind of relationship Phil had with him. A sort of laughing camaraderie and she wasn't at all prepared for the chain of events that disrupted it. Especially after the episode of the spider.

That happened late one evening when the house was quiet and Anna was sitting in her room working on a tapestry she'd been working on for a good six months without notably coming a great deal closer to finishing it.

When I do, though, she thought as she stitched neatly, I'll frame it and hang it in pride of place—no, I won't. I don't really like framed tapestries. Then why are you doing it? she asked herself. You've carted it around Queensland with you and worked on it in some highly unlikely places.

Because I've run out of books to read and...well, it soothes me, when there's nothing else to do. And that's the truth. I...

Something caught her eye at that moment, in the middle of this dissertation she was conducting with herself on the soothing aspect of handiwork, and she froze. For it was the largest, most hairy-looking spider she had ever seen, and it was advancing across the white rug beside her bed, towards her with a horrible military-like precision, not hurrying but purposefully as if it was not to be deflected.

She swallowed and cleared her throat and thought, stay calm, and threw her tapestry at it—only to see it emerge from beneath the khaki-coloured canvas unharmed, still marching purposefully towards her feet. She took flight then, through the french windows on to the verandah, and immediately thought, how stupid! Because if it's gone when I go back in, I'll never be able to sleep. I'll keep thinking it's lurking there somewhere. It has to be killed! How do people kill giant spiders?

'With their shoes, idiot,' she told herself, and bent down to take off her sandal, which was a pretty flimsy affair. 'I need a boot,' she muttered, and glanced around. But there was no boot in sight—not surprisingly, she thought. Her eyes alighted on a heavy cast iron ashtray. 'That'll do it!' She picked it up and peered around her verandah door— to see that the spider had stopped in the middle of the rug. And her eyes widened because it was all of three inches in circumference including its legs, and horribly hairy.

My God, she thought, I've never seen one this big. It'll make a mess on the rug. All the same, if it thinks it's going to share my bedroom with me, it's mistaken!

She raised the ashtray to shoulder height and prepared to hurl it—and nearly died of fright as someone tapped her on the shoulder.

'Oh!' she gasped, and turned to see Richard Gillespie regarding her quizzically. 'Oh...! You scared the living daylights out of me,' she added breathlessly.

'I'm sorry.' His eyes glinted with laughter. 'But I couldn't imagine what you were doing. You shot out of your room like a bat out of hell. Then you started to move around with such a great deal of stealth I was reminded of someone who'd found a body under the bed!'

'Nothing like that,' she said with a feeble grin. 'Only the biggest spider I've ever seen.' Her grin broadened. 'To tell the truth, I was sitting in there sewing at the time and...and well, I feel a bit like Little Miss Muffet, only she was eating. Do you—seeing that you're here, would you mind?' She looked up at him ruefully. 'I'm not normally scared of spiders and things, but this one I *am* scared of.'

'With pleasure,' he said promptly, and stepped into her room. 'Ah yes. He's quite harmless, actually, just a Huntsman, but he's one of the bigger ones I've seen. There,' he said, coming out again with the spider clinging to his handkerchief.

'What...what are you going to do with it?' asked Anna, backing away warily.

'Deposit in the shrubbery,' he answered, and did so at the edge of the verandah. 'They're very useful, as I'm sure you've taught a few kids.' He looked at her amusedly. 'Don't worry, we don't often get them in the house.'

'I'm relieved to hear you say so,' she said wryly. 'Even if they are harmless—well,' she shivered suddenly, 'it's not nice to think of them crawling all over you.'

He gazed at her thoughtfully, then surprised her by saying, 'Come and have a nightcap with me. It might help put it out of your mind before you go to bed and lie awake imagining things.'

'I...thanks.'

'What were you sewing?' he asked a little later when they were both sipping long cool drinks in the lounge.

'I'm working on a tapestry,' she said, and added ruefully, 'I expect I'll be working on it for years to come too, at the rate I'm going.'

'You don't sound terribly enthusiastic. Why do you persevere?'

'Strange you should ask that. I was asking myself the same question when I looked up and saw the spider. I...' she leant her chin on her hand, 'I bought it not long after I left home. I found that being away from home—you know, living in other people's houses or rented rooms... Well, put it this way, back home I was never at a loss for anything to do. I had my own flat that I always seemed to be decorating, or I was making clothes or I was expecting people and cooking,' she grimaced ruefully, 'or cleaning up. And I always had plenty to read and I had my own record player when I felt in the mood for music. But you can't carry sewing machines and record players and libraries round with you, and...and sometimes I wish I had just a single pot plant to water and talk to! But you can't carry them around either. So I hit on the idea of the tapestry. But it's not quite my creative line, I think.'

He didn't answer for a while and Anna looked around the room. It was lit by two tall Chinese lamps with turquoise shades that matched the raw silk coverings on the long settees, between which was the most magnificent Chinese carpet in delicate shades of turquoise and rose pink.

Then he said idly, 'How long do you plan to continue in this...homeless state?'

Anna raised her eyebrows and shrugged. 'I'd planned on two years. It's lately begun to occur to me that I might not last the distance...' She stopped abruptly, surprised to discover that this was an insidious thought that had really only surfaced as she had spoken the words, and she found herself feeling suddenly awkward. I wouldn't want him to think...read anything into it that isn't there. 'At least,' she amended with a smile, 'that it could take me two years to see Queensland this way, let alone the rest of it.'

'Is that such a bad thing, Anna? Do you have any special plans for when the two years is up?'

She sipped her drink. 'No. It's hard to plan that far ahead. I did think I'd like to teach...well, in a different kind of school from what I'm used to. Like...the one your mother taught at on Thursday Island. Letty was telling me about it,' she added hastily as his eyes narrowed.

'I think that would be a good idea. I think you have a gift for teaching.'

'I do love it,' she said honestly.

'And have you never thought of a more—lively kind of life?' Richard asked curiously.

'What do you mean?'

'Perhaps I shouldn't get into this with my record,' he murmured, 'but wealth and riches, and being able to go where the whim takes you, but in style. Being able to...have your clothes made for you. That kind of thing.'

She looked at him with a faint smile. 'With *my* record I hesitate to answer that honestly,' she told him.

'Why?'

'You might think I'm being disdainful...' Anna set her teeth and felt a faint colour come to her cheeks. Why ever did I get on to that? she wondered, and looked away.

He laughed softly and his grey-green eyes glinted appreciatively. He said, still sounding amused, 'I promise I won't.' Anna looked across at him in the soft blue light and he added gravely, 'Scout's honour.'

She relented a fraction. 'I guess everyone thinks about it and dreams about it. I do too.' She grimaced. 'I have to confess to a secret weakness as well. I take a ticket in the casket whenever I'm in the vicinity of a casket agency. Sometimes I take two. But to be serious,' she grinned, 'I don't think about it that much. I...don't really have much cause to. All I have to support is myself. It could be different if I had a family and so on, then I might hanker after it much more. But...' she stopped, 'I...when we had that barbecue, we were lively and I think we all enjoyed it tremendously. But it wasn't an essentially wealthy thing to do.'

'No,' Richard said slowly. He drained his glass and set it down.

'You don't sound so sure,' she said uncertainly after a minute or two. '*Did* I sound smug and disdainful? I didn't mean to.'

He had been looking away from her at nothing in particular yet with a strange fixity. But as she spoke his eyes came back to rest on her face swiftly and his expression softened. 'No, you didn't. Just very earnest and rather solemn, and I know—now—you mean every word you say. I'm sorry,' he stood up as he spoke in one lithe movement and reached out a hand to draw her to her feet, 'I'm sorry for what happened the night I got back, Anna. And every other time we've...I haven't understood. But you're wrong about one thing,' he said very quietly as she stared up at him bemused. 'That *was* an essentially wealthy thing to do, that barbecue. It was wealthy because Phil is a little nicely mad and Letty and Samson are two of the nicest people I know and Colonel Jackson is actually very sane, though not pretty,' his lips twitched, 'and for some strange reason likes to surround himself with nicely mad people, some nicer than others. And you. You remind me of the Colonel in a way, so sane yet touched with an understanding of these things. But more than pretty... Then there was Chrissy, and Chrissy is...well, we all know the kind of enchanted web she weaves. That's an amazing array of wealth of spirit, don't you think?'

They stared at each other until Anna said, 'That puts it in a nutshell. But,' her voice was husky and her eyes searched his face, 'what about you? You were there too?'

He grimaced. 'I might be the poor relation.'

'Why?' she whispered, conscious of a sudden, compelling urge to get to the bottom of this man who puzzled her immensely, she found.

'It's a long story, Anna,' he said dryly. 'But it's a long time since I felt much wealth of spirit.'

'I know,' she said involuntarily, and winced at her own temerity. But I do know, she thought. How could I not know when I've seen the other side of him? The cold, cruel side. 'You...but when you're with Chrissy, and the others, you're...transformed,' she said haltingly.

'I guess Chrissy's my saving grace.' He shrugged. 'Who would have thought...' He stopped abruptly and it was as if he deliberately changed the direction of his thoughts. He smiled down at her, that devastating smile that always seemed to make her heart beat a little faster. 'You don't have to worry about me, though. Phil and Letty and Samson do enough of that.' His eyes glinted devilishly. 'By the way, I'm quite sure there must be a sewing machine on Yandilla, and I know there's a record player,' he pointed to the magnificent hi-fi set in the corner of the room. 'As for books, I know there are plenty of them too. Please feel free to borrow them and play the records. I'll also speak to Letty about letting you potter around her kitchen and...'

'Oh—thank you,' Anna said confusedly, 'but I'd rather you didn't speak to Letty. She's...well, she's accepting me more and more into her kitchen and so on, really she is. And I'd rather it came naturally.'

'All right,' said Richard after a moment, and looked at her thoughtfully. 'Maybe you're right. The other thing is, you haven't had any time off—I mean off Yandilla—since you came here. Part of the arrangement was...'

'Yes, I know,' she interrupted hurriedly. 'That I have a weekend off every month. But I really haven't felt the need to get away yet.'

He lifted his eyebrows. 'I'm sure it will come,' he told her. 'You can get island claustrophobia too, you know. But it's up to you. Well, think you can get to sleep now without worrying about spiders?'

'Oh yes,' she said wryly. 'You must think I'm a bit of an idiot.'

'Not at all. In fact I was beginning to think you were the most terrifyingly...competent person I've ever known. So it's a relief to find you're human after all. Goodnight, Anna,' he added with a wickedly amused look, and held the heavy double lounge doors open for her.

'I...goodnight,' she said uncertainly, not sure whether to be cross or gratified or what. Here we go again, she thought. He's *done* it again. Turned the tables on me somehow...but no, I won't be cross. He's been so nice tonight. She looked up at him as she passed through the doors and smiled. 'Thanks,' she said quietly, and walked unhurriedly in the direction of her bedroom.

But she didn't get to sleep immediately, though not on account of spiders.

And she was struck by a strange thought the next morning. That there was absolutely no reminder of Chrissy's mother in the house at all. At least, no photos, framed or otherwise. And nothing amongst Chrissy's personal possessions that she treasured particularly because it had belonged to her mother. It was almost as if she had never existed, Anna thought with an inward shiver. Except that she was undoubtedly still there in the heart of the man who had lost her. Perhaps he can't bear the pain of seeing her face even in a photo, she mused.

I wonder what she was like? If one had known her, you might have a better idea of...at least it would be easier than wondering how you measured up to a ghost...

She closed her eyes abruptly and found herself feeling hot and cold at the same time. Whatever was she thinking? And she resolutely pushed the thought out of her mind.

CHAPTER SIX

'LOTUS LADY just called,' Samson announced, and deposited a canvas bag on the verandah table. It was mid-afternoon and Letty had just served tea.

'Oh, good!' enthused Phil. 'I'm running short of carbon paper and I ordered some ages ago—perhaps it's come.' She untied the string of the bag and delved into it and withdrew a bundle of mail. 'Who's going to play postman? If my carbon paper still hasn't arrived . . .'

'I will,' Richard said, and took the bundle of letters out of her hand as she started to look distracted. He leafed through them. 'Two—no, three for you, Phil, one for Sunshine, a whole lot of ominous-looking bills for me,' he said wryly, 'and . . .' His voice trailed off in a way that made most of them look at him enquiringly.

'Whatsa matter?' asked Letty. 'You look as if you've seen a ghost.'

'No,' he said slowly, but his voice was oddly grim as he studied the letter in his hands. Then he raised his eyes and looked straight at Anna. 'But perhaps I didn't make one thing clear to you, Anna. Nobody on Yandilla has anything whatsoever to do with Mike Carmody. And if you wish to stay here, you'd be wise to make it plain to him that that includes you.'

Anna gaped at him. 'I don't know what you're talking about!' she said at last.

He looked at her coldly. 'You might when you've read this,' he said, and tossed the letter he was holding on to the table in front of her. Then he stood up and walked inside abruptly and a moment later, for all to hear, the study door was closed ungently.

Anna stared at the letter and noted that it wasn't postmarked and was simply addressed to Miss Anna Horton, Yandilla. She reached for it and opened it with fingers that weren't quite steady. And her eyes widened incredulously as she scanned the letter, not taking in the contents because the big bold signature seemed to leap at her—Mike Carmody.

She looked up to see four pairs of eyes resting anxiously on her. 'I think somebody ought to explain,' she said helplessly. 'How did he know who it was from? And why would that make him so angry?'

Letty was the first to break the silence. 'Er...why, Chrissy love, I think our pavlova for dinner might be ready. Going to help me whip the cream and make the filling?' She held out her hand.

Chrissy looked at Anna and for a moment it seemed as if she was going to refuse. Then she slipped her hand into Letty's and went with her surprisingly docilely.

Phil sighed audibly and Anna looked at her bewilderedly as Samson too departed, but in the opposite direction and with a rueful shake of his head at Anna.

'Please tell me what's going on, Phil?' Anna begged.

'I...think it's up to Richard to tell you,' Phil said at last.

'Oh, that's all very well!' Anna exclaimed angrily. 'But if the way he looked at me is anything to go by, I don't particularly feel like asking him! And anyway, he can't dictate what I do with my free time or who I see. Can he?'

Phil wrung her hands—an indication she was deeply troubled. 'I suppose not. But he can make your life hell on account of it,' she said candidly. 'Does...do...I mean, is it important to you to...keep in contact with Mike Carmody?' she added delicately and a touch curiously. 'Because I can tell you he and Richard are—well, don't get on.' She pulled a face.

'No. At least, not particularly. Oh,' Anna sighed exasperatedly, 'that's not the point! The point is I'm legally of age, as the saying goes, in fact I'm more, and I'm employed here as a governess, but that doesn't mean he owns me body and soul and can dictate to me who I may or may not see!' She took a breath, her face flushed and her eyes bright and angry. 'And to do it that way too,' she went on furiously. 'So that I felt like a child being reprimanded! But for something I didn't even know about! Nor am I likely to, by the sound of things,' she added caustically.

Phil winced visibly. 'My dear, some things are hard to explain. And of course you're right! There was no need for him to do it like that. Oh, I'd be a little angry with him for doing it like that, certainly!' she conceded. 'But...'

'A little angry?' Anna fumed. 'The trouble with Richard Gillespie—I'm sorry, Phil—but the trouble with him is that he gets away with murder! And,' her gaze fell on the letter and she read the brief contents swiftly, 'all it says here,' she lifted her eyes to Phil, 'is that if I have any free time, he'd be happy to show me the Hinchinbrook Channel. Now I can't see how that could affect...my *boss* in any way or that it's any concern of his. And furthermore,' she stood up, 'I'm going in there to tell him that right now, and to arrange to take a day off as soon as I can!' She set her lips in a stubborn line and stalked inside, leaving Phil staring after her dazedly.

FIVE MINUTES later Anna had relieved herself of these same sentiments in no uncertain terms and she stared at

Richard Gillespie across the broad expanse of his desk, undaunted and unshaken by the coldly unmoved look she was on the receiving end of.

'You can be as angry as you like,' she said furiously. 'And if I have to resign to prove my point, I'll do it. But you seem to think you can get away with murder where I'm concerned so long as you apologise afterwards!'

'I have no intention of apologising to anybody on the subject of Mike Carmody,' he said violently. 'Nor do I have any intention of allowing myself to be dictated to on my affairs by anyone, but least of all *you.*' He looked at her contemptuously, his eyes smouldering.

'But this isn't your affair,' she pointed out hotly. 'That's what I'm trying to say! And I'm also trying to say that I object to the way you handled the whole business out there. I don't have to take that from anyone. And you've now treated me that way just once too often, Richard Gillespie,' she stormed.

'If that's the way you feel, then it is better if you go. In any case it's better that you go, Anna,' he added curtly, and his eyes glittered strangely.

'I...*why?*' she demanded, not sure she was hearing right and totally taken aback by this unexpected twist.

'Because you were right,' he said tightly. 'Chrissy needs a mother, not someone who'll be here today, gone tomorrow or in a few weeks or a couple of months or whenever the whim takes you. It's going to break her heart to see you go today, as it is.'

'I...I...' Anna whispered, and sank down into a chair as if she'd received a body blow.

'I thought you might get some satisfaction from being able to say I told you so,' Richard said grimly, his grey-green eyes raking her face mercilessly.

Anna licked her lips. 'If you did think that,' she said in a low choking voice, 'then you're more of a bastard than even I thought.'

'Then that's another reason why we should—part company, don't you think?' he said evenly. 'Although I'm quite sure one of the reasons you feel that way is because you can't forget that I kissed you once and you enjoyed it. But you won't allow yourself to admit it, despite the fact that you can't help thinking about it still.'

This was so true, yet so unfair, Anna could do nothing but stare at him disbelievingly. Then she found her voice, although it was strangely husky, and she said with a world of angry contempt, 'I've made allowances for you, you know. I've tried to convince myself that you are the way you are because of losing Chrissy's mother. Because you can't find anyone to measure up to her. But I always felt it didn't quite ring true. And now, despite the fact that everyone here thinks you're an inconsolable widower, I don't think it's that way at all. Oh no,' she said, 'and they might change their opinions if they'd seen the side of you I have. You're nothing but a...a...' she searched for the right word, only to find there was no other than one she'd already used, although she embellished it, 'an arrogant bastard, and you deserve to be pursued by fortune-huntresses and all the rest, because you don't have a heart!'

But to her astonishment he only raised his eyebrows at this outpouring and looked, if anything, faintly amused. 'Who told you I was an inconsolable widower?'

'It doesn't matter,' she gritted through her teeth.

'But I'd like to know. Because I can't imagine anyone here telling you that.'

Anna frowned. 'Well, indirectly they...' She tailed off uncertainly.

'How very loyal of them,' he commented. 'But you see, Julie was a faithless, treacherous woman, and the only reason we weren't divorced was because she died before it could happen.'

For the second time that afternoon she stared at him with her mouth open and a look of supreme shock and stunned disbelief in her eyes. 'But...' she whispered at last, 'this...you're talking about Chrissy's mother!'

'Do you think I don't know that?' he said angrily. 'Do you realise that not a day goes by that I don't look at Chrissy and wonder how she could be such a perfect little girl when she had two such mismatched parents? Do you think that prevented her *mother* from using her as some kind of a bargaining tool?'

Anna winced.

'Yes, she did,' he said coldly. 'That's the kind of woman Chrissy's mother was. And that's why I'm not exactly an inconsolable widower. And no, I don't think I have a heart. At least, what I have left tells me that if I ever do remarry, this time it will be to someone who's prepared to be a good wife and mother in the old-fashioned sense of the word. Someone who cares about her home and her children and values and non-material things I can give her more than the material ones. That's the yardstick I'd use now. *Look,*' he said savagely, 'for what it's worth, I don't...didn't blame Julie so much for the fact that we cooled off towards each other. Or to put it another way, I blamed myself equally, because it was a violent mutual attraction that didn't take into account the basic differences between us until it was too late. But when that became apparent, there should have been a civilised way of dealing with it for Chrissy's sake. In fact I offered her one which she declined although she *knew* I was going to fight her every inch of the way over custody of Chrissy.'

Anna stared at him. 'I didn't know,' she said shakenly.

'Well, now you do,' he said shortly. 'And since we're being so beautifully frank, in case you're wondering what Mike Carmody has to do with all this, I'll tell you that too. The last words Julie said to me before she died were that she was going to Mike, who really loved her. Not that I needed telling that he was infatuated with her. Most men she came in contact with were. Nor did I need telling that they'd become lovers . . .'

Anna closed her eyes, still trying to take in what she had just learnt. And she found that a lot of little things suddenly fell into place, things Phil had said, and Letty, things she had not understood at the time or misinterpreted. *If only someone had just told me the truth*, she thought despairingly. *It explains so much. Why he treats women the way he does* . . .

She looked up at him at last, her eyes clearly expressing some of the turmoil she felt. 'I . . . I'm truly sorry,' she said haltingly. 'I had no idea—if I had, I wouldn't have said some of the things I did.'

'Oh, I think you would,' he observed. 'I think you have a habit of speaking your mind.'

'I might never again,' she murmured, still feeling totally floored by what she had just learnt, and with an effort she attempted to wrench her mind away from it. 'I . . . but to get back to Chrissy and what we were saying earlier. I *can* see how fond she is getting of me. And it's by no means a one-sided thing,' she added painfully. 'I just didn't realise it was possible to become so attached to someone else's child. I honestly don't know what to do. Maybe you're right, maybe it is better if I go now rather than later.'

There was a long silence. They didn't look at each other. Then Richard said abruptly, 'There's another solution, Anna. You could marry me.'

Anna felt suddenly as if she was suffocating and she flushed brightly. 'I don't think that's in very good taste,' she said stonily.

'I do,' he answered surprisingly. 'In fact I think it's the perfect solution—for both of us.'

She sprang up agitatedly. 'But you've just *told* me…how could you ask anyone to marry you after what you've just told me? But as for me, when you think of the number of times we've quarrelled I'm surprised—I'm really surprised you would even consider me. Particularly if you mean what I think you mean when you talk about an old-fashioned wife. Someone who'll meekly accept everything you choose to throw at her!'

He smiled slightly. 'I'm sure I'd have to learn to duck if I tried that with you!'

'If you think this is something to joke about…'

'No,' he interrupted, and came to stand beside her. 'Why don't you sit down and we can discuss this rationally?'

Anna trembled and thought distractedly, this can't be happening to me. Does he really think I can sit down and talk about this rationally? As if we're discussing the price of eggs? She took an uncertain breath and stared at him— and was unwittingly flooded with an acute sense of proximity so that every other time she had been physically conscious of him faded beneath this particular onslaught. It's almost as if I'm seeing him for the first time, she thought dazedly. But in an old context—as I could see him if I accepted this incredible offer, making love to me, stroking my body with those lean, strong hands, watching me with that clever, probing grey-green gaze, holding me against that tall, strong body…

She sat down abruptly amid a confusion of clamouring pulses and with a lurching heart in case he could read her thoughts.

But if he could, he gave no indication of it. He merely waited with a polite, grave attentiveness until she said stiffly, 'All right. I suppose we can discuss it at least.'

'Good,' he drawled, and sat down on the corner of the desk. 'Anna, I've just told you how I feel about these things. And the reason I thought we'd...be right for each other is because you once told me how you felt. You said you didn't think you were made for a—quote—grand, hit-you-on-the-head kind of passion—unquote. You spoke of a slow sort of warmth that grows and feeds on a mutual interest. I think we have that. We have Chrissy, and you've fitted into the lifestyle of Yandilla so well, I can't believe we wouldn't have that in common too.'

Anna moved restlessly. If I'd had the slightest inkling how my own words were going to be used against me, she thought tormentedly, I'd have sealed my lips for ever. 'I...'

'No, hang on, let me finish. There's a lot more we have in common. You also told me once you're not particularly interested in a madly jet-setting existence. You like your pleasures to come more simply. That's how I like it too. She...Julie was bored to tears here after a while. Then too, we agree that children need stability and care and nurturing and they need to have time invested in them. We needn't, incidentally, confine ourselves to Chrissy either. We could have as many children as you liked, and I think you'd like that.' He looked at her probingly before he went on, 'So you see, in a sense we could make a better marriage than most because we have all these basic elements and perhaps, most importantly, we've each suffered our disillusionments and wouldn't be going into it with any...inflated expectations.'

'I...it sounds so sane when you say it like that. But I think you've twisted my words a little out of context,' Anna said with an effort. 'I didn't mean that my parents weren't in love when they married. I only meant that it...didn't strike them like a bolt of lightning. And,' her voice shook a little, 'what you're suggesting is that we get married for a variety of very...well, businesslike reasons, some of them...or practical ones, put it that way, and *then* hope that it happens that way for us too.'

'You don't think it could?' Richard queried.

She looked away. 'I don't know. How could I?'

He waited for a moment, then he said, 'Anna, there's something else, from your point of view. If, and I don't know exactly what kind of an unhappy experience you had, but if it means you find it hard to contemplate marriage because of it, wouldn't this be a...better way for you? At least you like me, I think. On my better days, of course.' He grinned faintly.

O, what a tangled web we weave... She sighed. I should tell him now, she thought. I should set the record straight about this for once and for all. But is it so important? I can't—in all sanity, I can't marry him for these reasons. I couldn't marry anyone like that.

She took a deep breath and started to speak, but was stopped by a shaft of pain that struck her heart like an arrow. Least of all him, she thought dazedly. Because...

'Anna?'

'I...I'm sorry, Richard,' she said confusedly. 'I...do you know that's the first time I've ever called you that, directly? Surely that demonstrates how crazy it is for us to even think of getting married?' she asked huskily with sudden tears in her eyes.

He looked at her steadily. 'Perhaps,' he said sombrely. 'If that's the way you feel...'

'*Yes*. But what will we do?' she asked, brushing away the tears.

'You tell me, Anna.'

'Do you want me to go? For Chrissy's sake I will. But— oh God! I've... all these weeks I've known that it was getting harder and harder to even think of leaving...'

'Don't cry,' he said with an unexpected compassion that, if anything, made it harder for her to stem the tears.

She stood clenching her fists and biting her lip. Then she whirled on her heel and ran from the room. And he didn't try to stop her.

IT WAS Phil who found her lying on her bed, dry-eyed now but staring fixedly at the wall opposite.

'Anna?'

Anna didn't move. But she said tiredly, 'Come in.'

'Are you all right?'

'No.' Her eyes didn't leave the wall.

'I tried to warn you,' Phil said diffidently. She closed the door.

'Yes,' Anna answered bleakly.

'My dear...'

'But you didn't tell me,' Anna broke in, her eyes at last leaving the wall. 'No one told me about Chrissy's mother. And I've made the most awful fool of myself...'

Phil picked up one of her hands and massaged it gently, but there was a curiously alert look in her blue eyes as if she was pondering something unseen. Then she said quietly, 'We don't talk about it, for Chrissy's sake. We pretend it never happened that way.'

'What was she like?' Anna found herself asking after a minute or two.

'Julie was beautiful. She had the kind of beauty that could turn the worst day of your life into something worthwhile just to see her. And she was fearless and stimulating—in that respect she and Richard were well matched. She could surf and sail as well as he could, she loved to scuba-dive, but it was also a headstrong kind of fearlessness that was always seeking new challenges. She could never sit still unless she was planning what to do next. She was also stubborn to a fault, but I think a lot of that was due to a difficult childhood, a rather poor one, and a particularly repressive father who invoked authority as much for the sake of it as anything else. I think Julie grew up resenting authority similarly, for the sake of it, blindly and often mulishly.

'But in other respects,' Phil went on slowly, 'they weren't well matched. I don't think she ever realised just how much Yandilla means to Richard, as a lifestyle and not in the way that it's lovely to have your own island to retreat to now and then and bring your friends to. She was never happy for long here. And I don't think she ever understood that spending money in itself, more or less simply because it's there, buys you very little in the long run. Which led Richard to wonder often, I'm sure, what she enjoyed most about their marriage—him, or spending his money.

'Oh,' Anna whispered, her eyes wide. 'Did she marry him for his money?'

Phil sighed. 'I don't honestly think so. I think the attraction was so strong, in the early days, she'd have married him if he'd been a pauper. But what she couldn't grasp was that if it was there, why not spend it? And while Richard isn't mean at all he...well, when you've always had it anyway, I think you find it in not very good taste to throw it about at whim. It's also harder, when you've always had it, to understand how it affects people who haven't. Some people anyway.'

'No...no wonder he's rather...'

'Wary?' Phil supplied, and smiled. 'I suppose so.'

'Is Chrissy like her at all?' Anna asked huskily.

'Oh yes,' said Phil. 'In lots of ways. Enchanting, fear-less about some things, a little more highly-strung than most of us, but even though she's so young, I can see a much more *caring* personality developing in Chrissy.'

Anna lay still and listened to the faint, familiar sounds of the house as dusk approached. She said at last, 'If it hadn't happened, would they have divorced, do you think?'

'Who could say?' Phil answered thoughtfully. 'Things were bad and I can't deny that Richard can be...hard, very hard. But he did offer her a compromise which amounted to them virtually living their own lives but staying married for Chrissy's sake. I don't know if that kind of thing ever works very well, but anyway, one thing he was adamant about was parting with Chrissy.'

'She wanted Chrissy?'

'Yes. Stubbornly, furiously and determinedly too, al-though she left her to Letty's care most of the time. But Chrissy adored her—when she saw her. She adored them both.'

'She told me she can still remember her,' said Anna.

Phil smiled wistfully. 'I doubt it.'

'How...sad,' Anna said with an inward shiver.

'It was sad. These things always are,' Phil shrugged. 'But it got sadder in a curious way, unfortunately. No one in their right minds could have wished that kind of a so-lution to it. And I think Richard will always be a little haunted by it and experience a sense of guilt.'

'But it wasn't his fault that she died?'

'Oh no. The actual...the way it happened was typi-cally Julie. She took a boat out on her own one night

without even telling Samson, and got caught in a squall
that blew up unexpectedly. It was the way she lived, and
there was always the distinct possibility that one day she'd
take up a challenge that was too great for her. But unfortunately, Richard wasn't here. He'd been at a sugar board
conference in Cairns for two days when it happened. And
they'd had a monumental row when he left.'

'And then she was dead,' Anna said slowly. 'I think I
understand what you mean. Would—she have gone to
Mike?' she asked involuntarily.

Phil shook her head sorrowfully. 'I don't think so. But
there's no doubt she'd led Mike on to believe she would
one day. He was very young then, Anna, and absolutely
infatuated, and she was the kind of person who...used
other people. But that too provided a further source of
bitterness. Mike was so infatuated he was beyond much
good sense for a while after she died. And he put it around
the community that Richard had...that she'd been so
desperately unhappy she'd taken her own life.'

Anna stared at Phil in horror.

'But that wasn't true, Anna. However unhappy, Julie
would no more have dreamt of doing away with herself
than I would imagine I could fly.'

'I'm surprised he still has the Yandilla contract...'

'Oh, that was my doing,' Phil said, brightening a little.
'I put my foot down there. Men do funny things when they
imagine they're in love and I didn't like to see him penal-
ised for her...well, I've known Mike since he was a baby
too,' she said ruefully, 'and at that stage he only had one
leaky old boat and the Yandilla contract was about his
only sure form of income.'

'You're so very sweet, Phil,' said Anna with a break in
her voice.

Phil contemplated her silently for a long time. Then she said, 'And you're more upset about this, Anna, than someone who has recently come into our midst need be. Would you like to tell me why?'

Anna sighed. 'Phil, you're not going to believe this—but Richard just asked me to marry him.'

To her astonishment, Phil didn't even look faintly surprised. She merely grimaced wryly and said, 'I was afraid of that.'

Anna sat up abruptly. 'What do you mean? Did you *know* he was going to?' she asked incredulously.

'I suspected. For two reasons—you and Chrissy get along so well. You have a rapport that makes it more than a governess-pupil relationship. And for some time now I've wondered whether he wasn't thinking of marrying again for Chrissy's sake.' She looked at Anna candidly. 'There's something else too. In lots of ways you're the antithesis of Julie, Anna.'

'So he told me,' Anna said dryly. 'None of which leaves me feeling much complimented or enthusiastic about his proposal.'

Phil sat forward. 'That's what I was afraid of. And you said no?'

'Of course I said no!' answered Anna, feeling angry tears welling. 'Would you have done any different? You don't marry for those reasons!'

Phil hesitated. Then she said carefully, 'You might do it for another reason, though. You might do it because you're attracted to him quite strongly.'

Anna closed her eyes and was silent. 'How did you know?' she said finally. 'I haven't even let myself... really admit that.'

'People often think I see a lot less than I do,' Phil remarked wryly. 'And I might have noticed it because you, in fact both of you, have been at great pains to hide it.'

'He...' Anna stopped and bit her lip. But she thought almost immediately that it was obviously useless to try and hide much on Yandilla. 'He hasn't always tried to hide it. In fact it's given him great pleasure on occasions to—to take advantage of me quite unfairly. But the point is, Phil,' she said bitterly, 'he's done it in a way that's left me certain I could be any reasonably pretty girl—just a face and a figure, no more. In fact I think he can take me or leave me without a second thought, as he probably can all women. And if you must know, the thought that I might have joined a succession of... of star-struck nannies fills me with a sense of humiliation and horror.' The tears trickled down her cheeks and fell on to her hands unheeded as she stared at Phil.

'Then you do think you might have fallen in love with him?' Phil asked gently.

'I...I've no idea what it is,' Anna said wearily. She grimaced. 'What is this thing they call love? If it's this... this mixture of uncertainty, of...sometimes I'm sure I hate him! Quite sure and not without cause. In fact I think I hate him right now.'

'My dear!' Phil said concernedly.

'I shouldn't,' Anna sobbed. 'I've learnt so much today which I never knew that *explains* so much. But I can't help feeling as if I've had a slap in the face, somehow, all the same.'

'Anna, I think that one of the problems of this kind of situation is that it's hard not to have preconceived ideas about love.'

Anna stared at her. 'Oh, Phil,' she said grimly, 'don't let me get on to that subject. If I hadn't thought I was wise on these matters, and insisted on delivering myself of my wisdom to him, together with a whole lot of other rubbish, I might not be in this mess. Look, all I know now is that not so long ago I was happy and carefree. Then I met Richard Gillespie and I haven't known whether I've been on my head or my heels since. And I haven't been happy either, and if that's love, I think I'd rather live without it.'

'The thing is,' Phil said quietly, 'if it is, it's not something you can turn off like a tap. It's not something that you can say to yourself, now look, this is silly! I've got to stop this! It will still be there.'

'Then all the more reason to test it,' Anna said bleakly. 'I have to go in any case, Phil. The longer I stay, the harder it's going to be for Chrissy. And even if it does turn out to be…true blue, as they say, there isn't a great future for it. Would you care to marry a man who doesn't love you in return?'

'Go?' Phil looked suddenly disconcerted.

'Yes. In fact, in lieu of marrying him, that's what Richard wants me to do—and he's right. And the sooner the better.'

'Oh, but you can't go just like that, Anna! You see, I…I'm expected in London in a week's time.' Phil looked suddenly embarrassed. 'Believe it or not, they're making a series of television plays from some of my books and they want me there to consult with the scriptwriters. The letter came in the mail today, as a matter of fact,' she said breathlessly, and drew a crumpled airmail envelope from her pocket. 'At least, confirmation of the dates. It…it… well, I'd really love to do it, but of course I don't have to,' she said confusedly. 'It's not as if it's a contract thing, more of a courteous gesture to me, but—well, it's not that important! Certainly not as important as Chrissy…I mean, if you and I both deserted her…I mean…' And she looked as flustered and remorseful as only Phil could.

Anna stared at her. 'How long for?'

'Oh, only six weeks to two months, but…'

'Does Richard know?'

'Oh, yes! But he might have forgotten. He was rather surprised when I accepted. I'm generally such a stick-in-the-mud… But that's neither here nor there. These things can't be helped, can they? Now promise me something, you're not to worry about this, not even to give it a second thought.'

'Phil,' Anna said helplessly, 'there must be some arrangement we could make!'

'Anna,' Phil smiled at her, 'it was only a little ego trip really. Please, I don't want you to think about it any more. You've got enough to worry about as it is.'

CHAPTER SEVEN

'CAN I talk to you?' Anna said hesitantly.

It was late, and if it hadn't been for Phil's revelation earlier in the day about her trip to London, Anna would not now be in the boatshed trying to talk to her boss, she knew.

In fact, she had had to force herself to go to dinner, although it hadn't turned out to be the ordeal she had feared. But only because Richard had received a phone call before the meal, a business call that had been a lengthy one, and Letty had finally taken his dinner to him in the study on a tray.

Yet it hadn't been a bed of roses either. Chrissy had been visibly tense and Phil unsuccessfully trying to project the image of not having a care in the world. Only Letty had appeared normal.

Richard looked up from the bench he was working at. He was still wearing the same jeans and khaki bush shirt he had had on earlier—for that matter, Anna was still wearing the simple lime green sundress she had worn all day that showed off her smooth tanned shoulders and went with the darkness of her hair. He said, 'If you want to. Where's Chrissy?'

'She's asleep.'

He glanced at his watch and looked surprised. 'It's later than I thought.' He stretched and stood up and leant back against the bench, folding his arms across his chest and regarding her impersonally.

'I . . . was waiting for you to come up,' Anna said awkwardly. 'But perhaps this is a better spot anyway. More,' she hesitated and looked round and up at the exposed rafters and the shadows the light threw on the whitewashed walls, 'private . . .'

He smiled, but without humour. 'I thought we'd dealt with everything of a private nature between us, Anna,' he said coolly. 'Not that it's possible to keep anything private on Yandilla for long.'

'I had worked that out,' she answered dryly. 'But this is about Phil. Has she said anything to you since we talked this afternoon?'

'No. Nothing she wouldn't normally have said. Why?' He sounded curious.

'I . . . this afternoon I told her I was leaving.' Anna looked down at her hands, then she raised her eyes and their gazes locked.

'You don't waste much time, do you, Anna?'

She flushed faintly, but said resolutely, 'I'd thought we'd decided it would only make it harder if I did. But something's come up which has made me wonder . . . well,' she broke off helplessly, 'I think you should know about it at least.'

He frowned. 'Like what?'

She told him about Phil's overseas trip.

'Hell,' he muttered. 'I'd forgotten about it. But I'm sure it wasn't due just yet. She hasn't got the dates mixed up, has she?'

'I don't think so,' Anna said slowly. 'No, she got the letter today. Maybe she had the dates mixed up when she first told you about it?'

'That's more than bloody likely,' he said impatiently. 'And she wants to go?'

'Very much, I think. But she said there was no possibility of going if I was leaving too—that it wouldn't be fair to Chrissy if we both deserted her at the same time. But I think too she was really disappointed, although she covered up as quickly as she could, and I doubt if you'd get her to admit it now.'

Richard stared past her for a moment. 'I see,' he said at last. 'And how did she take your news otherwise? Was she surprised?'

'Oh yes,' Anna replied glibly, having anticipated this question, and she prayed that he would leave it at that.

He raised his eyebrows. 'What did you tell her?'

She looked at him uneasily and resolved never to utter futile prayers again. 'The truth,' she said baldly at last.

'Did you now,' he remarked with some irony. 'You surprise me.'

'I surprised myself,' she replied truthfully. In more ways than one, she thought but didn't say. Then, because just looking at him leaning negligently against the bench with his fair hair ruffled and his tall figure etched darkly on the wall behind him had the power to disturb her, she found, she added with a barely muted sort of hostility, 'As a matter of fact, she wasn't that surprised. It seems she's suspected all along that you would remarry for Chrissy's sake and that I might be a likely candidate because I get on so well with her.'

Richard laughed briefly. 'I'm quite demolished! I shall never scoff at feminine intuition again. But let's get one thing straight, Anna...' His eyes roamed over her in a way that was becoming familiar, and she tensed and vowed not to let herself be affected by it. 'That wasn't the only reason I wanted to marry you.'

'It was the main reason,' she forced herself to say unemotionally.

'It was *a* reason,' he countered. 'And one that I'd surely have to take into account—don't you see that?'

'Of course, but...'

'But so far we've only...skated over another vital element. I've always been intrigued at the thought of taking you to bed. In fact I told you about it when it first occurred to me, which was at our very first meeting—if you recall.' His lips quirked, although his words were deadly serious.

'Yes,' she said grimly. 'You did.'

'And you were very angry with me,' he supplied. 'Although for a brief moment I got the impression you were a little intrigued yourself even at that early stage of our relationship. Were you?'

Anna set her teeth. 'This is beside the point,' she said with an effort.

'It's not so far as I'm concerned,' he said quietly. 'And I've thought of it since.'

'You...you told me once,' she said raggedly, 'that you'd quite lost your—half-formulated desire to see me without my clothes. Which I took to mean you'd lost interest in taking me to bed...' She trailed off frustratedly, cursing herself inwardly in case her words had sounded piqued which was the last impression she wished to create.

'And you were very angry with me again.' His lips twitched. 'And rightly so. I do admit I can be a bastard sometimes. But I said that not because I meant it, but because you were so cross and so determined to put me in my place...which I deserved at the time,' he added wryly. 'Then too, it was after that I kissed you despite the fact that I shouldn't have done that either. And for a little while you were soft and pliant in my arms and your mouth trembled under mine as if you were enjoying it as much as I was. So I think it's fair to say we're . . . a little intrigued about each other.'

'And I . . . I wonder if we should place too much importance on that,' she said shakily.

'You mean you don't think it has any place in a marriage?' he asked after a moment.

'No . . . I mean, yes, obviously it does, but . . . oh!' she sighed despairingly. 'Look, this isn't helping Phil!'

'Forget about Phil for a moment.' His voice was curt. 'I'm interested to get to the bottom of this. Are you trying to say that because of what happened to you once, you're not going to allow yourself to enjoy sex ever again?'

'No! I'm not trying to say anything of the kind,' she retorted angrily. 'But I am, as usual, a little confused about *you.* You were the one who . . . mocked me when I said,' she hesitated briefly, then plunged on thinking, well, the principle's still the same again, 'when I said I didn't trust those kinds of feelings. Then only this afternoon you basically agreed with me when you told me about Chrissy's mother. Now you're trying to say they mean something after all.'

'I think we're talking about two different things, Anna.' He surveyed her unsmilingly. 'You seem to want to pretend that you've been turned off the physical side of a relationship altogether, whereas I . . .'

'Obviously haven't been,' she muttered tautly, and thought, oh, why did I get myself into this in the first place?

'No. But I *can* put it in its proper perspective. If two people want to go to bed with each other and can enjoy it, that's fine. But don't call it love. Why call that love? There are other far more enduring things from my point of view—like trust and respect. But from your point of view,' he said compellingly, 'I think one of the reasons you're

trying to pretend we don't feel this way about each other,
that we could enjoy each other in bed too, is because I've
never whispered a whole lot of drivel in your shell-like ear
about undying admiration and love and God knows what!
That's it, isn't it, Anna? Despite your brave words to me,
you're as romantic at heart as the rest of them.' He smiled
briefly.

She stared at him as he studied her sardonically, and
thought with a shaft of pain that seemed to pierce her heart
again, he's right. Oh God!

Then she forced herself to take a steadying breath and
to think. He's also wrong about these things, surely?
Otherwise why would I feel this way? But how to tell him?

'I,' she said huskily, and cleared her throat, 'I don't
know what to think,' she confessed. 'I know I said a lot of
things about love which might have led you to believe
I——'she shrugged helplessly, 'well, that I knew what I
was talking about. But if one thing is clear to me now, it's
that I don't really have the slightest idea. Yet one thing I
do know,' she said honestly, and couldn't help the note of
bitterness that crept into her voice, 'I'm not sure about
having a lot of drivel talked into my ear, but it seems it's
just not acceptable to me to be made to feel "like that" by
someone who with not much effort—perhaps an ad in the
paper would do it—could find someone else just as suitable.'

'I advertised before,' said Richard with a sudden, dag-
ger-like glance at her.

She winced. 'Now you're angry. I shouldn't...'

'You're damn right I am,' he said shortly.

'Well, I think I'm the one who should be angry!'

'Oh?'

'Yes,' she cried passionately—and found that she was
angry and intolerably confused. And hurt, so inexplica-

bly hurt, it made her angrier. So that she said precisely, 'And I've just worked it all out. I loathe and detest you. I'd be only too happy to never have to see you again. And if,' she went on, her anger now white-hot and past caring, 'you had the slightest regard for Chrissy, who is after all the cornerstone of this whole business, you'd see that a marriage of convenience isn't the answer... What are you doing?' she gasped as Richard reached across the intervening space and hauled her into his arms.

'This,' he said savagely. 'Try and talk your way out of this, Anna!'

'This' turned out to be a repeat of what had happened to her the night he had come home from America. Yet it wasn't quite the same, because he didn't deal with her frenzied struggles with the same kind of easy strength and tolerance he had used that night. This time he quelled her bruisingly and as if he didn't care. And he swept her up into his arms and crossed over to a pile of sails and lowered her on to them, imprisoning her, half lying, half sitting, with his own body.

Anna sobbed with frustration and despair and tried to wrench an arm free, although she knew she was fighting a losing battle.

Then it changed. He looked down at her hot face and agonised eyes and it all changed, but with a suddenness that took her completely by surprise. His arms were no longer like bands of steel around her and his eyes no longer violent but broodingly sombre.

'Richard?' she whispered his name pleadingly.

'No, Anna,' he said very quietly. 'We've both said too much. The time's come now to show you what can't be said. Don't,' he held her closer as she moved convulsively. 'I'm not going to do anything that will be regretted...'

But won't it? she thought fleetingly not much later as his fingers and lips traced a devastating path across her skin, discovering and exploring tender spots that she hadn't known existed in that sense. Places like behind her ears and the nape of her neck which he was stroking just gently, and the inside of her wrist which he was kissing at that moment. Can this be undone? Can I ever forget just this? Is there anything earth-shattering about having your wrist kissed, or your eyelids? Surely not...

Then she wasn't so sure, as her whole body trembled beneath his wandering touch and came alive as he slid his arm around her and drew her close to him and kissed her throat. And he moved one hand gently and slid the strap of her sundress off her shoulder and undid the top few buttons of the heart-shaped bodice so that the swell of her breast gleamed like ivory where the dress fell away. He watched the satin smooth curves he had exposed rise and fall to the tune of her accelerated breathing intently for a long moment. Then he lifted his eyes to hers and she trembled again down the whole length of her, because she knew what he was going to do—knew too that she would let him because she didn't have the will power to resist, didn't want to have it.

'Anna?' he muttered, his lips barely moving.

'Yes...?' she whispered uncertainly.

'This is what you've been thinking about every time you've worn a swimming costume in my presence, isn't it? Every time you couldn't wait to get your everlasting towelling dress on?'

'I...' She looked up at him tormentedly.

'Well, I have,' he murmured, and slid his fingers beneath her dress. 'I've often thought about undressing you somewhere in the sunlight or the moonlight or lamplight, and laying you down and touching you with my hands and my lips—exciting you as I think I could.'

His gaze rested on her partly open lips, then moved to her wide eyes and the fluctuating colour in her cheeks; he moved her a little away from him and undid two more buttons and very gently slid the other strap off her shoulder, exposing her breasts completely.

She took a tortured breath but could not stop herself from looking down. And it seemed as if the impact was doubled, to see and to feel his lean, strong fingers touching her nipples delicately, then moving away to cup each breast with a caressing gentleness, and to see each rosy bud harden in a response that she felt with a shuddering intensity through to the pit of her stomach.

A flood of colour poured into her cheeks and she looked away—anything rather than have to look into those grey-green eyes and see the triumph and perhaps the mockery in them.

But when he made her turn her head to him with his fingers beneath her chin, there was no triumph, no mockery, only an expression she couldn't fathom. He said softly, 'Don't...look like that, Anna.' He traced the outline of her mouth with one finger. 'It's not a crime to respond like that. In fact for a man and a woman to excite each other in this way is like nothing else that ever happens to you, and it's a pity to spoil it with feelings of guilt and shame...or something you can't forget, won't let yourself forget.'

'What...what if those feelings come afterwards?' she queried unhappily after a long hesitation.

His eyes narrowed and he looked at her piercingly as if he could see right through to her soul. 'All right,' he said at last, and sat her up against the wall, buttoning her dress up and slipping the straps back into position. 'We'll leave it be.'

But perversely those words seemed to cut her to the quick and to her horror she felt hot tears well and trickle down her cheeks. 'I...' she said despairingly, and lifted her eyes to the ceiling in a gesture of helplessness.

'You don't have to say anything, Anna.' His voice was steady and even compassionate as it had been earlier in the day.

'Yes...yes, I do,' she said with an effort, and brushed her hair back from her flushed, tear-streaked face. 'I have to try to explain.' She looked at him. But in the very act of beginning to tell him how she had misled him originally, she paused, and discovered suddenly that she couldn't do it. But why? she wondered shakenly. Is it because I'm using that lie like a coat of armour? Is that why I went along with it in the first place because I realised subconsciously even then that I was going to need some protection against him? Against a terrible attraction that's turned into something more? Perhaps turned into the very thing he mistrusts most?

'Go on,' he said quietly.

She licked her lips. 'I wish I had the courage to go to bed with you,' she said in a low husky voice. 'But I don't. It...it's something to do with the way I'm made I think. Nor do I have the...whatever it takes to marry you, knowing you don't love me so much as want m-me.' Her voice shook, but she went on resolutely as he moved restlessly, 'And like me and respect me as I do you.'

Richard didn't say anything, just watched her carefully as she tried to think clearly because although she couldn't tell him the whole truth, it seemed desperately important to get across to him what was still the truth she felt in her heart. 'I think *you* must be right—this time. I must be as insanely romantic as the rest of them after all. I do want someone to fall madly in love with me and I probably will fall madly in love myself one day with all the trimmings I was so scathing about.' Only I'm terribly afraid that might have happened already, she added to her heart.

They stared at each other for a long time, then he smiled at her with a heartbreaking gentleness and touched her cheek lightly. 'He'll be a lucky man, Anna, when you find him. You can tell him that from me.'

'Richard,' she began, the tears falling more rapidly now, 'I'm sorry...'

He thought for a moment with his head bent. Then he looked up and said with a curious wryness, 'Perhaps not as sorry as I am.'

'That...that's the nicest thing you've ever said to me,' she answered tremulously. 'I...I'm not sure if I deserve it.'

'Oh yes.' He stood up in one lithe movement and she jumped. 'No, don't you move, Anna.' He grinned down at her. 'We've still got a few things to work out. And I reckon we could both do with a bit of this.' He pulled open a cupboard and withdrew a bottle and poured some of its contents into two battered old tin mugs. Then he switched the overhead lights off and came back to sit down beside her.

It took a moment or two for her eyes to adjust, but it wasn't really dark. There was a bright swathe of moonlight coming through the open slipway doors. Another Yandilla moon, she thought.

'Here, it's brandy,' he said offering her one of the mugs. 'We keep it down here for medicinal purposes.'

'That—sounds like a good idea,' said Anna, accepting the mug.

'Yes.' He glinted a smile across at her. 'Letty doesn't approve, however.'

'Oh?'

'No. Probably because on the odd occasion Samson and I have abused its medicinal qualities. Letty is a zealous teetotaller. So is Samson, but every now and then he gets melancholy.'

'Letty has good reason not to—from what she was telling me, about Samson's father.'

'So I believe. Do you know, she's a tower of strength, Letty. She was to my mother, she is to Phil and to me and Chrissy. The only person she doesn't exert too much influence over is Samson. Otherwise she'd have had him married years ago and had a whole tribe of grandchildren!'

'That's often the way with mothers and sons, isn't it?' remarked Anna. 'But talking of Samson, you *think* he's melancholy, then he surprises you and you know he's not melancholy at all but secretly...I don't know, more in tune than most people.'

'How right you are!' he said with a glinting look of amusement. 'Feel better?' he added abruptly.

'I...I guess so.' She sniffed and licked her lips.

'Have some of your brandy.'

She obeyed, and was grateful for the strengthening warmth that slid down her throat.

'To get back to the subject of Phil, how long does she think she'll be away, did she think?'

'Six weeks to two months,' said Anna.

'That's not...so long.'

'No,' Anna agreed quietly. She stared down at the mug in her hands, then looked up to see him looking thoughtfully into space.

'I...' he said at last, 'feel rather guilty about Phil as it is.'

'I don't think you should—apart from this,' Anna said. 'She loves Chrissy. I don't think it's been any burden to her to... be here for her.'

Richard's eyes came back to rest on her face. 'No,' he said slowly. 'And certainly, every time I've tried to tell her she needn't bury herself on Yandilla for Chrissy's sake, she's got rather hurt. But all the same, on account of Chrissy, I think she deliberately shut the door on something that could have blossomed into a... beautiful friendship, let's say.'

Anna's lips parted and her eyes became alert. 'Do you... do you mean Colonel Jackson?' she said slowly.

He looked surprised. 'Has she said something to you? The one time I tried to talk to her about it she told me I was imagining things and that she was far too old to be indulging in that sort of thing.'

'No, no, she hasn't said anything to me. But I saw the Colonel looking at her that night at the barbecue and...and it popped into my mind that he was in love with her. But she didn't—I mean, she didn't give any indication that she even knew about it. So I thought *I* must be imagining it.'

'Yes, well,' he said, 'I rather allowed myself to be lulled into the same kind of thinking. She and my uncle were one of the happiest couples you could find. But every now and then I can't help thinking that Phil and the Colonel would be perfect for each other. Yet I haven't wanted to push anything in case she was genuinely not interested.'

'What does Letty think?' asked Anna.

He smiled slowly. 'Do you know, I never thought to ask her! How foolish of me not to think of consulting the oracle!'

She smiled back at him, understanding perfectly. Then they both sobered and he said abruptly, 'We can't hope to solve that problem overnight, but would you consider staying while she goes overseas?'

'I...'

'You needn't be afraid of me, Anna. What's past is past now,' he said levelly, and stared at her searchingly.

'There's still Chrissy, though,' she whispered. 'We agreed that the longer I stayed, the harder it's going to be.'

'Yes. But I don't suppose six weeks or even two months is going to make such a difference. We might even be able to... prepare the ground a little. I did tell her at the beginning that you wouldn't be here for ever.'

Anna winced inwardly and thought of the child who had somehow managed to touch her heartstrings, and was shaken by a sudden thought—will I ever be able to leave here? Will I honestly ever have the strength to walk out on Chrissy and... Isn't it better to go now before the trap closes completely? I saw the trap, she thought despairingly, yet I kept on walking into it. I couldn't help it—I don't think I wanted to...

'Anna?'

She lifted her head and sighed. 'All right. I too owe Phil something. She's been so kind and she's so concerned. I...some days I feel as if she's my aunt as well. So I'll stay.'

'Thank you,' he said very quietly.

'Phil,' Anna said determinedly, 'you're going and that's that!'

It was eight o'clock in the morning and bright sunlight was streaming into the kitchen where Anna was helping Letty clear away breakfast while Sunshine started on the bedrooms.

'But I don't understand!' Phil said bewilderedly. 'I really don't! *Yesterday*...'

'Yesterday was yesterday,' Anna said idly. 'Gone and done with.'

Phil frowned. 'It's all very well to say that now,' she protested agitatedly, 'but if you recall...and anyway, we'd have to consult Richard. I mean...' She twisted her hands together awkwardly, and seemed to have some trouble continuing.

Anna looked at her affectionately. 'I've already consulted Richard, Phil.'

Phil's mouth dropped open. 'You have?' she said weakly at last.

'Mmm.'

'And what...?'

'We agreed to...disagree about some things, but we found ourselves in total agreement that you're going to London if we have to deliver you there personally!' She laughed at Phil's look of astonishment. Then she said softly, 'Trust me, Phil. It's going to be all right—and promise me you'll go with a clear mind and a happy heart, because Chrissy will be just fine with me. And of course Letty. Won't she Letty?'

'...Sure will,' said Letty after a moment, and began to stack the dishwasher energetically. 'I don't understand what all the fuss is about!'

Anna suffered a moment's remorse as she suddenly remembered that Letty for once wasn't privy to everything that had happened. Unless—Phil's told her? she thought. But no, I doubt it. And maybe I will tell her one day, because it doesn't seem right somehow to have secrets from Letty and I wouldn't want her to think badly of me...

CHAPTER EIGHT

'DO YOU think Phil's missing us, Anna?' asked Chrissy one hot and rainy day about ten days later.

'I guess so, honey.' Anna ruffled Chrissy's hair. 'You missing her?'

'Yes,' Chrissy said ruefully. 'And I worry about her sometimes. She told me she had to change planes in Rome. What if she gets on to the wrong plane? And what if she loses her glasses? She's always losing them around here and she can't read or write without them.'

'I think she might manage better on her own than we give her credit for, love,' said Anna. 'And I bet in a few days' time we'll get a fat letter from her. Tell you what, since we're thinking of her let's write to her.'

'Oh yes,' Chrissy said enthusiastically. 'I'll do it in my best running writing.'

It took Chrissy about an hour to perfect her letter to Phil. Then they took it in to Richard to get the address.

'Well, ladies,' he said, surveying them with mock gravity across an untidy, paper-laden desk, 'what can I do for you?'

Chrissy giggled and ran round to climb on to his lap. 'Anna's a lady, Daddy. I'm only a little girl.'

'I just hope you'll grow up to be as nice a lady as Anna is,' he said seriously.

'So do I. I've been trying terribly hard ever since Anna came to be just like her! Haven't you noticed?'

Anna stirred and went faintly pink and looked wryly into two pairs of grey-green eyes. 'Thank you both kindly,' she said with a mock curtsey. 'But I think Chrissy Gillespie is very nice just being Chrissy Gillespie. Don't you think so, Mr Gillespie?' she queried seriously.

'You're right, Miss Horton,' he replied but with a smile tugging at the corners of his lips. 'In fact I think she's going to be a real heartbreaker.'

'That doesn't sound very nice!' Chrissy protested. 'Anyway, I think you two are teasing me.'

'When do I ever do that?' Richard Gillespie said to his daughter, feigning offended surprise.

'All the time,' she said lovingly. 'Except when you get cross with me. But you haven't been cross with me for ages—and do you know why?'

'I'm agog,' he drawled. 'No, why?'

'Because I've been following Anna's example and trying to be good and ladylike, of course, silly,' she answered, and patted his face tenderly. 'Letty reckons I'm reformed since Anna came!'

'Letty should know,' he said a touch dryly, but he shot a laughing look at Anna.

BUT LATER that night when Chrissy was in bed and Anna was sitting on the verandah outside her room mending one of Chrissy's nightgowns with tiny, delicate stitches, he came to sit beside her.

'Anna...' He stopped and grimaced as the mosquito coil she had lit billowed its acrid smoke in his direction.

She stitched conscientiously for a few minutes. Then she looked up to see his eyes resting on her. 'What is it?' she asked. 'You were going to... ask me something?'

'Only...how things were going. Not that I need to ask on Chrissy's behalf. But—on your behalf?' He looked at her questioningly.

'I'm fine, thank you,' she said steadily enough and with a faintly surprised grin that she thought she managed very well. But inwardly she trembled and wondered if he could possibly have noticed what she herself had only become aware of in the last couple of days. That the fact that she had had trouble sleeping lately was beginning to show in the form of faint shadows beneath her eyes. And that she had had to move the buttons on a couple of skirts because they had become too loose...

'If you say so,' he said after a moment. 'But if there was something bothering you, I'd like to think you at least...trusted me enough to tell me. Is it—the thought of leaving Chrissy?' he added, his eyes narrowed watchfully.

'No...I mean, of course I worry about that, but...well, often these things have a habit of working themselves out anyway.' She smiled slightly.

'Then there's nothing else, Anna?'

'No, not that I can think of. Have I been looking worried? I didn't mean to! I'll take more care in future,' she said with a laugh, trying desperately to make light of the whole matter.

'All right,' he said after a moment. 'I'm glad to hear it.' He stretched and yawned. 'Well, I think I might make it an early night. Samson and I have an expedition tomorrow to Cardwell and Hinchinbrook. Two American scientists I met on my last trip are in Queensland to study our mangroves.' He grimaced. 'You know what that means, don't you—being eaten alive by sandflies. Goodnight, Anna.' He stood up.

'Goodnight. I'll think of you tomorrow, among the sandflies,' she added cheerfully, and they exchanged rueful smiles.

But as she watched his tall figure disappear round the corner of the verandah, she felt her heart contracting as if it was being squeezed and she thought despairingly, I could never tell you what's bothering me. How could I? How could I tell you I'm so afraid I spoke no less than the truth that night in the boatshed when I said I would probably fall madly in love one day. But that ironically, since saying those fateful words it's been almost as if they were the magic password, a kind of open sesame but to the door of my heart. Because I can no longer pretend to myself that I don't know what I feel for you, Richard. I know now...

But how do I know? she asked herself exasperatedly and with a shimmer of tears in her eyes.

Because nothing else could hurt this much, Anna, she told herself, and not for the first time. And nothing less could make the prospect of leaving this place seem as if it would be a kind of death—as if your source of life was being cut off. And nothing else surely would make you wonder if you shouldn't after all have accepted his offer of marriage even when you know you've been assessed and... could almost have come up on a computer!

She sighed and laid her head against the back of the chair with her eyes closed. How did this happen to me? she mused. How could one man, without even *trying*—or at least only to prove a point initially—make me so conscious of him that I can't even sleep any more? What is it about him? Perhaps if I can work it all out, I might have some chance of lessening this thing.

But she found her mind was flooded with images of Richard that didn't help to work anything out. Richard teasing Chrissy, Richard and Phil sharing a joke, Richard meekly accepting Letty's strictures but with his eyes laughing devilishly at her, Richard and Samson together—friends with a bond so strong, Richard telling her about the reef, and letting her see how painfully he cared for Chrissy. So many Richards, and not the least, Richard kissing her, holding her, even being angry with her, justly and unjustly.

'It's been like a revelation,' she whispered. 'Oh, what a fool I've been! So many things I've said…if only I hadn't, I might not be feeling so bad now.

'But then again,' she whispered, and licked the salty tears from her lips, 'the fact that I feel a bit foolish isn't the worst part of it, is it? The worst part is that he doesn't feel the way I do. That's by far the worst part.'

THE DAYS continued very hot, although not as hot as on the mainland. And the rain went away and stayed away for nearly two weeks which almost constituted a drought in that part of the world. And life on Yandilla ran its quiet course, but there was a difference for Anna.

A sense of strain had her firmly in its grip now, for the most part that she should unwittingly give herself away. And she found she had a curiously new feeling of vulnerability not only towards Richard, but to so many little things, almost as if she had lived her whole life with most of her senses partly blinkered. The beauty of the butterflies she and Chrissy were cataloguing seemed to affect her more deeply, and the orchids they found hurt her to look upon them. It was as if the world had broadened or that her sensibilities had been heightened, to make her feel that way.

It *has* to be love, she thought one day. Is this what love does to you?

It was the day after she had asked herself this question that she bumped into Mike Carmody. In a conscious effort to start cutting the ties that bound her to Yandilla, she had started to take more interest in visiting the mainland and on this occasion had gone over with Samson to do some shopping for Letty and herself. Samson had driven her and Chrissy to Tully, left them to spend a few pleasurable hours wandering through the not so extensive shops Tully had to offer, but when you haven't been shopping for months they were more than adequate, she found. Then Samson had reappeared and he and Chrissy had gone on ahead to the car, laden down with packages, while Anna slipped into a chemist for something she had forgotten.

She came out and cannoned into him.

'Well, well,' he drawled as he restored some of her packages to her. 'If it isn't Anna!'

'Mike!' She looked up at him with wide, troubled eyes and a trace of pink coming to her cheeks. Because she had never answered his note, although she had thought of doing so, only to find she didn't quite know what to say. 'I . . . I'm sorry,' she stammered. 'You must think me very rude.'

'Then you did get my letter?'

'Yes . . .'

'Oh, *I* see,' he said after a moment. 'They've barred you from having anything to do with me, haven't they? I'm surprised you let yourself be pushed around like that. I thought you had more spirit,' he added with a defiant look.

'Mike, it's difficult,' she said awkwardly.

'Is it? I thought you only worked there. I didn't think Richard Gillespie owned you. Perhaps I'm wrong, though? You wouldn't be the first sheila who's fallen for him. He's got a lot going for him. But one day you might find out he can be a right bastard too.'

Anna gasped, and would have turned and run from him, but he put a hand on her arm and held her fast. 'Not so fast, Anna!' he cautioned. 'You see, I've spent the past few months carrying a vision of you around in my mind that's been mighty hard to shift. I know that's not your fault, but then the fact that the Yandilla mob treat me like a leper shouldn't have to extend to you either. Believe me, Anna, if I could undo some of the things I did, I would. But if it's any consolation to Richard Gillespie, that's going to be my burden for the rest of my life. That I can't. That I was a thoughtless stupid fool and I'll always have to live with the knowledge of it.'

Anna was arrested by the bitterness in his voice and his eyes. 'Oh, Mike,' she said at last, 'if it's any consolation to you, they don't all want to treat you—like that. They— Phil anyway understands...'

'But he doesn't?' He stared at her searchingly.

'No. I don't know, it's none of my business,' she said confusedly. 'Do you...really expect him to?' she added uncertainly.

He dropped his hand from her arm. 'Nope,' he said laconically. 'But if it's none of your business, why won't he let you have anything to do with me? He won't, will he?' His brown eyes, that she had once seen so open and bright, were now dark and brooding.

Anna hesitated. '...No,' she said very quietly.

'So you think he has the right to dictate to you like that?'

'Mike...'

'Or is it that since you've found out the whole dark story, *you* don't want to have anything to do with me, Anna?'

'It's not that,' she said desperately, feeling a flood of compassion for him.

'Then prove it,' he said simply.

'I . . . you don't understand, Mike,' she said helplessly.

'No? I think I do,' he said at last. 'Well, then I guess I won't be seeing you again, Anna. Goodbye.' He turned away abruptly.

Anna watched him walk away and shivered suddenly, as if the day had gone inexplicably cold.

SIX WEEKS went by, and still Phil made no mention in her letters of coming home. For that matter, she didn't make much mention of the television series she was helping to script either, but wrote a lot about London and the great time she was having revisiting favourite spots. Richard remarked once that her butterfly brain was at its most evident in her letters, but added that she had always been loath to mention her work.

Anna winced as she thought of the lurking grin in his eyes as he had said this, and she thought, I hope Phil comes home soon, because I don't think I can stand much more of this, living side by side but always trying to hide what I'm thinking and feeling. Always afraid I'll break down one day and go to him and tell him that I feel like a flower withering because I can't get the thought of his mouth on mine or his hands on my body out of my mind— that I need those things to keep me alive. But most of all I need him to love me. Oh yes, the sooner Phil comes home the better. But what about Chrissy? Chrissy needs me . . .

'I WONDER when Phil will be home, Letty?' she said later that same morning. They were sharing a coffee break at the kitchen table.

'Darned if I know,' Letty replied absently. She was flipping idly through a calendar. 'Hey, look at this!' she exclaimed. 'Chrissy has an appointment for a dental checkup in Innisfail tomorra and I'd clean forgot! Want to come, Anna? We usually make a day of it. Samson takes us over, then he drives us up.'

'Yes. Thank you,' Anna said slowly, and frowned. 'Letty, just now you sounded as,' she moved her hands, 'as if Phil might never come home...'

Letty pursed her lips and hung the calendar up carefully. 'She'll come home, Anna,' she said at last. 'I wouldn't count on it being too soon, though.'

Anna stared at her. 'I don't understand,' she said with a curious feeling at the pit of her stomach.

'Don't you?' asked Letty with a wise little smile. 'It's simple. Phil doesn't want you to leave here until you're very sure about it. That's why she went overseas when she did, although she isn't due in London for that TV thing yet even.'

'But *why?*' Anna's eyes were wide and disbelieving.

'Why don't we want you to leave here? I don't either, Anna. Look, there's an old legend on Thursday Island. There's a funny kinda tree there called the wongai tree, and they reckon if you eat the fruit of it you'll always go back to Thursday Island some day. Well, there isn't no wongai tree on Yandilla, but I reckon for you, if you leave here there'll always be something calling you back. And it'll always hurt like hell if you can't come back.'

There was a tense little silence, at least on Anna's side it was tense. Then she said hoarsely, 'Letty, you and Phil are as bad as Chrissy.' She stood up and moved over to the sink to look out of the window. But she turned away almost immediately because she could see, through a gap in the shrubbery, Richard and Chrissy on the beach skimming stones into the sea.

'Are we?' Letty's voice was gentle. 'Honey, do you think I can't see you eating your heart out for him?'

Anna caught her breath, but relaxed slightly, although it was shortlived, as Letty went on with a little shrug, 'I can't understand why he doesn't see it, but then men can be so blind. Now you just tell me it's not true, Anna. That you don't ache for Mr Richard.'

Anna put her hands up to her face and just stood there for a minute. Then Letty got up and put her arm around her and she burst into tears and sobbed into Letty's shoulder.

'There, sweetheart,' Letty said soothingly. 'You want to tell me about it?'

'Yes. I...he doesn't love me, Letty. Oh, he likes me and thinks I'd be good for Chrissy, but he doesn't love me. I don't think he even believes in love any more. But even if he did, I don't think it would be me. I...I just have the misfortune to be a good governess who might make a good wife because I'm all the things—*she* wasn't. Chrissy's mother.'

'You seem mighty sure of all this,' Letty said quietly.

'Of course I'm sure,' Anna wept. 'You see everything, Letty, and I think you must know he asked me to marry him. And that I said no! But can you see that it's made the slightest difference to him?' She raised her flushed face to stare into Letty's eyes. 'Can you? I can't,' she said bitterly. 'But you can see what it's done to me.'

'Here.' Letty pulled a hanky from her pocket and handed it to Anna. 'Sit down. I'll make us some more coffee.' She glanced out of the window. 'Don't worry, they're still down at the beach. What you might not have taken into account, Anna, is two things,' she went on a few minutes later as she set the coffee on the table. 'Does it make you love him any less because he don't love you?'

'Not...no, but...'

'Okay, so you're gonna have to live with it whatever happens. Aren't I right?'

'Letty...'

'Hang on, we gotta sort this all out. Is that right or isn't it?'

Anna sighed. Then she said with a mixture of bleakness and anger, 'I don't know.'

'Don't you?' Letty looked at her with an eagle eye.

'Very well, I do,' Anna said at last. 'What does that prove?'

'That you're gonna be miserable too if you go! Maybe more miserable.'

'I wish it was that simple. I wish I had a set of scales that could measure it up. But that's not the point, Letty.'

'What is the point?'

'What's the point of *staying* if I'm going to be miserable? And eaten up with despair. What good is that going to do anyone?'

'Honey, you don't know that you will be! So we all have dreams over the moon that don't come true. But not many of us get as close to them as you could. Look, I've seen you two together and while he might tell you he don't believe in love, he gets along pretty damn well with you!'

'Sometimes.'

Letty snorted. 'Most of the time. And you ain't ever gonna find a man you get along well with *all* the time, believe me,' she said, slipping into a less grammatical form of English than she normally spoke. 'But the other thing is, he might have some cause to *believe* he won't fall in love again. She—Miss Julie, she gave him a rough time. For that matter I reckon they gave each other a rough time. But she couldn't change no more than he could, and when whatever it was between them burnt itself out it left behind one helluva mess. So he has some cause to be bitter, and if she were alive, she might too. Bitter and wary and hurt. But I'll tell you something, Anna, there's no man or woman alive who can say for sure they won't fall in love again...or perhaps for the first time, in his case. Who's to say? But if you don't believe that, take Phil and the Colonel. There's two people who thought it could never happen to them. Both of them had happy marriages, although the Colonel lost his wife young and I wouldn't be surprised if he hadn't looked at another woman till his eyes lit on Phil. Mind you, she's about as stubborn about it as you are. But at least she has cause. She don't want to leave Chrissy.'

'So...that is true,' Anna said slowly.

'True as I stand here!'

'But to get...to get back to Richard,' said Anna, and blinked away a fresh set of tears. 'Who's to say I'll be the one he falls in love with?'

'For one thing, you'll be the one on the spot.'

Anna shivered. 'I...I just can't think straight,' she said tearfully. 'And you're right about being on the spot, Letty. Phil...shouldn't have done this.'

'Well, can I tell you why she did? Because she was pretty damn sure Richard was more than a little in love with you already, only he won't...can't, whatever, admit it!'

'Well, I'm afraid that's where I have to differ,' Anna said tautly after a moment. 'In fact I'd like to have a bet with you, when I go...*if* between the two of you I ever manage to make it, he won't lift a finger to stop me. You see if I'm not right. So I can't agree with Phil.'

'And that's what you can't live with, Anna?'

'No, I can't.'

'That might only be a small thing compared to the things you could share.'

Anna was saved from answering by the sound of footsteps down the passageway and Letty took a look at her face and said, 'Slip out the other door, love. I'll tell 'em you've got a headache and gone to lie down. I'll watch Chrissy.'

ANNA DID lie down for a couple of hours. Then she forced herself to reappear as if she was quite restored.

But the next morning, the accumulated strain told and she woke up with a blinding headache, the likes of which she hadn't seen since being prone to them for a few months after her parents had died. And she knew that the last thing she felt like doing was making the trip to Innisfail.

Letty and Chrissy were both concerned and quite ready to cancel the trip, but Anna wouldn't hear of it. 'I'll be fine,' she said weakly. 'Honestly I will.'

'Well, if you're sure,' said Letty. 'I'd leave Sunshine with you, but she hasn't been off for ages and she wants to do some shopping... I'm coming!' she called stridently to Samson, who could be heard pacing the verandah impatiently. 'But anyway,' she brightened, 'Mr Richard will be here. He just went off for an hour or two to look for some specimens. So you'll be right!' Letty beamed, and Anna winced inwardly but agreed.

And after they had gone she tottered back to bed, and maybe because the house was so quiet or simply because she felt so emotionally exhausted, she fell asleep and slept for hours, and woke feeling more genuinely refreshed than she had for some time and with the headache gone.

But there was no sign of Richard when she went into the kitchen to make herself some lunch, and she frowned faintly and then decided he must be down at the boatshed.

But a walk down to the boatshed after lunch proved that he wasn't, and she came to the conclusion that he had gone off the island again because the small but powerful shark cat was not at its moorings, which meant two boats, including the one that Samson had used to get to the mainland this morning, were missing from Yandilla.

'Which also means I'm the only living soul here at the moment,' she said out loud as she walked round the beach back towards the house. 'Unless you take into account all the possums and wallabies and so on.'

The afternoon was very hot and still, and even just strolling along, the humidity left one drenched in sweat. But she noticed a massive build-up of cloud out to sea and thought thankfully that at least some rain was on the way.

But as the afternoon wore on she found herself grappling with a strange trickle of apprehension. There was still no sign of Richard and an eerie wind had got up to blow in short ferocious gusts that slammed doors and then subsided, only to rise again. And it began to rain, but intermittently too and as if the raindrops were being flung at the windows.

Then she was struck by a sudden thought and ran to turn the transistor radio on in the kitchen—only to gasp in disbelief as she heard what sounded like an air-raid warning siren being broadcast and then the steady tones of the station announcer reading a cyclone warning alert for areas from Cairns to St Lawrence.

Anna stared at the radio and swallowed several times. Then she realised that the same steady voice was dispensing information on just how to batten down for a cyclone... Secure all loose objects around the house, because winds of that ferocity could turn even relatively harmless objects like metal garbage bins into lethal weapons... Leave some windows open on the side of the house not in the path of the wind to reduce pressure. Remember that bathrooms were often more solidly constructed and offered more protection . . . stock up on batteries for torches and transistor radios and, above all, stay tuned to your radio.

None of this was new to Anna. Having been born and bred in Queensland she'd heard it all before. But as Richard had said only a few nights ago, very few cyclones vented the full force of their fury as far south as Brisbane. What stunned her was to think that she was quite alone on Yandilla and right in the path of one.

'I don't believe this,' she whispered—and jumped about a foot into the air at the sound of a sharp crack and a dull thud, then ran outside to see to her horror that a branch from an overhanging mango tree had broken off the tree and fallen across the telephone wires, uprooting them from their connection against the verandah roof.

Now I'm cut off, she thought. But no, the boatshed might still be connected. Let me think carefully... The line comes by submarine cable from the mainland—yes, and for the most part is underground on the island until it gets to the house, so it might... but no, she realised almost immediately, you can switch a call through to the boatshed from here, but you can't get one directly there . . . oh God! So I am cut off, because it all works off this line!

The telephone confirmed this by being quite dead when she tried it. All the same, I'll go down to the boatshed and see, she thought, maybe there's a radio transmitter . . . But first I'll batten down as much as I can up here.

The trip down to the boatshed was a weird experience. Depending on what direction she was going in she was alternately being pushed along by the wind or fighting to take each step, and all the time she was fighting for breath as the wind seemed to gain momentum and the rain started to fall with a stinging vehemence, and as the light faded she could see coconuts being bounced off the palms like missiles and her heart contracted with fear for two reasons, because it was three hours before the full force of the cyclone was due to hit, so what would it be like then? And because, unless by some miracle Richard was in the boatshed, he must be out somewhere in this...

But he wasn't in the boatshed and the phone didn't work, and there was a two-way radio, but it was lying on one of the benches in pieces as if it was being repaired. In fact the only piece of good news she found was that the cutter, the third and last part of the Yandilla fleet, was up in its cradle and under cover and not moored in the water. Not that it was of any immediate help to her, because she knew she had no chance of getting it into the water, even if she could sail it which she knew she couldn't. But at least it had less chance of being damaged or sunk. Then she realised that at least something else was in her favour. The heavy double doors of the boatshed, which didn't fit very well in any case, were faced away from the wind—at the moment at least, so it seemed a fairly safe place to stay.

Not that she felt she had much choice, because she didn't think she was capable of making the return trip to the house, beside the fact that it obviously would be a dangerous thing to do.

'In any case,' she muttered to herself, 'this is the best place to be, because this is where anyone who does come will come to. If anyone comes. Oh!' Her eyes dilated as she thought of Letty and Samson. 'Surely they wouldn't attempt to cross in this? But at least they know I'm here. Although they might think I'm safe with Richard...oh God! Where is he? He must know I'm here on my own. But he hasn't come back, which can only mean he's out there somewhere, caught in this awful wind...'

The next three hours were the longest she had ever experienced. The wind grew steadily in intensity until it was shrieking and howling dementedly, clearly to be heard over and above the torrential rain that was hammering on the roof. And the roof was her worst worry, because while the walls seemed to be standing firmly enough the roof was creaking and she was terribly afraid it was going to lift off or come crashing down on top of her.

She crept under one of the strongest-looking laboratory benches and tried to close her ears and began to pray as she'd never prayed in her life before, and to cry and sing...anything to keep at bay her terrible fear of the savage, maniacal wind and the other even more terrible fear that was gripping her heart.

When the lull came, she didn't realise it at first, but finally it was borne into her that the wind had died somewhat and she dared to crawl out from under the bench, only to wonder if it wasn't the eye of the cyclone passing overhead and that soon the wind would blow again but in the opposite direction.

Then when the lull had lasted for a good half an hour and she was just beginning to breathe more easily, a tremendous gust slammed the boathouse doors open inwards and she knew her worst fears were realised. But at the same time, or perhaps only moments before she heard another sound, a curious grating like tearing metal on concrete, and she reached for the torch as a blast of rain blew all over her, and though she was dreaming because the beam of light picked up the figure of a man staggering up the slipway in the driving rain.

'Richard...?' Her lips moved, but no sound came.

But he turned to the source of the beam of light that had picked him up and switched on his own torch. Then he covered the last few steps towards her at a run and swung her up into his arms. 'Anna! Thank *God*...'

'Oh, Richard,' she sobbed, 'I thought you were dead!'

'No, but we might both be if we don't move fast. Come...'

'Was it only the eye?'

'I think so...listen, just do as I say now.'

She did, with no clear idea of what she was doing except that she was being bundled into a cupboard that was fairly big and that she tripped over a pile of what felt like canvas and that Richard followed her in and pulled the heavy wooden door closed behind them. But it wasn't a cupboard, she realised as she came up against the back wall and felt that it was stone. Then Richard switched her torch on again and she looked around to see that it was a store room of sorts and that he couldn't stand upright in it because the ceiling was so low, and that it was narrow but quite long and that the canvas was a pile of tarpaulins and sails.

'It used to be a cool-room,' he said, 'so the walls are stone and doubly thick. We'll just have to hope the door holds...' He stopped abruptly as a new tearing sound came through the seams and cracks of the door and there was a tremendous crash, and Anna flew into his arms, trembling with fear.

'That...that was the roof going,' he said into her ear.

'I kn-know,' she stammered. 'I've been expecting it to go... Oh!' She shuddered as there wee more horrible tearing sounds and the wind shrieked and he held her hard against him.

They stood like that for an age, breathing as one, waiting for the wooden door to split into matchwood and for the awful wind to fill every crevice of the old cool room and break it up. But the door held and he moved at last as if to let her go.

'Don't!' she pleaded. 'I mean... not just yet.'

'I'm not going to, but we might as well be comfortable. Come...there,' he said a moment or two later when he was sitting on the pile of canvas with her in his lap. 'How's that?'

'...Fine,' she whispered.

'You must have been very frightened on your own.'

'I...was. I was singing...how silly!'

'No. I didn't know you were here, you know.' Richard touched her cheek.

She frowned. 'Didn't you? But...'

'No,' he said again. 'I thought you'd gone with the others. I went out to look for specimens this morning and the outboard packed up. So I drifted mostly and ended up on Bedrock—where I spent the morning with Colonel Jackson and his strange assortment of boarders trying to fix my motor. They persuaded me to stay for lunch, which I did thinking there was no one on Yandilla anyway.'

Anna expelled a shaken breath. 'I thought you must have come home and gone out again. It...never occurred to me you didn't know I was here, although I suppose it should have. Then...how did you know I was here after all?'

'When I heard the cyclone warning I was all set to leave and come home, but Colonel Jackson pointed out that seeing as it was moving in pretty fast and there was no one on Yandilla, it might be wiser to stay there. That seemed to make sense—until we got a frantic call on Bedrock from Samson and Letty. By that time the wind was well and truly blowing and they'd been trying to raise Yandilla for some time...'

'A branch of that mango tree fell across the line,' she explained.

'Ah! Well, anyway, in the slight confusion I said not to worry just to look after themselves. In fact I was intensely relieved to hear from them and to know that they were in the care of a State Emergency Service team and not driving down from Innisfail unaware... But then Letty said, tell Anna Chrissy sends her love. They thought you must be with me on Bedrock. Well, of course, that let the cat out of the bag, thank goodness. But by then the wind was so strong that although we got the boat launched three times, it just got steadily blown back on to the beach and it wasn't until the eye came over... but you know the rest.'

'I thought... I thought you were out there.' Anna swallowed painfully. She turned her head into his shoulder and said in a muffled voice, 'Are they really safe? Chrissy and...'

'Yes. But very worried, I've no doubt.'

She bit her lip as she thought of Chrissy. Richard felt the tremor that shook her as she pictured the child waiting and worrying, and his arms moved round her, drawing her closer. And together with the sounds of terrible devastation going on around them, it all became too much for her and she started to cry.

'Don't, Anna,' he said into her damp hair, but she couldn't stop until he lifted her face very gently from his shoulder and began to kiss her tears and then her lips, but very gently, as if he was kissing a distraught child.

But very soon it changed into something deeper. She couldn't resist the urge to touch his face with trembling fingers and there was no urgency about it, no stunned surprise on her part, just something slow and beautiful and so profound she couldn't explain it, except to think dazedly that she had never in her life got so intrinsically close to anyone. And when it ended, she fell asleep in his arms, as much exhausted by this new facet of her relationship with him—as if this intensely physical act had moved it outside a purely physical plane somehow—as by the trauma of the cyclone.

Richard held her in his arms while she slept, careful not to wake her and stared fixedly into the pitch darkness.

CHAPTER NINE

BUT THE next morning, when they eased themselves out of the old cool-room and stared round disbelievingly at what was left of the boathouse—a few twisted girders, and Anna turned to him in the patchy sunlight and tried to thank him for risking his life to come back and save hers, Richard only shrugged and said lightly, 'Any time, Anna. By the way, what...happened last night between us, I think should be struck from the record.'

She stared at him with parted lips.

He shrugged. 'After all, in those circumstances,' he said wryly, 'I don't think anyone should be made to account for their actions. Do you?'

'I...no,' she said with an effort. 'No.' And was surprised that she could speak at all because her heart seemed to freeze into a lump of stone in her breast. But she made a further effort. She turned away so that he wouldn't be able to see what was in her eyes, and said with a genuine unsteadiness, 'It's just...been blown away. I can't believe it. The cutter too, all your specimens...oh! The house!'

'Anna...' There was an odd note of urgency in his voice, but whatever he had been about to say was lost as they heard a faint shout and both swung round to see the only remaining member of the Yandilla fleet bearing down on what was left of the boatshed jetty.

IT WAS a tumultuous reunion. Chrissy was beside herself
as she hugged her father and Anna repeatedly, laughing
and crying but dangerously close to a sort of nervous hysteria. And Letty hugged them both, although more re-
strainedly outwardly, yet with an inner thankfulness that
needed no words. Sunshine too was visibly moved and
shedding happy tears of relief, and for the first time Anna
saw Samson smile a wide white smile that threatened to
crack his face.

Then another shout was heard and they all turned to see
Colonel Jackson's cabin cruiser puttering in, but this time
his oddly assorted crew were singing, 'Onward, Christian
s-o-l-d-i-e-r-s, marching as to war...'

'Oh, God,' Richard muttered, 'this might turn out to be
quite a day!'

YES, ANNA thought later—much later, when she was getting ready for bed. Quite a day...

By a miracle, or perhaps not, because it was the oldest,
most solidly constructed building on Yandilla, the house
had escaped with very little damage. A lot of water had
come in, three windows had been broken, but structurally
it had remained sound, although some of the verandah
furniture had been discovered quite far away, one chair
even lodged in a tall tree.

'I forgot,' Anna had said, conscience-stricken. 'I
brought the garbage in and all the pot plants...'

'Honey,' Letty had said soothingly, 'you did well. Don't
worry about it.'

But Phil's studio had suffered the same fate as the
boathouse. It was a wreck and the garden was strewn with
debris.

'But I tell you,' the pilot of the Emergency Services hel-
icopter which had arrived on a routine check of all the is-

lands said, 'you're bloody lucky! There are some poor folks who've lost everything they possess.'

YES, ANNA thought, as she brushed her hair, we were lucky.

She stopped brushing as Chrissy stirred but settled. In the end it had been the only way to get her to sleep. Not Richard, not Letty had been able to soothe her over-wrought imagination as dark had closed in and the tension of two days had finally claimed the child as Anna had seen it would. The only thing that had comforted her was to be rocked to sleep in Anna's bed with the promise that she could stay there all night.

Anna got up from the dressing table and moved over to the bed and knelt beside it. She slid her hand into Chrissy's and murmured, 'I'm here, baby.'

Chrissy's hand closed over hers and she relaxed, and Anna marvelled as she had once before at the long shadows her lashes made on her cheeks.

Then she turned her head as the bedroom door opened with no invitation and Richard stood there.

For a moment they stared at each other and Anna felt her heart turn over in a way that told her it was not dead but painfully alive, as she took in everything about him that tormented her so. His tall, powerful body, his intelligent grey-green eyes, his thick fair hair, his well cut mouth... She turned her head away and thought in despair, I must have imagined what happened last night. Perhaps he's right, it... was the circumstances. Otherwise he would have felt it too, surely? It seemed—to me anyway—to be so... special...

'Anna,' he said quietly.

She took a breath. 'Yes?' she whispered.

'Is she all right? Chrissy?'

Anna looked down at Chrissy, now sleeping peacefully again, and gently released her hand. She stood up and moved away from the bed, suddenly conscious but strangely uncaring that she wore only a slender white satin nightgown.

'Yes. She's fine.'

'Thanks to you,' he said abruptly.

Anna shrugged. 'A little, perhaps.'

'No. A lot. Anna . . .'

'Don't,' she interrupted.

'You don't know what I'm going to say.'

'I think I do,' she whispered. 'You're going to thank me for . . . coping with Chrissy tonight, but it's not something I want to be thanked for. It's . . . my job.'

'Is it?' he said, his eyes searching her face.

They stared at each other until she licked her lips and said with a strange reluctance, 'Yes, of course.'

'Yes, of course,' he repeated, and smiled bleakly. 'But I'd still like to be able to thank you. Sleep well, my dear,' he added, and went out, closing the door softly.

It was a long time before Anna got to sleep. Even with Chrissy curled up in her arms like a kitten, breathing easily, the turmoil in her mind refused to be quelled. But one thought kept returning above all else—when I thought he was dead, I wanted to die too. And not even what he said this morning can change that. So what do I do? I can't go on like this, I just can't. But then there's Chrissy . . . Round and round it all went, until her tired brain gave up and she slept.

BY MIDDAY the next day a lot had been done to restore Yandilla. The garden had been cleared with the help of Colonel Jackson's crew again, the phone restored and a lot of the debris from Phil's studio carted away. And two insurance assessors had come to estimate damage to boats and property and a building contractor had inspected the remains of the boatshed.

And after lunch, when all the activity had quietened down a bit, Anna knocked nervously on the study door and entered as bidden.

'Yes, Anna?' Richard said briefly, looking up from his desk.

'Are you very busy?'

He looked at her penetratingly, taking in the shadows beneath her eyes that she'd tried to hide with make-up which she didn't usually wear. His gaze flicked down her rapidly and something about her brought a slight frown to his eyes. She wondered what it could be, because she was only wearing a soft pink blouse and a full cotton skirt with green and pink strips on it—an outfit he had seen a dozen times before.

'No. Sit down,' he said finally.

Anna sat and gripped her hands in her lap and wondered how to say what she'd come to say. Perhaps the best way was just to take the plunge.

'Richard . . . do you still want to marry me?'

There, the fateful words are out, she thought, staring down at her hands and wondering briefly if it was her imagination or if the world had gone very still. She forced herself to look up, to see him studying her intently with narrowed eyes.

'You surprise me, Anna,' he said at last. 'What's made you change your mind? Even as late as last night you were determined to make it clear to me that this was a job and nothing more.'

A faint tinge of colour came to her cheeks, but she said surprisingly steadily, 'Chrissy, mainly. It's hard to put into words how I feel about her. But I can say that I just don't think I could leave her.'

'Is that all?'

'No,' she said slowly. 'There are other things. I feel . . . curiously as if I belong here. It's like being part of a family, something I've missed. Another thing is that having experienced . . . I don't know, I guess the kind of security of being surrounded by Letty and Chrissy and Phil and Samson has made me realise that I don't want to be heading off for the wild blue yonder any more. I . . . seem to have got that out of my system.'

'I see.' There was a strange, tense little silence during which his eyes roamed over her expressionlessly until she bit her lip and said huskily, 'But you might have changed your mind. Of course I'd understand if you had.' She looked down at her hands in a misery of hot confusion and wished desperately that she had never spoken.

'No, I haven't changed my mind,' he said quietly, and her lashes flew up at some note in his voice that she couldn't decipher.

'But . . . you don't think it's such a good idea any more?' she whispered uncertainly.

He smiled slightly. 'Are you asking that, or hoping it, Anna? But no,' he went on without giving her a chance to reply, 'I still think it's a very good idea—with one proviso. If it's going to make you look a picture of misery, and lose weight as you have done lately, and a lot of sleep, then maybe it isn't such a good idea. But on every other count, I haven't changed my mind since we last discussed it.'

'How . . . did you know?' she asked unhappily.

'I'm not blind, Anna,' Richard said dryly. 'What *has* made you change your mind?' he asked directly, and looked at her enquiringly. 'Only those things you mentioned? Chrissy and so on?'

Oh God, she thought, don't do this to me. How can I tell you that in the final analysis, it was *you!* Even though I tried to pretend to myself it was Chrissy—and it is—but it's also you… Perhaps I should tell you? But no, that wouldn't be fair to either of us. Because that would make it a lopsided relationship. She shivered inwardly and thought, no, I can't do that to myself.

She stood up and walked over to the french windows, staring out over the garden for a moment and trying to take a grip on herself. Then she turned back to him. 'I have been unsettled lately. And unhappy and confused. One half of me has been saying that the only sensible thing to do is leave Yandilla while the other half,' she grimaced ruefully, 'seems to want to stay. And not only on account of Chrissy,' she said honestly. 'I can't,' she looked away, 'I find I can't help wondering what it would be like to be married to you, although I'm sometimes still not sure…about that. But,' she raised her eyes to his, 'I think what cast the deciding vote was the night before last when you came back in the cyclone. I…it made me feel…as if I had an anchor. And,' she went on quietly, 'when I thought about it, it seemed to me as if out of all the things I've thought and said, that was one solid fact, and it might be worth as much as all the rest in any case.' And that's the truth, she realised with some surprise. At least part of it. The other part of it is that you hurt me unbearably the next morning when you said what you did, but that's my affair, isn't it? And just something I'll have to guard against. Besides, as Letty said, there might be things to more than compensate for that kind of foolish hurt.

'O.K.,' he said. 'If you're sure, so be it. I think you've made a wise choice, Anna. From my point of view I know you have, and from your point of view I'd only like to say

I'll do everything in my power to make sure you don't regret it.'

He stood up and came over to her and tipped her chin up with his fingers. 'Would you like to kiss me to seal the bargain?'

She closed her eyes briefly and for a startling, blinding instant, wished she could say no. But that's what it's all about, isn't it, Anna? she thought. You can't say no to this, can you?

Then she could think no more as his lips descended on hers.

THE NEXT two weeks passed in a whirl of activity and something of a daze for Anna. Chrissy's joy had been unbounded, and her touching declaration to Anna had brought tears to her eyes.

'I prayed for this, you know, Anna,' she said, her hauntingly look-alike eyes shining. 'Daddy told me I mustn't even think about it and I tried hard not to, but all the while I couldn't help just hoping a little bit and keeping my fingers crossed. And saying a prayer *every* night! You couldn't call that interfering, could you?'

'Not really, sweetheart.'

'And I couldn't help feeling rather m-mortified,' she said experimentally, 'to think what my meddling could have done!'

'What meddling? Oh—you mean . . . ?'

'Yes! But it's taught me a lesson! To think that I could have married Daddy off to one of those others and missed out on you. I shall never meddle again. I'll just leave it all up to God in future,' Chrissy said dramatically. Then, being Chrissy, she got straight to the heart of something she was wondering about. 'How long does it take to have a baby, Anna? I'd love to have a baby brother or sister.'

'That's not something you can predict, Chrissy,' her father said, coming up unexpectedly and shooting Anna a wry glance as she coloured faintly. 'We'll just have to wait and see.'

'Oh! Oh well,' Chrissy said philosophically, 'I don't really mind waiting. I'm so happy as it is . . .'

Letty was also happy, it seemed. 'You did right, honey,' she said. 'But there, I knew you would.'

'Did you, Letty?' Anna said curiously. Then she added quietly, 'I hope I have done the right thing.'

But Letty didn't reply, just smiled wisely as if to say, wait and see . . .

Then Phil created a diversion by arriving home out of the blue two days later.

'Phil,' Richard said exasperatedly, 'I've been trying to contact you in London to let you know we're all right. And all the time you've been on the plane home!'

'Of course I was on the plane home!' Phil said tartly. 'As soon as I heard about the cyclone I hopped on the first plane. They did tell me at Australia House that there were no fatalities, but I wanted to make sure for myself. You've no idea what it's like sitting around waiting for news!'

'But you must have known I'd get on to you as soon as possible. And what about your series?'

'Oh, that!' Anna said airily, going faintly pink about the ears. 'I'll tell you about that some time.'

'Aunt Phil! Aunt Phil! Guess what? Daddy and Anna are going to get married!' Chrissy cried, hurling herself at Phil and adding to the confusion considerably.

'They . . . are?' Phil said weakly, looking at Anna and Richard in turn and then at Letty.

'Sure are,' said Letty.

'Well . . . what a surprise,' said Phil, and turned away from a distinctly—oh yes?—look she discerned in Anna's eyes. But she turned back almost immediately. 'Then it's a jolly good thing I did come home after all, Richard,' she said militantly. 'If you thought you were going to get away with a wedding without me, you were much mistaken!' And she stuck out her chin in an aggressive gesture that was so unlike her, everyone burst out laughing.

'Dear Phil,' Richard said finally, and put an arm round her. 'It wasn't that at all. And I'm very glad you're home. I should have hated to get married without your presence. But I just thought...'

'Well, don't you think any more,' Phil said fondly, and blinked away a tear. 'I wouldn't miss this for anything!'

'ANNA?' PHIL said several days later when they had sunk down exhaustedly in their Townsville hotel room. 'You're very quiet. Wasn't this trip to Townsville to shop for your trousseau a good idea after all?'

Anna looked across at her affectionately. 'It was a lovely idea, Phil,' she said quietly. 'Most of your ideas are.'

'Then... it's the idea of me paying for it all that you don't like?' Phil said hesitantly.

Anna got up suddenly and knelt beside the older woman's chair. 'No. It's a wonderful gift, and I love you for it, Phil.'

'What is it, then, pet?'

'I think... I think,' Anna said tremulously, 'it's a good old-fashioned dose of bridal jitters.'

'Anna,' Phil said gravely, 'please tell me, because I'm a little tormented about it, shouldn't Letty and I have interfered the way we did?'

'Probably not,' said Anna with a glint of humour. 'But I'm glad you did. You see, at least I know that you...approve of me and like me. And that means a great deal to me.'

Phil put out a hand and touched her hair. 'You mean a great deal to us, my dear. That's why I'm a bit conscience-stricken, do you see?'

Anna took a deep breath, 'Phil,' she said steadily but with a shimmer of tears in her eyes, 'I'm marrying Richard because I can no longer pretend to myself that I don't love him. And that's not anything to do with you or Letty, except that you've made it easier.'

'And—Richard?' Phil queried.

'Will go out of his way to make me happy and secure,' Anna said slowly. 'If I didn't believe that I wouldn't be doing this. But not so much because I'm me as because I'll be a suitable . . . wife who he can trust.'

'Is that going to be enough for you, Anna?'

'Yes, Phil. More than enough,' Anna said huskily but firmly. 'And I'll get over these jitters, you see. I guess being a virgin bride at my old age is enough to give anyone the jitters,' she added wryly, but thought wincingly, that's the heart of the matter, isn't it, Anna? You still haven't told him, can't seem to find the right time or the right words, but soon it will be too late. Will it matter very much, though? And it's not always such an earthshattering thing, if you can believe what you read.

'Anna?'

She looked up at Phil. 'Sorry . . .'

'I was only going to say, if that's what's worrying you, I was a virgin bride at the grand old age of twenty-six. And even in those days we weren't quite so prudish about these things as we like to make out we were now. So I was quite convinced I was some kind of a freak. But in the end I was very glad I'd saved it up . . . Dear me, did I say that? It sounds awful when you say it like that. But you know what I mean.'

'Yes, Phil,' Anna murmured with a loving little smile.

ONE WEEK later she was married to Richard Gillespie in the garden of Yandilla homestead.

She wore a frothy cocktail-length dress that wasn't quite blue and wasn't quite grey and was romantic enough even to satisfy Chrissy, who had had visions at one time of seeing Anna in something like the Princess of Wales had worn. Her dark hair was uncovered and it gleamed almost blue black and lay smooth and naturally curved to her shoulders. She also wore a pair of diamond studs in her ears that had been Richard's present to her, together with a diamond engagement ring that wasn't large but was exquisitely cut so that every facet of it sparked a blue, unmistakable fire. And she was to carry a bouquet of orchids, tiny white, star-like ones that Samson had picked himself and Letty had wrought beautifully into two bouquets—one for Anna and a smaller one for Chrissy.

'You look—I've never seen anyone look as pretty as you do, Anna,' Chrissy said with tears in her eyes.

'Nor I you, sweetheart,' Anna answered with a lump in her throat as she adjusted her bow and smoothed her long fair hair. 'Chrissy, we won't be gone for very long. Will you mind?'

'Oh no! Letty explained to me about honeymoons. And Phil's here and she says the Colonel has some treats in store for us. I wonder what they are?'

'Special treats for a special little girl, I suspect.'

But strangely, it was Mrs Robertson who spent the last few minutes with Anna before she was married.

Her arrival on Yandilla had come as a complete surprise to Anna the day before. Richard had escorted her up to the household and announced, 'I have a very special guest, Anna.'

'Oh! Mrs Robertson... Oh!'

'Anna!'

And now, in those last few minutes before the service began, Mrs Robertson said with a funny little smile, 'I have to tell you, Anna, Bob Wetherby sends his regards—and said to tell you he hasn't ever seen me struck dumb before, but I was when your Richard rang.'

Anna had to smile. 'It is hard to imagine, isn't it? If it hadn't been for your Mrs Lawson, I'd never have come here.'

Mrs Robertson settled her enormous, flowery hat more securely and suddenly her bright, bird-like eyes were a little misty as she surveyed Anna. 'It's only what you deserve, though, love. It couldn't have happened to a nicer person! And the very next time anyone tells me I'm an interfering old busybody—Bob Wetherby, for example—I'll tell him, nothing ventured, nothing gained, and look what happened to Anna!'

'Mrs Robertson, I love you,' said Anna, a little mistily herself.

'Well, you just promise me one thing, love. Be happy—sometimes it takes a bit of working at when it isn't all so new any more, but it's worth it.'

'I'll... work at it, I promise.' They hugged each other warmly.

IT WAS the Colonel who gave her away. And it was his flock who formed the greater part of the congregation. In fact the minister who performed the service looked faintly incredulous as he surveyed them.

But the Colonel said in a quiet aside to Anna as they came down the verandah steps, 'They will behave, my dear. Don't worry about that.'

'I rather like them when they don't, Colonel.'

'Funny you should say that, so do I. Nevertheless a wedding is a wedding! Not something you do every day!'

No, she thought. Thank God!

But despite its strange origins and strange assortment of guests it was somehow a solemn occasion. Phil and Letty cried openly and Samson, who was best man, cleared his throat after those final words had been pronounced and said, 'Richard and Anna, you two best take care of each other like the man said. 'Cause you're mighty precious to us all.'

The congregation had answered, 'Hear, hear!' and then begun to sing beautifully and obviously rehearsed, 'All things bright and beautiful, all creatures great and small! All things wise and wonderful...'

Richard and Anna looked at each other fully for the first time, Richard with eyebrows slightly raised, and she said, 'Th-that sounds like Chrissy's choice. It's her favourite.'

'The Lord God made them all...it was,' Phil sang.

Richard turned and Chrissy flew into his arms, while Anna looked at the two fair heads so close together and felt her nervous tension drain away as a kind of peace claimed her.

'ANNA.'

Anna turned away from the window of another hotel bedroom, this time overlooking the lights of Sydney, and took a deep breath.

'Yes?' she whispered.

'Come here,' Richard said gently.

She obeyed mutely. 'You're tired,' he murmured, and touched her pale face with two fingers. 'And all wound up.'

She could only nod helplessly after a moment. For it was all too true. Her state of peaceful euphoria had lasted through the long day, the drive to Townsville and the long flight to Sydney. It had seen her through dinner at a premier Sydney restaurant, and then quite suddenly it had deserted her when the door of their suite had closed on the rest of the world and Richard had taken off his jacket and thrown it over the back of a chair and pulled off his tie. She had looked at him and in a moment of panic seen a tall, attractive stranger whom she was expected to go to bed with shortly—and discovered to her horror that that was the last thing she wanted to do because incredibly she was as fearful about it as some silly teenager.

And even now, showered and changed into one of her new nightgowns, she felt no better about it.

'There's no need to be,' he said, his grey-green eyes searching her face. 'We don't have to rush anything. We have all the time in the world.'

'I . . . I'm sorry,' she said with a catch in her voice. 'You must think I'm awfully silly . . .'

A shadow of a smile crept into his eyes. 'Not silly,' he said very quietly. 'Quite wise, in fact. Come.' He took her hand and led her to the enormous bed and pulled aside the lavender silk sheet. 'Lie down.'

She did, and he pulled the sheet up and sat down beside her. 'Some things are better left until they happen . . . spontaneously.' He pushed a wayward strand of hair behind her ear as if she was Chrissy. 'So why don't you go to sleep and stop worrying. Then tomorrow—well, that's another day. Goodnight, my dear,' he said, and kissed her wrist. 'Sleep well.'

The surprising thing was that she did.

And when she woke with the faint half-light of dawn coming through the uncurtained windows, she lay quietly for a few minutes, then felt a movement beside her and turned with her heart in her mouth to see Richard propped up on one elbow, watching her.

'Have you been awake long?' she whispered.

He reached out a hand and cupped her cheek. 'A little longer than you, Mrs Gillespie. I'm an early riser. How do you feel?'

'Fine.'

'You look…more beautiful than you usually do,' he said gravely, and his hand slid down to her shoulder.

So do you, she thought as her gaze slid involuntarily to his wide, bare shoulders. She smiled, her lips just faintly unsteady, 'You have a nice line in early morning lies, Mr Gillespie,' she murmured. 'I'm sure I look a mess.'

His eyebrows rose and he shot her a wicked look that made her tremble. 'All right,' he said, 'put it this way. Your hair is gorgeously rumpled, your skin faintly flushed, your eyes still calm and dreamy and you have an unguarded air of *déshabillé* about you that makes me long to complete the process.' He lay back with his head beside hers on the pillow. 'Would you mind very much if I did?' he asked, his eyes suddenly completely sober.

'Not…not when you ask so nicely,' she responded, suddenly filled with a quivering tenderness as she thought of how understanding he had been last night when he need not have been. When many men wouldn't have been in the circumstances. And she took a deep breath and thought, it's now or never. Perhaps I could still tell him? But no, it seems cowardly somehow to do it now…

She slid her fingers through his, then lifted his hand to her mouth and kissed it.

She thought later, dimly, that she was doing well. But almost immediately she realised that she personally was not all that responsible for what she was doing. Because Richard was slowly and expertly arousing her to a pitch of fevered desire that was wringing responses from her that she had no need to mime in any way. And that somehow, his hands that were so sure, and his lips, were doing things

to her body that were unmercifully releasing the flood-
gates of longing she had been so carefully and for so long
keeping tightly leashed.

Then, in spite of herself, she tensed as he took her, and
her body convulsed with a tearing pain. Richard lifted his
head and felt the tremors that racked her; he held her hard
against him and said with a kind of despair, 'You haven't
ever done this before, have you, Anna?'

'I...no...'

'Why did you lie?'

'I don't know,' she whispered tearfully. 'But you mustn't
blame yourself. I seem to make such a habit of doing
foolish things. And I thought you might not necessarily
ever have to know...'

'Oh, Anna,' he sighed into her hair, still holding her as
the pain began to subside. 'It's all too late to change it
now.'

'I don't want to. Please don't stop... It would have
happened anyway.'

'Perhaps,' he said with an effort. 'Although there are
ways to lessen it if you *know.*'

'Richard,' she wept, 'don't make me feel worse.'

'All right—don't cry,' he said quietly. 'Relax, if you can,
and we'll start all over again.'

He began to kiss her body slowly, and all over again she
fell prey to the exquisite beauty of his touch on her until
finally she was transported to a kind of heaven with her
senses reeling and that tearing pain only a shadowy memory.

They lay in each other's arms for a long time afterwards. Then Richard put her away from him and stared
down at her. 'You should have told me, Anna,' he said
sombrely. 'Why did you let me think that?'

She sighed tremulously. 'I was—I don't know, when you assumed what you did that day, I was angry and I thought, *let* him think that if he wants to...'

'So you haven't had an unhappy love affair? Or didn't it get to the going to bed stage?' His eyes searched hers.

'No, I've never been in love,' she whispered.

'Then—O.K. I can understand what happened that first day. But why didn't you tell me later?'

Why? How can I tell you why? Her eyelashes fluttered and were beaded with tears. 'Because I felt an incredible fool,' she said huskily. 'I think that's why. But was it so important? Unless,' her lashes flew up and her eyes widened painfully, 'unless you wanted someone experienced? Not gauche and fumbling...' She closed her eyes and felt herself shrivelling like a fallen leaf. 'I never thought of that. Men do, they say,' she added shakily.

'Who says?' he asked, his voice suddenly strangely dry.

'Well,' she moved helplessly, 'I've read it.'

'You shouldn't always believe what you read, Anna,' he said ironically. 'Did you also read somewhere that virgins can pass themselves off as experienced women? Did you read up about that?' His eyes bored into hers.

She coloured and turned her head away, wishing miserably that she could die. 'I'm sorry,' she whispered. 'I see now that it's quite natural you would have wanted someone more...more...'

'I didn't say that,' he interrupted.

'But if you'd known—I think you're trying to tell me that if you'd known, you wouldn't have married me. Yet I honestly didn't think it would make much difference. I mean, the other things stand, don't they? All the other reasons for us getting married?'

'Oh yes.'

She stared up at him with her heart beating like some dead, muffled drum. 'But you wouldn't have, would you? If you'd known...?'

'No.'

The single syllable cut her to the quick. 'W-won't you tell me why, at least?' she stammered.

Richard looked over towards the window where the dawn was losing its early rose colour to a shimmering, pale blue. 'Because I thought, with the basis of some experience to work on,' his eyes came back to her face and they were bleak, 'you'd be able to make a reasoned, rational judgement when I asked you to marry me.'

'I did that in the end,' Anna whispered. 'I worked out that what you said made sense. In fact, that what you said were my original thoughts on the subject. And that really I could spend my life looking for love never to find it or to find that it wasn't the real thing after all and then I'd regret turning my back on things that do mean a great deal to me. Like...Chrissy and Yandilla and in a sense, you.'

Liar, Anna, something rose up inside her to taunt her.

But at the same time she knew too, with a deeply hurting honesty, that she could no more tell him the truth than she had ever been able to. Less able to now, in fact.

'And what do you know now, Anna?' he asked with a haunting gentleness. 'Was it worth it to take such a gamble?'

'I...that depends on you,' she said unhappily.

'Ah! There you've unconsciously put it in a nutshell, my lovely deceiver,' he said with a wry twist to his lips. 'If you knew anything about me, you'd know that I didn't want to be burdened with a virgin bride because that's a situation I'm not best equipped to deal with. I thought we were two people who'd suffered some...disillusionment which had left us ready to deal in realities. I *don't* think anybody's first lover, whatever the outcome, should have to be someone like that—like me, a rather coldblooded, cynical realist. But I have to hand it to you, Anna. I've heard of this particular deception being practised the other way around...hell!' he said with a sudden savagery and his eyes dark. 'Don't look like that. I'm *sorry!*'

He pulled her into his arms. 'Forget what I said,' he murmured, holding her close as her body shook in a paroxysm of despair. 'We'll make it work somehow.'

And a little later, when she had subsided exhausted against him, he tilted her chin up gently and smudged the tears on her lashes and said, not quite smiling, 'Who knows, I might turn into a Prince Charming for you after all. You're beautiful enough to bewitch me, and despite what you read, I found your...inexperience charming. So much so, I suspect that'll be the least of our problems.' But the last part of his sentence was said inaudibly to Anna, and he stared across the top of her head at nothing in particular but with a curious look of pain in his eyes.

CHAPTER TEN

IF THERE was one word she could apply to her honey-moon, Anna often thought afterwards, it would have to be 'unforgettable'.

Yet while that was true enough, it didn't express so many things. The heights and the depths, the laughter that sometimes hid tears, the uncertainty that she couldn't al-ways hide, the sensation that she'd once suspected—that to be his lover would be like flying too high, or the fact that love could grow as hers did. Nor did it express the fact that only once during those two weeks did the things said on the first morning of their marriage surface again and that for all the rest of the time he seemed determined to try to wipe them out. And he was so successful, she found that she could often pretend that Richard Gillespie didn't regret having married Anna Horton.

They did everything they couldn't do on Yandilla—went to the theatre, art galleries, antique auctions. They shopped for things the cyclone had damaged in the house, and more besides.

'It's your home now, Anna,' Richard told her. 'It should reflect your personality.'

'But I like it the way it is!'

'I didn't think there was a woman alive who could resist that kind of invitation,' he said, looking at her quizzi-cally.

'That's because you don't think much of women,' she retorted before she could stop herself. But she managed to grin at him almost immediately as if she was only teasing. And because she had so nearly fallen into the trap she knew she must avoid at all costs, she allowed herself to be partly persuaded. They bought some paintings and china that she especially liked, some silver cutlery that he had monogrammed with their initials, and a beautifully crafted mahogany rolltop desk—the kind which had fascinated her ever since she could remember—for her own personal use. They also shopped for Chrissy and spent some time and some hilarity trying to find presents for Letty and Sunshine, Samson and Phil.

They went to the races and to the cricket. Richard had managed to get tickets for the third day of an Australia versus England test match at the Sydney Cricket Ground.

Anna, who was not a particular cricket fan, said after a few hours with a lurking smile, 'If I'd known you were such a cricket fan, I might not have married you.'

'I thought you must have guessed,' he replied innocently.

'How should I have guessed?'

'Why do you think we came to Sydney for our honeymoon? This week particularly?'

'Oh . . . you! No, seriously . . .'

'Seriously, Anna,' he said, laughing at her expression, 'why don't we leave them to it? I can think of something I'd much rather be doing, after all.'

She stared at him with her lips parted. 'You don't mean . . . ?' And her cheeks grew pink at the way he was looking at her. 'But it's only two o'clock in the afternoon!'

'That's a very good hour for what I have in mind,' he said with his lips quirking. 'When most other sober citi-

zens are diligently pursuing their lawful pursuits, it adds a
certain spice to it. Besides, the cricket is awfully dull.'

'Well!' she exclaimed indignantly.

'And besides all that,' he said, and lifted a hand to trace
the outline of her mouth with one finger, 'I haven't seen
you without your clothes for hours now. That's too long.'
He didn't attempt to lower his voice.

'*Richard,*' she whispered, and looked around uneasily,
to see a few people staring at them amusedly. 'Oh! Let's get
out of here,' she muttered, with her colour fluctuating deliciously.

They did, and he made love to her laughingly in the
sunlit bedroom of their suite and teased her about being so
awfully prim and proper. Then they slept until it was dark,
showered together and went out on the town and didn't get
back to the hotel until three in the morning.

'See what I mean about making love in the afternoon?'
said Richard, his eyes glinting devilishly as he removed her
wrap and shoes and swung her up into his arms to sit down
with her in his lap on the settee. 'It leaves the night free for
other things.'

Anna, who was still drifting on a cloud of the bewitch-
ing music they'd been dancing to, cast him a sudden suspicious glance from beneath her lashes. 'Like what?'

'This,' he said gravely, and started to kiss her.

'Isn't that what we were doing this afternoon?' she asked
a few minutes later.

'Is it?'

'Richard, don't tease me,' she begged, 'or I'll...'

'Or you'll what, Mrs Gillespie?' he asked politely.

'Oh, really give you something to tease me about,' she
threatened, laughing as she said it but even closer to tears,
because her love for him was threatening to overwhelm her

and sweep her away to the extent that she would lose all caution.

'Hey,' he said gently, taking her face in his hands, 'what's this? Am I going to fast for you, Anna?'

'No...oh no!' she said tremulously.

He looked at her searchingly. 'All the same, you're a very new bride.'

'Not that new...'

His lips twitched. 'All of a week old. Perhaps we should have a moratorium—say, until this time tomorrow. I won't touch you or kiss you or mention anything in public about how beautiful you are without your clothes...and I'll take cold showers at hourly intervals. How does that sound?'

'Terrible! Oh, Richard, you are an idiot sometimes!' But she felt herself relaxing all the same and she snuggled up closer to him. 'I never dreamt you could be like this when I first met you.'

'That's because I was very cross with you,' he said idly, and stroked her hair.

'Yes, you were.' She sighed suddenly.

'What is it?'

'Nothing...'

He stroked her hair. 'Do you feel sleepy?'

'Mmm...'

'Go to sleep, then, Anna.'

'Here?'

'Why not?' He swung his legs up on to the settee and settled them both comfortably.

'Are you serious?' she asked drowsily.

But he didn't answer. Just kept stroking her hair until she fell asleep.

BUT THE façade did slip once. It happened the night they were to go to the opera, and Anna had no intimation of what was coming as she got ready, taking her time about it and making sure she looked just right.

She bathed, using an expensive and fragrant bath oil, then smoothed a matching body lotion all over so that her skin glowed with the sheen of silk. And she put on a matching set of French satin and lace underwear and carefully drew on a pair of sheer fine tights. Then came the dress, a thing of almost living beauty, she had thought when she and Phil had chosen it. Nor had it changed since she had tried it on in the shop, she saw as she studied her reflection in the long mirror. The coral chiffon was still the same vibrant colour, the pleated low-cut bodice that was supported by narrow, halter-neck ties still fitted perfectly, hugging her figure and emphasising the slenderness of her waist, and the skirt was still soft and clinging despite its yards upon yards of material. Gold sandals with very high heels completed the outfit.

She moved back to the dressing table and sat down to put the final touches to her appearance. She had put her hair up and the moisture from her bath had added just a touch of waywardness to it, but the effect was rather nice. In fact, she couldn't help feeling pleased with the whole effect as she applied perfume from a delicate cut-glass bottle to her wrists—a matching fragrance again. Her translucent lipstick and her nail varnish toned with the coral of her dress, a pale grey eyeshadow seemed to make her eyes look enormous and the mascara she had used sparingly made her lashes look even longer. And Richard's diamond earrings shone in her ears . . .

Her dark lashes lifted suddenly as another reflection joined hers in the mirror—Richard.

He had been waiting in the lounge of the suite for her, and even though she had seen him briefly in his evening clothes before he had left the bedroom to watch the news, something about him made her catch her breath. But it wasn't only that evening clothes suited his fair good looks very well—that the dark jacket of his dinner suit and the starched whiteness of his shirt sat as well on him as jeans and a bush shirt—it was something else too...a strange air of remoteness, as if this was some tall stranger and not the person who so often teased her and now played such an intimate part in her life.

'Have I taken ages?' she asked self-consciously. 'I'm ready now.'

But she didn't stand up. Because there seemed to be something magnetic keeping his eyes riveted to hers in the mirror.

Then at last he said, 'It was worth waiting for. You look sensational, Anna.'

'Thank you.'

'Yes,' his grey-green gaze roamed her reflection meditatively, 'too beautiful to take out, I'm afraid,' he added with a strangely twisted smile.

She stared at the mirror with parted lips as his hands came up and he undid the halter-neck tie at the back of her neck. Her eyes widened as he very slowly, lingeringly pushed the bodice of her dress down so that her breasts were revealed, cupped in the lacy strapless bra she wore.

She moved then, a tiny almost defensive movement that he stilled with his hands on her shoulders. Then he looked down and slid his fingers down her back and opened the zip at the back of her dress, then he undid the clasp of her bra and slipped the wisp of beige lace and satin off and laid it on the dressing table.

'I prefer you without one,' he said quietly.

Anna swallowed suddenly as she gazed at the images in the mirror. The softly lamplit room, Richard behind her, his head bent as he looked down at her...and herself, naked to the waist with her breasts gleaming like ivory and rose. And as she watched, he put his hands on her shoulders again and moved them slowly downwards.

She shivered slightly then, conscious of a confused mixture of emotions—a strange feeling of expectancy tinged with a desperate vulnerability. Because somehow the sight of him standing behind her looking austere and remote, yet doing what he was doing, made her feel like an expensive piece of merchandise, to be appreciated at whim—or discarded in the same way like a lovely but lifeless stone statue.

Is this a moment of truth? she wondered with a sickening lurch of her heart. Is that how he really sees me?

But there was nothing lifeless about the way her breasts swelled beneath his hands. And a bright wave of colour stained her cheeks and she said foolishly, 'We'll be late...'

He looked up at last and his eyes captured hers in the mirror and he smiled slightly, a cool, chiselled movement of his lips that didn't quite reach his eyes. 'What's the point of going if I'll be spending the whole evening wanting to do this, Anna?'

'You...you could do it when we got home,' she said haltingly and uncertainly.

'I might not have the will-power to wait that long,' he drawled ironically.

She bit her lip, not knowing whether to believe him or not. But surely he couldn't be serious? She said awkwardly, 'I think you're teasing me again.'

An undisguised spark of amusement touched his eyes. 'Then I'll have to show you otherwise, won't I, my much-misused Anna?'

She winced inwardly because the irony was still there and it hurt. And she looked at him in the mirror with eyes that were dark and troubled and lips that were not quite steady.

'What's wrong?' he asked softly. 'Isn't this after all what you set out to achieve—in fact what all women set out to achieve when they take a lot of trouble with their appearance? That some man will be moved to undress them and make love to them? Well, you've achieved that, Anna, here and now, so isn't it a little pointless to waste time on the rest of the charade?'

Anna paled and with jerky, unco-ordinated movements, freed herself and stood up, pulling her dress up clumsily as she did. '*No,*' she whispered, appalled. 'If that's what you think ...'

'It's what I know,' he interrupted dryly, and leisurely reached for her. 'I'm not *complaining* about it—just acknowledging it. Does that upset you? It shouldn't, because you could say the joke's on me.'

If she was pale before, she went white now. Because for the first time since he had taken her in a kind of ignorance and said that he wouldn't have married her if he'd known, he was showing her the side of him she had begun secretly to hope did not exist any longer. That part of him that viewed women so cynically—and perhaps what hurt most, she realised anguishedly, he was showing her too, that he had no cause to revise his opinions.

'Well, it does upset me,' she said raggedly. 'How would you like it if I told you I wasn't interested in spending any time with you other than in bed?'

His lips twitched and his eyes glinted devilishly and he started to speak, but she was so sure it was going to be something mocking and clever that she would have no answer for, a spontaneous spark of anger ignited within her, fusing all her hurt and love and uncertainty into a blazing rejection of his sentiments. Her arm flew out to slap him, but he caught her wrist in a grip that threatened to crush her bones.

'Don't do that,' he warned grimly, and with no further ado picked her up and tossed her on to the bed and sat down beside her, effectively imprisoning her with an arm on either side of her. 'It's quite a while since you've been angry with me, Anna,' he added.

'It's quite a while since you've been your usual objectionable self,' she retorted bitterly, close to tears of despair.

'I wouldn't have thought it was objectionable to pay you a compliment,' he said coolly.

'That…what you said wasn't a compliment. It was more like a shot fired in anger,' she answered tightly, and turned her head away defiantly.

'And I wonder what you would say this is,' he murmured, and despite every futile effort she made, finished undressing her carefully and somehow objectively until she was crying, tears of frustration and humiliation.

Then when he had finished and her clothes were lying in a heap on the floor, he stood up and started to take his own clothes off, but his eyes never left hers.

And when she said in a husky, goaded voice, 'If you think I'm enjoying this or feeling complimented, you're wrong!' he merely smiled slightly and said, 'We'll see.'

She did see not much later. She saw that her anger and hurt weren't proof against what he did to her, slowly and inexorably. She saw that while she could stop herself touching him, she couldn't stop herself trembling as his hands moved from her breasts to her waist to her thighs, stroking, cupping, exploring. She saw her puny defences go up in smoke, one by one.

But most of all, she saw why. That it was no good consoling herself as she had tried to once before, with the thought that he was sufficiently attractive and experienced to wring a response from her despite her better judgement.

No, she thought dimly. If I really didn't want him to be doing this to me, I could stop him because I'd be frozen with contempt and dislike and revulsion. But I'm not. I'd like to think I was, but I'm not... And why? Because Richard Gillespie fascinates me and torments me and makes me feel more alive than I thought possible even when I think I hate him. And if I think I hate him now, it's because he, of all men, is the only one I want in so many ways—and can't have in so many ways. I want his companionship, his admiration, his respect...his love. I don't only want to be someone he enjoys taking to bed. Oh God, she thought torturedly, I thought I could live with it, but I don't know if I can! Not this...

And a terrible sense of longing intermingled with frustration took possession of her heart, much as the hurt anger had consumed her earlier, and even though she knew tauntingly that she was handing him this particular round, game, set and match, she suddenly didn't care.

She came alive beneath his wandering lips and pushed her fingers through his thick fair hair and arched her body towards him in an unmistakable invitation. As she did so she ran her hands down his back, skimming over his smooth skin, then stopping every now and then with a firm but gentle pressure and with her fingers wide-spread. And when that seemed to please him, she began to kiss his body and trail her tongue along the strong lines of his throat and the smooth tanned skin of his shoulders, all the time touching him more and more intimately and caressingly and moving beneath him as her own pleasure and excitement seemed to increase with each movement she made. She grew even more daring, to the astonishment of one tiny corner of her mind, which was all that was left of her that was not totally absorbed in what she was doing. She eased herself slightly away from him and reached out to switch off the bedside lamp so that the only light coming into the room was through the doorway leading into the lounge, and sat up on her heels beside him, proudly so that every curve of her body from the swell of her breasts to the slenderness of her waist and the rounded sweep of her hips was outlined in a golden glow against the shaft of light coming in. She stayed as still as a statue, offering herself for Richard's inspection demurely yet tantalising, with her lips parted and her breathing not very steady and her nipples telling their own tale, hardening in anticipation of what his touch could do to them, of the pleasure he could inflict on her by just touching them.

They stayed like that for what seemed an age, with his narrowed gaze roaming over her as he lay with his head resting on one hand. Then he stretched out the other hand and plucked at each swelling, throbbing peak, and Anna watched his fingers for a moment. Then she closed her eyes and tilted her head back, and tremors of exquisite torment racked her until she could stand it no longer, and her head sank forward and her dark hair, which had tumbled down, shadowed her face like a silky curtain.

Richard's hand left her body abruptly and he sat up with a suddenly tortured breath and her lashes fluttered upwards uncertainly and she saw, in the intent way his eyes were devouring her and in the muscle that jerked in his jaw and the way he was breathing, that she had stirred him for the first time, she thought, to a pitch of such sheer naked desire for her that there was no place for any gentle mockery or teasing provocativeness or even anything protective, as there had always been in his lovemaking, in deference, she assumed, to the fact that she was a newcomer to it and he didn't want to hurt her again or frighten her. There was nothing of that now, just something white-hot and elemental between them that had him as relentlessly in its grip as it had her.

But the thought stumbled into her mind that she should be getting some satisfaction from this fact, yet curiously she wasn't. Because she was quite suddenly just a little afraid...

Then it was too late for fear as he started to kiss her breasts and run his hands from her waist to her thighs, and she moaned despairingly and pressed his fair head closer and began to say his name over and over, pleadingly and gaspingly and with an aching sense of love that she couldn't disguise. Until finally, when she thought she must faint from the savage beauty of his lovemaking, they reached a pinnacle of spinning intensity together, which made every other time she had experienced it seem pale by comparison, and she clung to him helplessly as they eventually floated down slowly from it, and she murmured anguishedly, 'Hold me...oh, please, don't let me go...'

'I'm...not letting you go, Anna,' he said huskily into her hair and as if it was an effort for him to speak. Then he held her hard until their bodies were still at last and she fell instantly asleep in his arms.

A PALE, marshmallow pink dawn greeted her eyes hours later through wide-swept curtains. Her first waking thought was that she had closed the curtains last night when she was getting dressed to go...

She bit her lip and a tide of colour rose up from the base of her throat to stain her cheeks as the events of the previous evening washed over in a living tide.

She lay for a long time with her eyes closed, remembering and feeling almost as shaken now as she had then. Until gradually it dawned on her that she was alone in the bed—in the room, probably in the suite, because she could hear no sound of Richard. And she was sadly glad—if that's possible, she thought—because she didn't feel in any condition to face him.

In fact, she mused, she felt as if she had been dropped from a great height and she was still lying sprawled with a sort of twisted, abandoned grace.

'Abandoned,' she whispered, 'that's a good choice of words in more ways than one. Not only do I feel literally abandoned at this moment, I feel totally abandoned in the wanton sense of the word. Languid, not sure if I have the strength or the energy or the will to move, but curiously fulfilled.' She grimaced ruefully and turned over—and couldn't quite stifle the small sound of pain that rose to her lips as the movement hurt her aching breasts.

'Anna...'

She jerked convulsively and turned back to see Richard standing beside the bed staring sombrely down at her. He was dressed in jeans and a fine wool sweater that matched his eyes and his hair was ruffled as if the wind had been tugging at it.

She trembled. 'I didn't know you were there.'

'I haven't been—for long,' he said quietly, and sat down beside her. 'Are you all right?'

'Oh yes... yes,' she stammered.

He studied her piercingly for a long moment with his lips set and pale. Then he said abruptly, 'It didn't sound like it just now.' And he prised the sheet from her fingers which were unconsciously grasping it tightly, and drew it away from her.

'Richard,' she whispered uncertainly, 'I'm all right.'

He closed his eyes briefly. 'You also bruise more easily than most people, or I was far too rough last night. I'm sorry, Anna,' he said tiredly, and laid the sheet back carefully and looked away.

She wondered if he didn't want her to see the pity and compassion in his eyes and realised that she didn't, that it would hurt her far more than a few bruises.

She put out a hand and touched one of his. 'Don't be sorry,' she said softly. 'I was there too, remember? And I'm not sorry. How could I be? You told me once that when a man and a woman... affect each other like that, it can be like nothing else that's ever happened to you. I know what you meant now. And,' her voice cracked slightly, but there was something painfully honest in her eyes as she went on, 'whatever else is... not quite right between us, I could only feel poorer for not having experienced that.'

His eyes had come back to rest on her face as soon as she had touched his hand. But as she stopped speaking he looked away again and it seemed to her as if he winced inwardly, and she wondered why. Wondered if she'd said the wrong thing.

When he spoke, at last, his voice was uneven and his fingers not quite steady as he fitted them through her own. 'Anna, what is—not quite right between us is the fact that you deserve *more*... because you're so courageous, so beautiful, so...'

'Don't,' she said involuntarily. 'Please don't. I'm not really.'

He smiled slightly, a smile that was more an expression of pain. 'Yes, you are. And it's breaking your heart that I can't give you more, isn't it? Can only give you the kind of treatment I meted out last night over the simple matter of going to the opera. I should be shot for what I said,' he added.

Anna felt as if her heart had stopped beating. He knows, she thought hazily through a sudden tensing of all her muscles.

But his next words made her wonder.

'That's—what I was worried about, you see,' he said, and traced a meaningless pattern on her hand with one finger. 'When it happens to you for the first time,' he looked up and captured her compelling gaze, 'it's hard not to be,' he hesitated, 'not to be all-encompassed by it. Do you have any idea what I'm talking about?'

Oh yes, she thought unhappily, I do. Only that happened to me first, long before last night. But even though you don't know that, you do obviously know something of what I feel now. Which is not so surprising, she thought with a sudden flickering of her nerve ends as she recalled the way she had acted. But how to put it into perspective, your kind of perspective which doesn't believe in it?

She looked up at the ceiling briefly, then back at him.

'Yes,' she said gravely, 'I do see. But although I'm,' she grimaced, 'running true to type—as romantic as the rest of them—there are other things that . . . that more than compensate. For one thing, at least we can talk about it. And the way we've been for so much of the time has . . . has meant a great deal to me. It's more than enough.'

She stared up at him with her heart now thudding painfully and was suddenly conscious that she meant every word she'd said and that her mouth had gone dry in case he rejected it, because it hit her suddenly, with almost the same force the cyclone had, that it was as much him as his love that she needed. Even in his cynicism, which was in any case slightly counterbalanced by the fact that he did care enough to try to make her understand.

'Richard,' she said on a sudden breath, 'I don't mind that it's not perfect. I knew...it couldn't ever be. But I think we can make the best of it.'

'God,' he muttered barely audibly, and gathered her into his arms, 'if you only know what a low, rotten kind of heel it makes me feel to hear you using my own arguments and philosophies!'

'No!' she pulled away from him. 'No, you don't understand!'

'Yes, I do,' he said, roughly. 'More than you know. I understand that I'm a bloody sight luckier than I deserve to be. And I just have to hope it stays that way. *Don't...* don't cry,' he added with a gentle bitterness, and kissed her eyelids. 'If there's one thing I wish, it's that I *could* be your Prince Charming,' he said huskily. 'Because you deserve no less.'

They stayed like that for an age until Anna was able to get a grip on herself. Then he held her away and said seriously, 'Did I hurt you very much last night? How do you feel?'

'I...I'm not sure,' she said huskily—and added with her lips quirking, 'Depends what you have in mind. I don't feel like doing anything too strenuous, like sightseeing or...'

His eyes softened. 'That wasn't what I had in mind.'

'Richard,' she said breathlessly.

'I like the way you say that.' His voice was perfectly grave.

'...Richard...'

'Yes, Anna?' But she could see the teasing smile at the back of his eyes and he took pity on her confusion. 'No,' he said with a grin, 'that wasn't what I had in mind either. Not yet awhile, my beautiful bride. What I did think of doing was something not in the least strenuous. I thought you might like to soak in a warm bath while I order a special breakfast, which you can have in bed.'

'Sounds like a good idea!'

But her eyes widened when she was back in bed and breakfast was wheeled in accompanied by a bottle of champagne in an ice-bucket, and she had to laugh. 'Letty wouldn't approve,' she murmured as he loosened the cork and poured two glasses and brought one over to her.

'Then let's not tell her,' he said with a wicked glint in his eye. 'Mind you,' he added as he put the cork back into the bottle, 'I don't think it would be a good idea to drink it all. We'll keep some for later. By the way, perhaps I should warn you. I fully intend from now on to feed you on oysters and asparagus...maybe a little powdered rhino horn—and myself, of course.'

Anna grimaced. 'Whatever for?'

'Because they're all supposed to be great foods for lovers, and in case I haven't mentioned it before, my lovely Anna,' he said with his eyes warm, 'you're a sensational lover. So much so, I'm going to have great difficulty keeping my hands off you at all times. Which means we both have to keep our...strength up.'

'Richard,' she said trying hard not to giggle, 'if you dare feed me anything powdered...anyway, you might only end up making me get fat!'

'Would it matter if we got fat together?' he enquired.

'I think it might defeat your whole purpose,' she said, laughing.

'Ah, I see what you mean...'

'No, you don't,' she answered, still laughing but feeling almost faint with love for him. 'You're just teasing me—yet again.'

His face sobered suddenly. 'Maybe about the one, but not the other, Anna. You were—last night you were everything any man could wish for.'

'I...I'm glad,' she whispered. But only because it was you, she added to herself. And if I was, it was only because it was you and what you do to me.

'Eat your breakfast,' he said a moment later. 'You can sleep all day if you want to.'

She didn't sleep all day, but after breakfast she did feel sleepy and relaxed, perhaps due to the glass of champagne, and she did sleep for a couple of hours, to wake with a curious sense of physical well-being and a feeling of peace in her heart. And she thought, how many people do have it quite perfect anyway?

THE REST of the two weeks passed uneventfully.

At least, if you could call the mere fact of being married to Richard Gillespie uneventful, Anna mused once. But at least she felt they had come to a kind of understanding, greater than any they had had before. And if she felt wistful now and then, she resolutely put the feeling away from her.

But all too soon the fortnight came to an end and she found herself possessed by another feeling—one of nervousness, which was very hard to explain. Why should she be nervous about going back to Yandilla? Particularly now that she'd crossed the biggest hurdle of her life, let alone one connected with Yandilla.

But the day they flew home it dawned on her what the reason for her attack of nerves was—in fact that there were two reasons. The first one, which was probably going to be a problem always, was the fact that everyone there seemed to be able to read her like an open book. She grimaced ruefully but decided it was something she had to learn to live with and not as worrying as the second reason.

She glanced at Richard and wondered why she had never thought of it before. Perhaps because we've been away from Yandilla, on new ground, so to speak? she thought. But there must be memories for him at home, she mused. Memories of Chrissy's mother. And she wondered in a sudden startled flash if it was any particular memory which had made him the way he was the night they didn't get to the opera—and felt a little flicker of outright fear prickle her skin unreasonably. But all it means really, she tried to reassure herself, is that I'll have to be on my guard. Which I am anyway.

And she deliberately made herself relax.

CHAPTER ELEVEN

ABOUT TWO months later Anna stopped what she was doing one day and thought wryly back to her fanciful fears. For in fact it had been a joyful homecoming. Chrissy, predictably, had been ecstatic, but then Phil and Letty had been hardly less so, and Samson had looked at them both and shrugged and said, 'Hey, man! Whatever you two are doing with each other, it seems to be agreeing with you! Never did go much on the idea of marriage myself, but I reckon I might give the matter a second thought after all!'

Richard had laughed and Anna had blushed, while Chrissy had hugged her adoringly and said brightly, 'I think it's just a simply super idea. It also seems to be c...' She stopped and clapped a hand to her mouth, but went on in a moment, 'We've moved you and Daddy into the biggest bedroom, Anna, come and see!' She'd tugged at Anna's hand and would not be denied.

But later that night when the house was quiet, Anna had looked around the biggest bedroom and felt a return of some nervous tension.

And when Richard had come in quietly and closed the door behind him, she had jumped slightly and his eyebrows had risen. He had come across the room and taken her in his arms and asked quietly, 'What's wrong?'

She had tried to smile. 'Oh, nothing. Just tired.'

He had frowned down at her, then looked around the room. 'Anna,' he had said slowly, 'I've never used this room before. My mother was still alive the—last time I got married, and although she offered to, in fact tried to insist on moving out, I wouldn't let her. It didn't seem right, to me, to move her for the little time she had left. Nor, eventually, did it seem right somehow to bring to this room, which had known a lot of love, the kind of…disharmony Julie and I shared. So there are no ghosts for you to worry about, here, except the nicest ones. You'd have liked my mother, I think. And I know she'd have liked you.'

For a moment Anna had been unable to speak, torn between anger at herself for being so transparent that the one subject she wanted to avoid had cropped up, and almost dizzy at the thought that he didn't mind sharing this room with her. Then she had said gruffly, 'Thanks.'

'A pleasure,' he had said gravely, and picked her up and laid her on the wide double bed. 'That's in lieu of carrying you over the doorstep, by the way. I'm surprised Chrissy let me forget that. But talking of Chrissy and the rest of our family,' he had gone on as he had lain down beside her and started to unbutton her blouse, 'did you by any chance get the same impression I got? That they were big with news?'

'I—now you come to mention it, yes.'

'Want to have a bet with me? What their news is?'

'Now you come to mention it, no. Because it's got to be—another wedding in the family, say?'

'Right again, Anna. Who would you say the parties involved were?'

'Well, seeing that Samson has only just begun to give the idea as a whole some thought, and seeing that Letty doesn't have a beau to my knowledge, I reckon it has to be Phil and the Colonel,' she had answered, and laughed

softly. 'Do you think the Reverend will take kindly to another Yandilla wedding?'

'Don't see why he shouldn't. I think they're very nice,
Yandilla weddings.'

'All the same, let's not let on we've worked it out!'

THEY HADN'T, and Anna smiled to herself as she recalled
Richard's expression when Phil had dropped her bomb-
shell the next evening when Chrissy was in bed and out of
earshot.

'You're . . . what did you say, Phil?' he demanded incredulously as they sat on the verandah.

Phil went pink. 'I said, I'm going away with the Colonel. We're . . . going to have an affair. And if it turns out
well we'll get married.'

'Phil, you can't be serious!'

'Richard,' Phil said awkwardly, 'I'm sorry to shock you,
but I think I'm old enough to work out what's best for me.
And I'm certainly old enough not to be stampeded into
anything. I . . . well, I'd like to be very sure. Besides, I
thought that was the accepted way of going about things
these days.'

Richard stared at her and then swore fluently, and Phil
went pinker with alarm.

It was Letty who intervened at that stage. 'She's right,
and swearing never helped anyone, Mr Richard,' she said
sternly. 'Because'm you done everything by the book, it
don't say the rest of us is bound to, and I reckon Phil's
earnt the right to do things the way she pleases. After all,
it's not as if she hops off every few months with a different bloke, now is it?'

Richard regarded Letty narrowly, but she was in no way
intimidated. Not even when he said, 'So you say, Letty, but
the only time your grammar ever deserts you is when

you're deeply disturbed about something! And don't try to...!'

'Of course I'm disturbed!' Letty cried, and fixed him with a belligerent glance. 'I'm disturbed 'cause they been eyeing each other, Phil and the Colonel, over this damn stretch of water,' she gestured widely, 'for years! And at last they've reached some kind of a decision. I tell you, that's a mighty step forward, but all you want to do is muck it up! And while I'm normally all for doing things by the book, I reckon there can be some exceptions! Mind you, I'm glad you didn't make no exception for Anna here, don't think I'm not, and I'd have told you pretty damn quick what I thought of you if you had! But for Phil, you be advised by me, you just be happy for her!' She leant forward aggressively.

'I don't need you or anyone else to tell me how I feel about Phil, Letty,' he said grimly, and stared back at her angrily.

Anna found herself intervening at this point as Phil muttered distractedly, 'Oh dear, oh dear!'

'Richard, Letty, I think you're both right,' she said soothingly, and could have laughed as she became the recipient of two sets of smouldering glances. 'You're both disturbed because you're so fond of Phil. But,' she went on calmly, 'I don't think it's our place to tell Phil she's either right or wrong.' She glanced suddenly and meaningfully at Letty. 'There are some things it's best not to meddle with,' she finished quietly.

Letty looked away and betrayed the first aura of discomfort Anna had ever detected in her. But something oddly acute entered Richard's eyes as he studied Anna and then Letty.

'Oh, I see,' he said at last, and Anna tensed.

'No, you don't,' Phil answered. 'You really don't, Richard.'

'I think I do,' he said slowly with a strange twist to his lips and a sudden clear, piercing look at Anna. 'Not that it matters, it's just strange that I should have been so blind...'

'Well, I have to confess I tried to hide it,' Phil said helplessly. 'But we have been...eyeing each other—I suppose that's as good a way of putting it as any other—for some time. So if you're thinking I've suddenly gone mad and am trying to re-live my youth or anything like that, Richard, it just *isn't* like that. It's been growing and it's nothing light or as if I'm embarking on a last flirtatious fling. Oh, how can I explain it!' She stared at him anxiously, seemingly unaware that they were talking at cross purposes at that precise moment.

But Anna was aware of it and it brought her an oddly apprehensive feeling. Letty, too, was looking at Richard with a strange expression in her eyes.

'All right,' he said abruptly. 'Perhaps Anna is right. What—or rather how—are you going to do it?'

'Well,' Phil said awkwardly, 'we're going to London for a couple of months because...' She stopped uncertainly.

'Ah yes,' he said. 'Your television series. That seems to be dragging on, doesn't it?'

'Well,' said Phil, and shot a flustered look at Anna, 'to tell you the truth I...got the dates mixed up. You know how awfully stupid I can be at times?'

There was silence while Richard studied Phil, this time meditatively and searchingly. Then he surprised them all by saying only, 'And what have you told Chrissy?'

'That...that,' Phil said tearfully, 'that the Colonel and I like each other very much and that we're going to go overseas for a holiday and that one day we might get mar-

ried. I must say Chrissy had no reservations whatsoever,'
she added. 'And she's too young to understand or even
think of the morals of it. Besides, in my heart, I just don't
feel as if I'm compromising my morals. Nor that it's anyone's business if I do.'

Richard's face softened suddenly. 'Oh, Phil,' he said
quite gently, 'it's not that. I guess—it did just take me by
surprise. But then you're often a surprising lady, which is
one of the reasons I love you as a person and an aunt.'

'Richard,' Phil said tremulously.

Anna and Letty faded away discreetly then and didn't
hear any more. But in the kitchen, they stopped and
looked at each other, and Anna said, 'Letty?'

'Don't you bother your head about it, Anna. Men just
don't like to think they aren't godlike creatures who don't
need a discreet shove in the right direction sometimes.'

Anna had to smile, albeit reluctantly.

'Anyway,' Letty said softly, 'were Phil and I wrong? I
know you don't hold with meddling, but didn't it work out
right for you? I only got to see the way you look at him...'

Anna flushed faintly. She said with a little sigh, 'Yes, it
worked out right for me, Letty.'

'Then what's to worry about?'

ANNA CAME back from her reminiscences with a little
grimace. Letty had been right again. After that night
Richard had never given any indication that he resented
what Phil and Letty had done. In fact he'd never even
mentioned it, and that nameless apprehension she had felt
had subsided.

And once Phil and the Colonel had left, life had settled
into a smooth, easy-flowing pattern, one that had seen
Chrissy blossom and lose much of that occasionally fine-
drawn highly-strung air.

This alone had delighted Anna and she was able to further contribute to it by putting into operation something she had thought of often. She enrolled Chrissy with the School-of-the-Air, which had its northern headquarters in Cairns. The results had been well worth it because for the first time in her life Chrissy was in contact with other children, and even though it was only via a special two-way radio transmitter set, she blossomed even more because of it and made a special friend, a little girl called Louise, of her own age, who as it happened lived on an island in the same area as Yandilla. Which meant that one day they would be able to see each other.

As for herself, there were no more sleepless nights, no more tortured confusion. Instead of that, a marriage that, for all it was not quite perfect, was more than fulfilling for her in those days. A blend of friendship and laughter that was not particularly loverlike in public—in that Richard wasn't particularly demonstrative in front of others, more as if they were good friends; and something that wasn't quite the same behind the closed doors of the biggest bedroom. Nor was the less public side of their relationship reserved for the nights, Anna discovered. Because sometimes, at the oddest times, she would look up and find him watching her with a look in his grey-green eyes that made her tremble inwardly.

The first time it happened she was confused and not sure if she was reading it right. It was late morning and she was polishing her new silver cutlery, while Chrissy was sitting at the kitchen table labouring over a composition she had been given as homework in an earlier session of the School-of-the-Air.

Richard came in through the back door. He and Samson had been out in one of the boats since early morning. He smiled at Anna, ruffled Chrissy's hair and pointed out a spelling error to her, then turned to get himself a cool drink. Anna went back to polishing the silver, but she looked up for some reason to see him leaning against the sink, watching her. Then he had turned away and walked out of the kitchen.

It was then that she found she couldn't get on with what she was doing, because she was filled with a strange restlessness and a clamouring of pulses that his look had aroused. And eventually she asked Letty to take care of Chrissy for a while and helped them to pack a picnic lunch to take down to share with Samson and Sunshine. But as she watched them walk down to the rebuilt boatshed, she was filled with a flood of uncertainty and her nails bit into her palms as she wondered if she wasn't making an awful fool of herself.

All the same, she went into the bedroom and stood in the middle of the room with her head bent and her fists still clenched.

But after a very little while Richard came. He closed the door and stood leaning back against it with his arms folded, not saying anything.

Until finally he spoke very quietly. 'Take your clothes off, Anna.'

She found, though, in spite of the way she felt, that one small part of her was rebelling against the fact that he could do this to her with just a look. And it was that part that enabled her to grasp one tiny straw of face-saving initiative.

She lifted her head and said just as quietly, 'Why don't you take them off?'

His eyes narrowed and glinted and the air between them was suddenly taut and threaded with a tinge of hostility.

'All right...'

He undressed her there in the middle of the sun-dappled bedroom, sliding her dress off slowly, his eyes never leaving hers and his lips moving in a slight, cool smile as her skin shivered wherever his fingers touched it.

Then he moved back and that grey-green gaze roamed her body leisurely. But a last remaining shred of that odd spirit of rebellion kept her head up proudly and her eyes faintly challenging.

But he had only smiled slightly again and said huskily, 'You're very beautiful, Anna. But I think I've told you that before. Come.' He held out his hand and she took it after a slight hesitation and he led her to the bed. 'Lie down.'

She obeyed and lay quietly, her hair spread across the coral pink pillowslip like dark silk. Richard stared down at her for a long heart-stopping moment. Then he started to undress and as she watched, her eyes grave, and the only indication of what the sight of his tall, powerful body was doing to her was a fluttering of the delicate skin in the hollow at the base of her throat.

And when he finished, she sighed and murmured, 'You're beautiful too...'

After that it was no contest at all. She gloried in the things he did to her and the knowledge, later, when she lay with her head on his shoulder, that she had pleased him.

But in the gentle aftermath of their lovemaking, he said against the corner of her mouth, 'Didn't you like the idea of me making love to you in the middle of the day, Anna?'

She hesitated, then thought, why not be honest? 'Yes and no,' she whispered, and her lips curved into a smile.

'Oh?'

'Mmm. I don't always like the idea that I'm going to keel over like a pack of cards every time you look at me. You've done it before, at the cricket.'

She felt a jolt of laughter shake his body and he said, still smiling, 'Why don't you think of it this way, then? *You* don't even have to look at me to put these ideas in my mind. Just the sight of you polishing silver has the oddest effect on me sometimes.'

She smiled back at him, but said almost immediately with a touch of guilt, 'What would they think if they knew? I mean ...'

'If you mean Letty and Samson, they probably exchanged knowing looks over Chrissy's head and had a quiet chuckle.'

'Oh!' Anna blushed.

'And in their heart of hearts,' he went on lazily, tracing the colour in her cheeks, 'envied us. By the way, I don't know how we keep getting back to this subject—there must be something in the air—but I've noticed Samson watching Sunshine when he thinks no one is watching him.'

'Really? Oh, definitely something in the air!' Anna teased gently. But she sobered suddenly. 'If you're right, though, how can that be? They're related.'

'I doubt that. The number of nieces Letty has had here over the years is prodigious. At the closest Sunshine is probably the niece of a niece of an old friend. Blood ties are not the only ones that matter to them. Also, I suspect Letty imports them to Yandilla at such an astonishing rate for more reasons than one.'

'Letty,' said Anna after a moment as this sank in, 'is...' She stopped abruptly. In a class of her own so far as being an indefatigable matchmaker, she'd been going to say, before she'd almost bitten her tongue off.

'Letty is ... ?' he queried.

'Well, you said yourself she'd love to have grandchildren,' she said lamely.

'So I did,' he remarked pensively. 'Anna?'

Oh no, she thought. Here it comes!

'Yes?'

'If you don't get up out of this bed very soon, I might start getting those odd ideas again.' His arms moved round her gently. 'How does that thought affect you?'

'Do you really want to know?' she said slowly, filled with relief and a sense of love that was almost too great for her heart to hold.

'Uh-huh...'

'I think, and I told you this once before,' her lips trembled in a smile, 'that there should be a law about men like you, Richard Gillespie! Especially at *this* time of day!'

And she fled the bed laughing as he reached for her and then subsided, laughing himself.

YES, ANNA mused on that day about two months after they had arrived home on Yandilla from their honeymoon and she'd found herself in a mood of reminiscent daydreaming, only a fool would complain about this marriage.

And even if it can't last in this same way, even if it must inevitably lose some of its fire, at least I'll have these memories to hold on to, these days when it was easy to pretend I was truly loved...

BUT IT was only a couple of days later that the whole fabric of her pretence was ripped apart and she was faced with the bare truth. Richard did not love her, and no memories were enough to compensate for it.

It all began with a perfectly harmless shopping expedition.

The weather had cooled down, not that it could be called cold, precisely, but there was a new zip in the air at night time and in the early morning and less humidity and Anna found herself correspondingly, feeling energetic, creative and brisk.

And for a time, two days exactly, she found plenty of outlet for this state of mind. She rearranged the furniture in several rooms, went through all Chrissy's clothes, sorting out the ones that no longer fitted, she re-potted all the pot plants on the verandah—but it was when she started on the kitchen that Letty intervened.

'You pregnant?' she enquired when she found Anna rearranging all the kitchen cupboards one morning.

Anna stopped what she was doing rather suddenly. 'No. Why?'

'Well, I did those cupboards out only a few weeks ago. Oh, I'm not saying I mind you doing them! Except you helped me do 'em, which made me wonder. See, being pregnant takes different people in different ways. Some lie about while others get the urge to do things.'

Anna half smiled. 'Well, I don't think I am.'

Letty looked at her affectionately. 'That could change overnight, pet,' she said.

'Letty!' Anna replied with a grin, but at the same time feeling a sudden deep longing.

'Well, it can!'

'O.K., it can,' Anna acknowledged. 'But at the moment I think I'm only suffering from a reverse spring-cleaning syndrome. I think it's the nip in the air, in other words.'

'Ah! So happens I am too. Always do at this time of the year. But between the two of us this house is so damn clean, there isn't anything left to do. Why don't we try our hand at something else?'

'Like what? Do you have anything in mind?'

'Yes. Batik.'

'Batik? But do you know how?'

'Reckon I do,' said Letty. 'There's a woman on T.I., she comes from Java and she was showing me how she did it last time I was up there. See, you paint part of the material with wax, then you dye it. I thought if we got the hang of it we could even teach it to the Colonel's crew when he comes back. Don't think they're into batik yet, and there's a market for sarongs and things like that. What do you think? Like to try it?'

'Love to,' Anna said promptly.

And so it was arranged that Anna should make a trip over to the mainland to purchase what they needed. Chrissy was to go with her, but at the last minute she remembered that one of her School-of-the-Air class-mates was having a birthday and a rather special lesson had been planned.

Anna set off with Samson and Letty's list and was soon driving Richard's car, which was kept on the mainland, into Tully. She had declined Samson's offer to drive her and arranged to meet him at the jetty that afternoon.

All the same, as she climbed into the low-slung car, she experienced a touch of nerves. It was so obviously expensive she would feel awful if she had damaged it. Not that Richard had had any qualms about her driving it, obviously, because he had kissed her goodbye with a lurking smile and simply handed her the keys.

But after a few miles and an encounter with a large, strange-looking bird on the road, which had illustrated to her that the brakes worked very well, she relaxed.

'That must have been a cassowary,' she told herself. 'Wait till I tell Chrissy!'

Then she found herself thinking of the first time she had been in this car and how it seemed almost like a lifetime away.

But the return trip, after a successful shopping expedition, turned quite suddenly into a nightmare. On a deserted stretch of winding, narrow road about five miles out from Mission Beach, one of the tyres blew with a deafening bang and the car slewed across the road and came to rest facing in the opposite direction with the other rear wheel resting in a fairly deep cane-irrigation ditch.

Anna climbed out shakily with her heart pounding violently, glad to be alive but horrified at the damage she might have done. Yet an inspection of the car reassured her somewhat. There seemed not to be a mark on it. However, it dawned on her that even if she did get the tyre changed, there was going to be the distinct possibility that the car would be bogged in the muddy ditch. She looked around, wondering if it wouldn't be easier to go for help rather than attempt anything herself, but knew it could be a long walk and her best hope was for a passing motorist either to give her a lift or give her a hand. But how long will I have to wait? she thought to a sigh of despair that immediately changed to a cry of joy as a large Land Rover hove into view like an answer to a prayer. It stopped in response to her frantic signalling and Anna ran forward thankfully—only to find herself staring up into a pair of sardonically amused brown eyes.

'Well, well, if it isn't Mrs Gillespie,' Mike Carmody drawled. 'Much as I dislike ignoring damsels in distress, perhaps I should drive on?'

'Oh...Mike,' she said awkwardly, 'please don't. I really need help.'

He glanced over the top of her head at the car, consideringly. 'You're not running away from Richard, by any chance, are you, Anna?'

'No, of course not! Why would you think that? Oh, I see,' she went on hastily as his eyes changed, and felt her face colour. 'No, in fact I'm going in the opposite direction, to Mission Beach, but I had a blow-out and skidded. The thing is, though, I'm due there in about twenty minutes and if I don't turn up Samson will start to worry...'

Mike looked at her. 'So you married him, Anna? That didn't altogether surprise me. But it's ironic, don't you think, this habit he and I have of fancying the same sheila. More ironic that he's always the one married to them.'

'Mike, please,' she begged. 'You and I barely knew each other.'

He laughed. 'Yeah—he made damned sure of that.' Then he shrugged. 'What the hell! Let's see what we can do.' He opened the door and stepped out.

'Oh, thank you, Mike!' she breathed.

'Will you tell him who came to your rescue, Anna?' he asked with a mocking look, but when she coloured, he relented. 'Forget I said that.' He grimaced. 'Okay, you've got yourself into a right mess, lady! Lucky I've got a tow-bar and some rope...'

It took them nearly an hour to get the car roadworthy again—at least it took Mike nearly an hour, for there was not much Anna could do to help. Then he suggested that he follow her to make sure she got to Mission Beach safely, seeing he was going there himself anyway.

But she had no further mishaps and garaged the car with a sigh of relief but still worried that she was over an hour and a half late. But the garage Richard rented was in sight of the jetty, and she locked the door carefully and turned to find Mike stepping out of his Land Rover.

'Mike, I can't thank you enough,' she said quietly. 'You're a real friend.'

'For you, Anna, any time,' he answered, and leant forward to kiss her on the lips. 'No, don't say it,' he warned, his eyes glinting devilishly. 'I've been dying to do that just once. Perhaps I'll be cured now... See you, Anna.'

He turned away and she started to hurry towards the jetty, her eyes searching for the Yandilla launch. It was there, she saw with some relief, and broke into a run as the person lounging on the jetty beside it straightened.

But it wasn't Samson she all but collided with. It was Richard.

And her apologies and explanations died on her lips as she realised that he was looking at her coldly, almost murderously.

'Richard...?' she whispered. And although she had not the slightest need to feel guilty, she looked round and realised instantly that he would have seen her and Mike, and a hot colour flooded into her cheeks. 'I...can explain,' she stammered.

'Don't bother. You just did,' he muttered through his teeth, his eyes on her hot cheeks. 'Get aboard,' he added grimly.

'No...'

'Don't argue, Anna,' he said violently, and picked her up bodily and put her in the boat, then climbed in after her.

'No...I mean, no I haven't explained anything! You've just jumped to a conclusion quite ridiculously and...' She gasped as the motor tore viciously to life and the boat surged forward away from the jetty, and she collapsed on to a bench in an undignified heap, dropping all her parcels.

Suddenly she was as angry as he was. 'I hate you, Richard Gillespie!' she cried furiously as she scrambled up and as he uninterestedly steered the boat in the direction of the sunset. 'I hate you!'

He only shrugged then and said, 'We'll see. You might think you hate me now, but you'll find you have good cause to really hate me if I ever catch you within a mile of Mike Carmody again.'

'If...' Anna struggled to speak through a red mist of rage, 'if I didn't know you better, I'd be tempted to think you were insanely jealous of Mike. But where there's no love, how can there be jealousy?'

But she took a precipitous step backwards as he cut the engine and reached for her, to dump her unceremoniously into one of the padded fishing chairs, where he imprisoned her by leaning over her with a hand on each arm. And in spite of her rage she couldn't help cowering back at what she saw in his eyes.

'You're right, Anna,' he said softly but with so much threatening menace, she shivered. 'There's no jealousy, only this—Mike did me an incredible disservice once, and as a result of it, I have this curious but nevertheless very strong aversion to him. And I don't care to have anything to do with him, let alone share any of my possessions with him. If I had a dog that would include it, and it includes you. So, if from being such a determined virgin, you've now begun to think longingly of all the years and all the men you missed out on, we might be able to come to some arrangement, but if it's Mike Carmody you particularly want, forget it, because I don't even share my cast-offs with him, and we shall just have to get along as best we can.'

Anna's jaw sagged and her eyes widened incredulously under this cruel onslaught. And something died in her heart, in fact she wondered dazedly if she had a heart left at all, because a frozen, alien object seemed to have taken its place in her breast.

'Do we understand each other now, Anna?' he said gently—the kind of gentleness, she thought, that would cut ice.

She swallowed and said hoarsely, in a voice quite unlike her own, 'Yes . . . oh yes.'

'Good.' He straightened up. 'Then perhaps we can get home.'

Home, she thought wildly. How can I go home to Yandilla with him, like this? how can I . . . carry on as if nothing's happened? How?

CHAPTER TWELVE

YET SHE did carry on as if nothing untoward had happened, although she never knew how she did it. She helped Letty get started on the batik, mothered Chrissy as usual—no, not as usual, even more caringly and warmly if anything, because she couldn't bear to think of Chrissy sensing that anything was amiss with her bright, perfect world that had endured for such a short time. She even managed to act normally towards Richard in public, although it was a different matter behind the closed door of the biggest bedroom. They still shared a bed, there was no way they could not without arousing at least Letty's suspicions, but he didn't try to touch her and only came into the room when she was already in bed, and he was gone when she woke in the morning.

For two weeks Anna carried on the charade. Then she snapped.

The breaking up process happened one night when Richard came into the bedroom for the first time in two weeks before she was in bed.

She was sitting at the dressing table brushing her hair and she was already dressed for bed in a white broderie anglaise nightgown that had been part of Phil's wedding present. It had a low-cut, square neckline with a ruched bodice and tiny puffed sleeves and red ribbons threaded round the sleeves. She was also wearing white satin mules trimmed with swansdown that complemented her tanned, bare legs visible from just below the knee where the night-gown ended. But as she brushed steadily, she was not thinking of how she looked. She was thinking of some-thing quite different, and she jumped when the door opened and Richard walked in and closed it behind him.

They stared at each other in the mirror for about a min-ute, then she looked away but didn't say anything.

'Anna?' His voice was contained and quiet.

'What is it?'

'Look at me, Anna.'

Why should I? she wondered. So that you can pin me again like some helpless butterfly? All the same, her lashes lifted and even as distressed and wounded as she felt, she couldn't deny with an inward tremor, the impact just his presence had on her.

But she forced herself to say calmly enough, 'Yes?'

His eyes narrowed and searched her face. Then he said abruptly, 'You don't look well.'

'I'm fine,' she answered quietly. 'Is that—what you wanted to say to me?'

'No...' He hesitated briefly. 'I've only just noticed it. Are you sure?'

'Quite sure,' she said steadily. 'I think I have the kind of looks that go off when I'm not...' She stopped and bit her lip.

'When you're not happy?' he supplied after a pause.

'Probably,' she agreed dryly.

'Then perhaps I can restore you,' he commented.

'...Oh?'

'Yes. Samson used the car today,' he went on with no further preamble. 'It's the first time it's been used since you took it to Tully that day. And when he discovered the blown-out tyre in the boot, and told me about it with quite some surprise, it wasn't hard for me to deduce what must have happened. And so I've come to say I'm sorry for the things I . . . inferred that day.'

Anna stared at him in the mirror with her lips slightly parted, but he merely returned her look dispassionately. She blinked confusedly and thought shakenly, no, you're not. You're just as angry as you were then. You're only trying to put a better face on it because . . . because . . . why? Are you trying to tell me we made a bargain and the time's come for me to hold my end up again? Or something like that . . . ?

She licked her lips. 'That's all right,' she said huskily, and started to brush her hair again, not looking at him.

But Richard leant over swiftly and removed the brush from her fingers. 'You didn't say that very convincingly, Anna,' he remarked.

Her uplifted hand sank into her lap and she literally felt the breaking up process begin within her, like an over-taut rubber band giving way at last.

'Is that so strange?' she answered bitterly. 'I wasn't particularly convinced by what you said. I don't think you're sorry at all!'

'Then why did you tell me it was all right?' Richard asked sardonically.

She swung round on the stool, her eyes suddenly bright with anger. 'Because I have no option!'

He smiled unpleasantly. 'Poor Anna,' he said with a steely mockery. 'You've had a rough time since you came to Yandilla, haven't you?'

'I . . . what do you mean?' she demanded.

'Well, this business of options, for one thing. I'm not quite sure why I didn't realise it at the time, but it's since become plain to me that Letty and Phil jockeyed you into a position where you thought you had no option too. *Didn't* they?'

Two things flashed across her mind at that point. That he was trying to force some sort of a confrontation with her and that it went even deeper than what had happened the day she'd gone to Tully. And secondly, that she had been right to worry about his reaction to the discovery of Phil and Letty's connivance, after all... But what does it matter? she thought suddenly. What does anything matter any more?

'Oh no,' she said tautly, that flame of anger burning steadily. 'No one jockeyed me into anything. I made my own mistakes, Richard.'

'Go on.' Their eyes clashed.

'What more is there to say?'

'Oh, I thought you might be going to add something like—I made my own bed and now I have to lie in it,' he murmured, his lips twisting ironically.

She gasped. 'If you think I'll ever willingly share a bed with you again,' she shot at him, 'you're very much mistaken!'

'I wonder about that,' Richard said coolly, his eyes mocking her. 'You were a quick learner, Anna. You even surprised me. And seeing that you're not going to have anyone else to share your bed until, and if, it ever suits me, I wouldn't make sweeping statements of that nature if I were you.'

She stumbled up with but one thought in mind, to attack him with her fists, anything...

All she succeeded in doing, though, was to end up clamped in his arms, her breath coming in tearing sobs of frustration and just about every other futile emotion she could think of.

He held her like that until her puny struggles ceased. Then he picked her up and laid her on the bed and stood looking down at her detachedly. 'Yes,' he said finally, 'you might find it's not as easy as you think to return to a life of celibacy, my passionate lady-wife. And when you're ready to admit that, let me know, won't you? I might put you out of your misery.'

He turned and walked out of the room without a backward glance.

ANNA STARED up at the ceiling with stark eyes for a long time, consumed with an unequalled sense of torment and despair. And when she finally fell asleep, it was with one thought in her mind—I have to get away from here...

THE NEXT morning not even her best friend would have told her that she looked well. She had dark smudges like bruises beneath her eyes which intensified the pallor of her face. But curiously, while she was wondering what to say when anyone taxed her with it, she found she had no need to say anything.

Because Letty, who was the first person she encountered after she had got up, took one look at her and exclaimed, 'Oh, you poor thing! Another of those headaches like the one you had the day the cyclone hit! Now you just get straight back to bed. And don't you worry about getting Chrissy to her friend—I'll take her.'

Anna bit her lip. She had forgotten in her turmoil that Chrissy had been invited to spend the next couple of nights with her new little friend, Louise. But she found herself thinking dazedly, if I really want to go, this might be the best opportunity I'll get—if Richard's out... But I don't know that. All I know is that he didn't come back to this room last night.

But it was Letty who solved this too. 'Now,' she said, sailing into the bedroom a little before ten o'clock, 'everything's arranged. Samson's gonna take me and

Chrissy across to her friend—not quite sure when we'll be back, after lunch, probably. Samson tells me Mr Richard went out to the Reef at the crack of dawn and won't be back till lunchtime, but I guess you know that? But just in case you're worried another cyclone is gonna sneak up on you, it's too late for them now, and in any case, Sunshine's here.'

'I'm not worried about that,' Anna said with a weak smile.

'Good. Then maybe you can have a nice long sleep. You sure look as if you could do with it!'

Anna stared up into Letty's eyes and wondered how much she had guessed. But all she could see was a warm look of sympathy.

Then Chrissy tiptoed into the room and came to lay her head beside Anna's on the pillow. 'Should I stay and look after you, Anna?' she asked softly.

'No, darling,' Anna whispered with some difficulty. 'I'll be fine. Are you sure you've packed everything you want to show Louise?'

'She's packed enough to stay a month,' said Letty with a grin. 'Drat, there's Samson pacing about like a caged tiger!'

And so with a flurry of goodbyes they left, but not before Chrissy gave Anna a last warm, fierce little hug. And Anna turned her head into the pillow and wept as she hadn't been able to last night. But even as she thought brokenheartedly of what it would do to Chrissy to come back and find her gone, she felt that in the long run it would do much more harm to have to watch her new mother disintegrate at the hands of her father.

'And that's what I'll surely do if I stay,' she murmured. 'Even although I'm going to have his baby…oh God! How ironic it's all been. I *was* pregnant and didn't know it that

day Letty asked me. But I can't any longer not admit it.
Especially after feeling distinctly nauseous these past few
mornings. But what am I going to do? I have some money
saved, though it's not a fortune... but I'll cope somehow.
I'll just *have* to. And if I'm going to do it, now's the
time... And I won't be quite alone.'

SHE MADE her preparations stealthily so as not to alert
Sunshine, whom she could hear singing round the house.
Not that there was much to prepare. It was simply a matter of pulling her two bags down from the top cupboard
and packing them with her old clothes. Then she waited
until she heard the back screen door close, and knew from
long experience that Sunshine would be occupied in the
laundry for some time, because that was her inevitable
routine every day, and she went swiftly into Richard's
study to make a phone call with surprisingly steady hands
and voice.

At least, until the bright young voice on the other end of
the line said still with a tinge of surprise, 'Yes, Mrs Gillespie. As a matter of fact the *Lotus Lady* is making the run
now, but I could contact her on the radio and get her to call
into Yandilla... let's see, it's only a supply run, so she
would get there in about a half to three quarters of an
hour's time. Is it a package you'd like to consign?'

It was then that Anna's nerve deserted her momentar-
ily. 'Er...' She closed her eyes as she thought of the *Lotus
Lady* and Mike Carmody. 'Yes,' she said breathlessly.
'Is... is Mr Carmody making the run?'

'No. He's away for a few days, Mrs Gillespie.'

'Oh. Well, look, I'm not quite sure if I'll have it ready
in time...' Anna! she chided herself. What's this? You
know you can't back out now.

But the voice at the other end of the line solved yet another dilemma for her, unwittingly. 'That's no problem, Mrs Gillespie. If you get it ready in time, just leave it at the end of the jetty. That's the arrangement we have, anyway. And if not, perhaps you'd care to give me a ring and we can make some other arrangement. But it's no problem for the *Lotus Lady* to check.'

'All right. Thank you very much.' Anna put the phone down with now shaking hands. Someone is going to get a shock when they discover what the Yandilla consignment is, she thought. But at least it won't be Mike, it'll be a stranger, so I won't have to make explanations. Not that there won't be a lot of speculation still...

She stood with her head bowed, in the middle of this room which had seen her make some momentous decisions. But as her resolution began to falter she heard his words again—if I had a dog, that would include it, and it includes you—I might put you out of your misery. And when you're ready to admit that... 'No!' she whispered on a gasping, trembling breath. 'No. I can't stay. I just can't.'

But it was so ridiculously easy to leave, that too seemed to rise up and taunt her for some strange reason. She could hear Sunshine singing distantly in the laundry as she went back to her room to collect her bags.

And all I have to do is go, she thought. If I leave the door closed, Sunshine won't even come in for fear of waking me. She looked around the room through a mist of tears and foolishly tidied up a few odds and ends as if that could eradicate the awful disharmony that had after all come to this bedroom. Then she licked the salty tears from her lips and picked up her bags and walked out.

She was half way down to the deep-water jetty when she tripped over a root of a tree. It was not a heavy fall, but as she tried to save herself she was conscious of a sudden flash of fear that she would never normally have experienced for such a mild tumble. Nor was the fear for her, she realised, but for the tiny, precious seed of life she carried within her. And as she sat on the path, examining this new dimension of her which until only so recently had not even been a certainty, a great tide of emotion rose up within her, making it difficult even to breathe. But one thought hammered at her brain insistently, refusing to be denied.

'I can't go,' she said out loud, with tears streaming down her face. 'How foolish I was to think I could,' she marvelled. 'Because for better, for worse, I made Yandilla a part of me that I can't tear out. I can't do it to Chrissy, I can't do it to this baby, but most of all I can't do it to myself. I just can't bear to think of living without any of them, even Richard. Especially, Richard,' she acknowledged, and shivered as a shaft of pain pierced her heart. 'How can he do this to me?' she whispered. 'How can he make me hate him but love him at the same time? Love him so that I *can't* leave him. How is it possible?'

She sighed deeply and sat with her chin on her knees. Then she got up carefully and looked around. She pushed her two bags into a clump of bushes and started to walk again, but not towards the jetty.

About twenty minutes later she heard the asthmatic siren of the *Lotus Lady* toot twice, yet she kept walking steadily along the beach in the opposite direction. But not long afterwards she began to feel inexpressably weary and she sat down beneath the slanting branches of a strangler fig. The sand was warm and soft and the light breeze ruffled the leaves above her gently, and she lay back. Then she turned over with her head buried in her arms and fell asleep.

SHE ONLY slept for an hour—to her relief. And she thought that with a bit of luck, she might even get back to the house without Sunshine discovering she had ever left it. 'Or anyone else, for that matter,' she muttered. 'But no one else should be back yet.'

It wasn't until she reached the front verandah and had her hand on the screen door that opened into the long central passageway of the house that she remembered her bags. She grimaced and half-turned to go back for them, when Sunshine erupted into the passageway from the bedroom, stopped dead at the sight of Anna, stared incredulously for a moment, then burst into tears, at the same time waving a hand distractedly at the doorway through which she had come. Then before Anna could say a word, she turned and fled towards the kitchen.

There's been an accident! was Anna's first reaction as she stumbled down the passageway. But the sight that greeted her eyes as she came abreast of the bedroom took her breath away. Because it was not the tidy room she had left. In fact it looked as if it had been ransacked. There were clothes strewn everywhere and cupboards open and drawers hanging out.

And with his back to her, standing at the window, Richard.

Anna made a small, unintelligible sound. He turned slowly and she saw that his face was pale and rigid and his eyes dark and violent. So violent, she took a step backwards and put out a hand helplessly as if to ward off the worst of his anger.

But it didn't come, at least not physically. When he spoke, though, it was there unmistakably. 'I don't know why you came back, Anna. But it's just as well you did, because it saved me the bother of fetching you back, which I wouldn't have done too politely. In fact,' he said, speaking clearly and distinctly, 'I might as well warn you not ever to do it again unless you wish to be treated less than...civilly.' And there was something so hard in his eyes, she shivered and paled.

'Do you understand, Anna?'

'I...no!' she cried brokenly. 'I don't! You...we...'

'Then I'll explain it to you,' he said remorselessly. 'I don't quite know how you did it. But you did—you bewitched me to the extent that I can't live without you. And seeing it was you yourself,' he said harshly, 'who once had such faith in a grand, hit-you-on-the-head passion like this, seeing it's *you* who did it, you're going to have to live with it whether you like it or not!'

'Richard...' she whispered incredulously.

He smiled unpleasantly. 'Didn't you know? Didn't you even begin to suspect? I thought it must be obvious...what a fool I was making of myself.'

Anna licked her lips, more totally confused than she'd ever been. 'I...wished it and hoped it,' she said tremulously.

'Did you?' he asked curtly. 'I wonder why? So you could say I told you so?'

'*No,*' she breathed, her distress showing plainly.

'But you didn't do anything about it,' he shot at her savagely.

'How could I?' she said helplessly. 'You've been so...lately, so...'

'Yet I'd have thought, if you cared at all, some time in the last two weeks you could have tried to tell me how wrong I'd been. You had the proof.'

Anna's eyes widened. 'Is that why you were still so angry?'

His eyes blazed with a bitter light of self-mockery that answered her question as effectively as words.

'I...I...' she stammered, feeling her heart beginning to beat somewhere up in her throat.

'But that's beside the point now, isn't it? And perhaps I wasn't so wrong after all. Mike must have been delighted to discover yet another Yandilla wife needing rescuing from my clutches.' He looked at her sardonically.

'No! Richard, I didn't...I came back.'

'Did you forget something?' he asked cruelly. 'Did you persuade Mike to bring the *Lotus Lady* back? Oh yes, between us, Sunshine and I were quite able to work out what had happened when you weren't to be found anywhere and your two bags and your own clothes and your tape recorder weren't here. And when she remembered hearing the boat toot twice, for no apparent reason, I rang their office. They said you'd wanted to consign a package. But I knew better. It was yourself, wasn't it?'

'Yes,' she conceded distractedly, and took a wavering breath as she saw his mouth tighten. 'I did plan to go. But I couldn't do it. I never set foot on the *Lotus Lady* and Mike isn't on her—I've no idea where he is! Nor do I want to... You can check—they'll tell you!'

For the first time a hint of doubt showed in Richard's eyes. 'Then where have you been? And where are your things?'

Anna looked around the dishevelled bedroom and swallowed. 'When I found I couldn't go, I went for a walk along the beach and...I fell asleep. My bags are stowed under a bush. I forgot about them.'

'If,' his voice was laced with pain suddenly, 'if you got that far, how come you couldn't do it? No, don't tell me. It was because of Chrissy, wasn't it?'

'Yes. Partly.'

They stared at each other and her heart contracted at the look of weariness in his eyes. As if he was drained now of all emotion.

'It's always been because of Chrissy, hasn't it, Anna?' He spoke unevenly and very quietly. 'That's why Letty and Phil got through to you with their machinations—I know that now.' His lips twisted in a bitter little smile. 'But I used Chrissy too, you know. In days gone past when I was still telling myself I could take you or leave you... even then I was banking on the fact that Chrissy would hold you here...'

'Well, you were wrong,' she said, searching his face and seeing what she had despaired of ever seeing. And the shock of it brought tears to her eyes that brimmed over foolishly and wet her cheeks.

'Was I? How was I wrong, Anna? Tell me,' he said huskily, his eyes roaming her face. 'I could make you— I've thought of it... You see, I've learnt too. I know how to make love to you just the way you like it. I know what makes you quiver and tremble. I know the secret, most sensitive parts of your beautiful body—I know every inch of you in a way I could never forget. Is that what you won't tell me? That you can't live without the way we make love to each other?'

'No,' she whispered, finding her throat strangely constricted. But then the words seemed to tumble out of their own accord, shakily and not very coherently. 'It's so much more. It's like an ocean that I can't begin to describe. That's why I tried to go. I thought I couldn't live like this any more, loving you and knowing—thinking you couldn't ever love me, didn't even trust me. I just couldn't stand the hurt any longer. And I thought I could do it, because, you see, I'm going to have your baby...' She stopped as he took a suddenly tortured, understanding breath. 'I thought—I thought I'd have that at least, something to live for, something of yours that I could care about even if you didn't care about me. But I couldn't do it, because I need you on any terms, it seems.'

'When did you know about the baby?' His voice shook and his hands were clenched as if to stop himself from touching her.

'Only a few days ago, for sure.'

'And that's why you've been looking so pale—oh God!' He closed his eyes briefly. 'How could I have been so stupid and so blind?'

'Richard,' she whispered, and reached out to lay a hand on his arm, 'I love you.'

'Why?' he said roughly. 'I'd understand it better if you said you hated me. Don't you know that I've been fighting you, and this, ever since I first laid eyes on you, covered in dust but still so beautiful and spirited and desirable?'

'I fought it for a while too,' Anna said softly. 'Remember? That—that was the real reason I let you go on thinking I wasn't a virgin. I—it—I know it sounds stupid, but it made me feel less...vulnerable, somehow. But the night of the cyclone, when I thought you must be dead, I felt like dying too. And I knew then that I couldn't go on pretending to myself any longer that I didn't love you.'

His eyes searched her face and one hand came up involuntarily to cover hers. 'Is that...what made you decide to marry me?' he asked huskily. 'Not, Chrissy, not what Phil and Letty did?'

'Yes. But to love you is to love Chrissy too.'

'Anna...'

'Oh, Richard, hold me,' she whispered.

He did. he kissed her hair and her eyelids and her throat as if he could never get enough of her. Then he picked her up in his arms and carried her to the bed. He returned to the door with a wry grimace and closed it, then he came back and lay down beside her and took her in his arms again. 'Sunshine thinks I've gone mad,' he said wryly.

'Why?' Anna pushed her fingers through his hair.

'Well, I told her, amongst other things, that I'd get you back if it was the last thing I did and I'd make you love me if it was the last thing I did too. I also told her she shouldn't be put in charge of a dog and if, when I did get you back, Letty couldn't keep her meddling fingers out of it, they'd all find themselves back on Thursday Island faster than you could say Jack Robinson. Just another manifestation of my insanity! Anna, my darling,' his voice was deep and unsteady, 'I still can't quite believe this.' He touched her face gently.

'Didn't you ever suspect—either?' she whispered, and kissed his wandering fingers.

'Yes—at least I wondered. When I found out I'd taken your virginity, almost casually, I wondered then. And I realised, looking back, that I should have known you were a virgin, but the mills of my mind grind exceedingly slow, I'm afraid,' he said grimly. 'And I was still not prepared to admit what I was feeling—still trying to tell myself that what I felt for you was a particularly strong attraction that then became coupled with a sense of guilt—you were so lovely, so eager to please, so easy to please...'

Anna trembled in his arms, but he drew her hard against him. 'Now, I know I loved that, more than you'll ever know,' he said very quietly. 'But *then,* in my heart I was still fighting you, Anna. Fighting the way you were growing more and more into my heart every day, every hour, it seemed. The night we were to go to the opera was one time I tried to buck against it.'

She moved her head so she could see into his eyes.

'Yes,' he traced the outline of her mouth with one finger. 'I thought, cope with this, Anna Horton, see what you can make of this. See if that—serene, virginal willingness can cope with these dark depths of my soul. I was doing battle with you in earnest that night, Anna. Did you know?'

His eyes roamed her face and there was something so tender in them she trembled anew.

'Not that it matters,' he murmured. 'You routed me completely that night. You loved me in a way that was so honest, so generous, so—special, it was like nothing I'd ever known before.'

'Only because it was you. And because I loved you so much and couldn't tell you . . .'

He winced. 'I'm sorry, so sorry. But that's when it began to dawn on me that I was fighting a losing battle. That's when things began to change and I found that instead of being preoccupied with my feelings, more and more I was beginning to think of yours. And I began to hope. But when you're in the twisted, paranoid frame of mind I'd been in for so long, it doesn't take much to dash your hopes. And the first setback mine received was to discover that Letty and Phil had been putting pressure on you too. I thought then, maybe you did only tell me the truth when you said you'd marry me.'

'I nearly did,' she confessed.

He held her close for a long time. Then he said on a curiously tortured note, 'All those things I said, all the things I thought—can you ever forgive me?'

'Of course,' she whispered, and kissed his hand again with trembling lips.

'You shouldn't. How come you do?'

'Because I know what you went through before . . .'

'Yes, Julie,' said Richard with a tiny frown of pain between his eyes. 'I lived in torment with her memory for too long. But now... I only wish there was some way I could make my peace with her. Does that sound strange to you?'

'Oh no,' she whispered. 'It makes me very happy.'

He stroked her hair and watched her with eyes that were loving and calm at last. 'And Mike,' he said, but moved his head negatively almost immediately. 'No, not Mike,' he added very quietly.

She looked at him, her eyes a little troubled.

'Oh, in my heart, yes, because I know now what he might have been going through with Julie. I've had the evidence of my own insanity where you're concerned,' he said with a slight smile, 'to understand. But if he admires you, and I think he does, then we're destined to be two people never to see eye to eye.'

'He... he... but I never thought of him like that. How could I?' Anna said tearfully. 'Since that day you nearly ran over me I haven't had a thought to spare...'

'Anna, sweetheart, don't cry,' he murmured remorsefully, and kissed her tears.

'Kiss me properly, then I won't,' she said with a trembling little smile. 'Although sometimes you do it so beautifully that makes me want to cry too.'

He did. And a little later, he undressed her and stared down at her searchingly, taking in every detail of her body. Until he lifted his head at last and said huskily, 'I can't see any changes.'

'It's too soon. But in a few months' time there'll be more... so much of me, in fact, you might not like what you see any more,' she teased gently.

'I wouldn't count on that,' he commented. 'I suspect I shall be just as proprietorial as I am now, if not more so. And jealous and proud and filled with a sense of my own importance as I watch you grow big with my baby. I'll probably be impossible to live with. Will you mind?'

She laughed softly. 'I suspect not.'

But Richard sobered and as he bent his head to kiss her breasts, he murmured, 'It's been so long, Anna.'

'Two weeks.'

'That's two weeks too long. Is it any wonder I was a raging lunatic?'

'Ah,' she said breathlessly, 'so that's the answer? I'll remember that the next time you get cross with me!'

'I don't think there'll be a next time,' he said between kisses.

'That might be a pity.'

'Why?'

'I've just worked out the way to deal with it,' she answered, her eyes dancing impishly.

Richard lifted his head. 'Tell me.'

'Oh—I thought I might try my hand at seducing you for a change but if you say...' She wasn't allowed to finish.

'Forget what I said,' he interrupted with the most wicked glint in his eyes. 'And why wait until I'm cross to do it? I...'

'I know all about *you,*' Anna said primly but with her eyes alight with love and laughter. 'You're one of those unprincipled men who is no respecter of ladies or conventions, and believes in making love at the oddest times.'

'Hell,' he said with a grin, 'don't tell me it's lunchtime again! Tell you what—I'll show you how reformed I am. I shall desist...'

'Don't you dare! Besides, I've got used to it now,' she said airily.

Richard's eyes danced. 'You do realise Letty and Samson and Sunshine are probably all in quite a state by now, wondering what's going on? Don't you think at least we should...'

'Later,' she said softly, and ran her hands along his shoulders, caressingly. 'Anyway, Letty will have worked it all out by now. She's always one step ahead of me.'

'And me,' he said wryly. 'Anna,' he went on, suddenly completely serious, 'will you say it again? And keep saying it while you...do what you're doing?' he added with an effort. 'Then I might believe it's not just a dream.'

'I love you, Richard. I love you. I...'

THE AUTHOR

LINDSAY ARMSTRONG married an accountant from New Zealand and settled down—if you can call it that—in Australia. A coast-to-coast camping trip later, they moved to a six-hundred-acre mixed-grain property, which they eventually abandoned to the mice and leeches and black flies. Then, after a winning career at the track with an untried trotter, purchased "mainly because he had blue eyes," they opted for a more conventional family life with their five children in Brisbane, where Lindsay now writes.

A Fool to Say Yes

Sandra Clark

Frankie worked hard as a dance therapist and professional dancer. She was doing fine until she met Tristan de Vere Manning.

Son of her exercise patient, Lady Manning, Tristan returned from abroad to run the family estate. Suspicious of her motives and methods, he made Frankie's life miserable.

He was attracted to her, yet clearly wasn't interested in marriage. Frankie wasn't either. But neither was she about to have an affair with him! Convincing the arrogant, self-confident Tristan was another matter....

CHAPTER ONE

FRANKIE ARCHED her back in a graceful arabesque. The long sweep of rippling brown hair that reached to her waist flicked back with an almost audible sound as she straightened. Lady Manning's wheelchair on its pneumatic tyres made no sound over the parquet floor as the dowager propelled herself from the practice room.

'Thank you, Francesca,' she had said, and the grateful smile she had given the diminutive brunette at the end of their session left a glow of warmth behind that made Frankie pirouette around the bare room with a wide grin on her gamine features.

At last poor Lady Manning was beginning to show some improvement. When Francesca had been asked to take on the job of dance therapist to the victim of a motorway pile-up, she had not expected the patient to be quite so helpless. There had been no movement in Lady Manning's legs for six weeks, but in the last session or two there had been a definite improvement.

Frankie had been surprised on another score too—that her patient should be a titled lady and one who lived in such apparent isolation. It was only later that she had learned that Lord Manning had been killed in the crash which had rendered his Mercedes fit only for the scrap yard and made his elegant wife a cripple.

Now the whole future of the charming Queen Anne mansion was in the balance. Lady Manning had been unable and, Frankie supposed, reluctant to move elsewhere in the weeks following her bereavement, but now that she was able to take stock of her situation, together with the gradual realisation that she might well be in a wheelchair for the rest of her life, she was slowly coming round to the idea that she would have to make some major changes.

It had seemed natural to Frankie that so grand a lady should confide in her. People of all kinds often did. And as a constant visitor at the house they had an immediate rapport. She had learned that Lady Manning had been trained in classical ballet herself. She had even studied in Moscow for a time as a young girl. But, she confessed, she had given it up in order to marry—an admission which Frankie had had the tact to note without comment.

Lady Manning had given a girlish giggle then. 'I admit to being mildly disappointed in bearing only sons,' she had flashed a quick smile in Frankie's direction then, 'neither of whom,' she went on, 'shows any inclination whatsoever to become a ballet dancer.'

Frankie pictured the two sons—neither of them she had ever met—striding about the estate in their Lovat green thornproofs, or driving husky Range Rovers over the many ploughed acres of the family farmlands, and she smiled faintly.

'I do have hopes, however,' Lady Manning went on. 'I have a granddaughter. She's a positive darling. Look.' She indicated a gold-framed photograph on the table beside her. A pert six-year-old smiled sunnily out at them and Frankie, noting the garland of flowers in the child's hair and the faery-like white organdie dress, had made polite noises, again tactfully keeping her opinions to herself.

Afterwards, sweat darkening the petrol blue of her Lycra catsuit as a result of a particularly tough workout at the dance studios, she had repeated the gist of the conversation to her best friend, Rani.

'People *still* think dancing is just a question of floating about looking sweet. They just don't understand the hours and hours of sheer physical hard work that goes to make a good dancer.'

Rani, sitting on a bench in the changing room, her legs spreadeagled in front of her, and her face damp with exertion, nodded in agreement. 'They're all soft,' she asserted, flexing one of her aching limbs.

Frankie paused with the brush still in her hand. 'I wouldn't say that about Lady M., actually. She's quite a tough lady in her way. It's just that her ideas are a bit feudal. She certainly doesn't slack at her exercises. If sheer guts and determination are anything to go by, she'll be walking again one of these days.'

'Maybe that's due to the magic touch of her therapist!' butted in Rani with a grin.

Frankie picked an old pair of practice tights off the bench and aimed them in Rani's face. 'Come on, let's go and see if Matthew has got the drinks dispenser working yet. I could do with a drink of orange juice after all that.'

Frankie tried to work out at the dance centre every day. It was expensive, but she managed to supplement her income from private teaching with any work that Matthew, an ex-professional dancer who owned the centre, could send her way. It had been through him that she had come to get the job at the big house. One way and another, she mused, over her orange juice, Matty had been a brick. It hadn't been easy, these last two years, after Mother had died, what with Dave, at sixteen, relying on her to take family matters into her own hands.

She had been poised to join a small contemporary dance company, but her mother's sudden illness and death had made it impossible. She could hardly have left a sixteen-year-old in the lurch. There was nobody else Davey could have gone to. She determined to fill her mother's role until Dave went to university. Now he was in his last term at school and, although she knew that, two years older, she would find it that much harder to get work with a good dance company, she was beginning to face the next few challenging months with mounting excitement.

Loving her kid brother as she did, she felt that two years had been stolen from her life and that now, at last, she was going to be able to get on with the proper business of fulfilling her destiny. She was born to dance—everyone had always said so. And now, at last, dance she would.

'You're quiet for once,' observed Matty, clicking his fingers several times in front of her eyes.

'She's exhausted by that new routine you gave us, Matty,' Rani suggested.

'Yes, I noticed you two slacking in there this morning,' whipped back Matty. 'I'll have a couple of armchairs moved in for you tomorrow.'

Frankie came to with a start. 'It's all right for some.' She finished her drink in one gulp and stood up. 'I'll have to love you and leave you, sweethearts.'

'Going already?' asked Rani in surprise.

'I've got an extra session with Lady M.,' Frankie shrugged. 'I told you she was a determined character.'

'Don't forget your lesson with me this evening,' called Matty superfluously to her retreating back. As if she would! She would sooner die than miss a lesson, as he well knew.

THE LITTLE 2CV roared and bucketed up the mile-long private lane that led up to the house. It wasn't until she rounded the screening privets on the bend and came noisily out on to the gravel oval in front of the house that Frankie saw the large pearl grey limousine parked plumb in front of the shallow steps that led up to the front door.

She was at once filled with curiosity. Lady M. had had numerous visitors in the last few weeks. Some time ago the son whose little girl featured in the gold-framed photograph had flown back from Africa for a few days. When he had thoroughly checked that the professional care being given to his mother was satisfactory, a full-time nurse having been brought in, he had flown back again with the promise that he and his family would be home on three weeks' leave in the summer.

Of the second son nothing had been mentioned, and Frankie had felt it would have been out of place to ask questions as his name never came up. There was, she noted, no photograph of him on display.

Other visitors called in from time to time, the wives of local landowners, and the tenants at the dower house down the lane, a middle-aged farmer, and his pleasant, capable wife who parked her little Metro round the side whenever she came to spend an hour or two with Lady Manning.

The impressive-looking vehicle which confronted her now, with—Frankie's mouth dropped—its own uniformed chauffeur sitting in the front seat was, however, another kettle of fish altogether.

She parked her old rattletrap brazenly beside the other car and reached into the back to get her bag containing practice gear. The driver scarcely looked up from his newspaper as she crunched across the gravel to the steps. She could just see the tip of his cap on his bent head across what seemed to be the unnecessary length of the car's gleaming bonnet.

All that's missing is the royal flag, she thought wryly.

Dismissing the matter of the car, which had made her momentarily guilty about the spreading rust on the nearside door of the 2CV, she ran lightly up the steps and let herself in through the glass-panelled doors.

The marble tiles in the hall made the heels of her high-heeled ankle boots click loudly as she tripped the few yards to the door of the practice room.

It suddenly occurred to her that if the arrival of the visitor was as unexpected for her employer as it was for her, the lesson might have to be cancelled. She muttered under her breath. Not for the lost fee but for the possible harmful effect the missed session would likely have on Lady Manning's progress.

It was vital to keep up momentum, she told herself, as, optimistically, she changed into a green Lycra catsuit and pulled on a pair of multicoloured legwarmers to complete her outfit. She did a few warm up exercises in the large airy room while she waited as usual for Lady Manning to come in.

Officially this was the green drawing-room—but all its furniture, apart from a small writing desk, a straight-backed chair and an uncomfortable red cretonne armchair, had been removed. A long mirror, judiciously placed so that the patient could watch her own progress, was the only addition to the furnishings. Two french windows afforded the only distraction in the room, giving a tantalising glimpse of the yew gardens and the gently rolling hills beyond the outer edges of the park.

Frankie studied her line at the end of the new sequence of steps Matty had inflicted upon them. It was cruel, the contortions he expected of them. Slowly she unwound, unaware, until she turned full face towards the door, that it had opened silently and as silently admitted someone. For a moment she stood stock-still, her breath held taut, an abrupt thudding starting up as her heart rate unaccountably increased.

'Well, well...' The voice was huskily attractive, but the note of derision in it chilled Frankie's natural impulse to smile a greeting at the man.

She watched without moving as he padded elegantly across the shiny wooden floor towards her. He seemed to move with such catlike sinuousness that he made scarcely a sound. Yet he was tall, strong-looking, athletically masculine, except for the almost flowing softness of the white cotton kurtah he wore and the elegant line of his impeccable white trousers.

Her eyes dropped to his feet. It was a sort of escape, she afterwards remembered thinking, from the burning look of scorn in his dark eyes that seemed to shrivel her to nothing. Peripherally she noticed that he wore leather Indian sandals.

Her startled expression on seeing him approach must have registered on her face, for he stopped a couple of paces in front of her and when she looked at his face again she saw him raise his eyebrows in some sort of silent question.

'I might well ask what you are doing here too,' he said at last, almost as if she had spoken.

Normally never at a loss for words, Frankie could only stare. The man's aquiline features, tanned to a healthful gold, were worth staring at. He himself knew that. She let her glance fall again, shielding from him at once the nature of the impact his sudden appearance had had on her.

'Well?' There was an impatience in his voice which told her that what she might have mistaken for a polite question was nothing of the sort. He was telling her by his tone of voice that she had better give an account of herself, and fast.

She prickled, straightening her neck. Even when she stood erect like this, the top of her head would barely reach the man's shoulders. 'I'm Lady Manning's dance therapist,' she paused slightly, her expression cool and uncharacteristically distant. 'And who are you?'

Rudely the man ignored her question. 'So you're the one!' His face seemed to harden. Insolently his eyes travelled over her body, clearly defined in its figure-hugging catsuit against the light from the window.

'And what's that supposed to mean?' She might have meant the look, or the words. The intruder didn't ask. He seemed amused by the brittle edge of her voice and laughed softly. 'Well?' Frankie's blood was boiling. She stared at him, forcing him to give an answer. 'What do you mean?'

He smiled, vulpine, with a brief flash of startlingly even teeth, but the smile had no humour in it. 'I mean,' he replied, 'so you're the one who's filling Mother's head with the crazy idea that she's ever going to walk again. I mean, dear lady, so you're the one who's fastening on to someone else's misfortune in order to make yourself a quick buck.'

'What?' Frankie first went cold with shock, then she felt waves of heat sweep up over her body. Had she misheard? Her wide grey eyes took in the full measure of the man's icy features. The son, she thought dully, the other son. 'I don't know what you mean,' she managed to stutter. The man's implacable dislike seemed to paralyse her limbs and her powers to think clearly. 'I don't know what you're talking about,' she repeated stupidly. 'Fasten on her? How? Why? I'm here to help...'

The man gave a snort of disbelief. 'Help? To build up her hopes like this? Have you really looked at her limbs? She's paralysed! She can't move!' His face came close to hers in the ferocity of what he was saying. 'Have you given a thought to what's going to happen when she realises she'll never walk again? Have you?' He was almost shouting.

Frankie forced herself to stand where she was, though her impulse was to run and run from such blind anger. 'She will walk again,' she countered in as quiet and controlled a voice as she could muster. 'She has already vastly improved on the state she was in six weeks ago.'

'Of course she has,' the man ground out, 'it's natural for some change to manifest itself, but—' He spun abruptly at the sound of movement in the hall.

The door, slightly ajar, was edged fully open, and a corner of the wheelchair nosed into view.

He was across the floor in an instant, but not before Lady Manning, smiling with amused satisfaction, had manipulated the chair through the doorway and was whipping smartly across the polished floor.

'Sorry I'm late, my dear,' she greeted Frankie pleasantly. 'You'll no doubt have guessed why!' She turned proudly to indicate her son, who was standing foolishly with his hand on the door knob. 'You see, Tristan, I can get around faster than you now in this little contraption. If it wasn't for Frankie I think I would be quite content to remain in a chair for the rest of my life.' She shot a look of open friendliness at the girl. 'But I don't think she's going to let me languish here much longer.'

Frankie's heart sank—not at the words, but at what they meant, for it seemed inevitable to conclude that she had heard what Tristan had been saying. She knew that the success of Lady Manning's therapy depended to a great extent on her confidence in it. Any little doubts planted in her mind would thrive at the first sign of remission. She tried not to glower at Tristan for the harm he might have done, but Lady Manning's next words abruptly allayed her misgivings.

'Tristan is a great believer in the unorthodox, aren't you, Tristan?'

He turned briskly towards the door.

'Oh, don't go, dear. I'd like you to see how far we've got.'

Frankie's heart plummeted again. It was an exacting process, working the way she did, with a mixture of persuasion and bullying and immense mental concentration. Both women finished the session as near the point of exhaustion as Frankie dared go. To have a witness, and one so patently unsympathetic as Tristan, was not an enticing prospect.

His mother might be convinced, for reasons as yet unknown, that he was a believer, but Frankie had no such illusions.

Tristan had paused by the door. Frankie watched to see whether he would go out. She would heave a sigh of relief on seeing it close behind him, but she was to have no such luck. With a smile that did nothing to raise her spirits, Tristan pushed the door to and came towards them both.

'What a good idea,' he agreed, resting his hand lightly on the handle of his mother's chair. He regarded Frankie coldly over the top of the invalid's head. 'It should be very enlightening to see what methods are to be utilised by Miss—er—?'

Lady Manning raised a hand to her lips. 'Heavens! I assumed you'd got around to introducing yourselves. How remiss of me!' She took Frankie's hand in her own. 'Francesca Redpath—Tristan de Vere Manning, my elder son.'

Solemnly Tristan proffered his right hand. As she took it, briefly and coldly, Frankie realised it was the handshake of generals over a peace treaty neither intended to ratify.

'MATTY, I shall kill him—I shall! It's the only thing to do with a man like that! I could scream!'

'Go ahead, don't mind me. You know I'm a believer in spontaneity. Let it all hang out!'

Instead of smiling, Frankie glowered darkly at him and tossed her head.

'Hey, you really are upset.' Matty's smile faded and he was all concern. His neat crewcut grey head bent as he pulled Frankie into a loose friendly embrace. 'There, there!' he murmured. 'He's not important. You're too sensitive, Francesca, my love.'

Frankie let him soothe her for a moment. When she looked up at him her large grey eyes were troubled. 'I'm worried about what his attitude will do to Lady M. She's not stupid. She's going to guess before long exactly what he thinks of the therapy, and you know as well as I do that without the inner conviction that she's going to walk again, she'll never do it.' She sighed.

Matty stroked her hair as if she was a little girl seeking consolation and said, 'I think you're worrying for no reason. After all, it is his own mother. I'm sure that once he realises it's working for her, he'll cool it.'

Frankie laughed bitterly. 'When he sees it working, yes! His very own words. He's given me three weeks to prove it. Three weeks! Then he goes back to the Far East, and if she's not showing definite signs of improvement by then— that's that!' She tossed her head. 'The man's inhuman, I tell you. Everybody knows you can't put an arbitrary time scale on a thing like this! He *wants* it to fail!'

Matty, stepped back and looked at her with his wise brown eyes. 'Do you really believe that?' he asked her seriously.

Frankie rubbed the back of her hand over her face. 'Where has he been all this time she's been ill?' she demanded. 'Certainly not at his mother's bedside. He's a louse, and that's all there is to it.'

She walked over to the barre, put her foot on to it and did a dozen bends without stopping. When she stood upright she saw Matty in the mirror standing behind her. Al-

ready he had that back-to-business look in his eyes. She
turned with a flourish. 'Right, don't say it—I'm being un-
professional. Let's get on.'

IT WAS a good hour later while standing in the shower that
Frankie had a chance to go over in her mind what had
happened that afternoon after the therapy session. She
grinned ruefully to herself. There was one thing to be said
for Matty's workouts—they successfully erased all thought
from one's mind. But now that her body was having no
demands made upon it and she was at ease in the caressing stream of water, her thoughts were free to roam again
over the cause of her outburst to him.

It could all be summed up neatly in one name—Tristan
de Vere Manning.

She glowered again as she remembered how he had taken
up his position in the red cretonne armchair where, she had
to admit, he had made his presence almost unfelt, making
neither sound nor movement, as she had encouraged and
coerced Lady Manning through her exacting routines.

When they finished he had remained silent for some
time, then with one lithe movement he had sprung out of
the chair. Frankie had been helping Lady Manning back
into the wheelchair and without pausing he had touched
Frankie peremptorily on the shoulder with the muttered
order to see him in the library before she left.

She remembered taking as long as she dared over the
coffee and hot home-made scones which were always laid
on for her in the kitchen afterwards, and when, with the
greatest reluctance, she had finally made her way up to the
library in her going-home clothes, her worst fears had been
confirmed.

Tristan had been sitting in a large leather winged chair
by the window. When she came in he had neither risen nor
turned his head. After a moment when she had begun to

doubt whether he had actually heard her come into the book-lined room, she had ventured to speak. Even then he had scarcely bothered to turn his head to look at her. With rising indignation Frankie had had to listen to him pour scorn on her ability, her methods and, worse, her integrity, before she had been able to bring herself to utter a word in her defence. Even then she had only been able to reiterate her belief in the approach she had adopted.

His finely drawn dark eyebrows winged upwards with a look of scorn when she mentioned that it had been Lady Manning's own G.P. who had suggested such a course.

'It beats me how James could bring himself to dabble in this sort of thing,' he countered. 'He's always been such a down-to-earth sort of chap.'

'It beats me how your mother could be so mistaken about you!' burst out Frankie before she could stop herself.

'Oh?' The expression was cold. 'Explain that, would you?'

'She seems to imagine that you would approve of un-orthodox methods—' Frankie didn't have time to finish what she had been going to say because Tristan suddenly changed colour, and he half rose from his chair with an angry oath on his lips.

Something about Frankie's startled gasp must have made him realise he'd gone too far. Instead of coming to his feet he abruptly slumped back in the chair and merely gave her a long weighing look from the shadows. Eventually when he spoke his voice, though harsh, was controlled.

'Take a look at that photograph,' he ordered, pointing to an ornate heavily framed photograph on the desk by his side.

Frankie had to move round between his chair and the corner of the desk in order to reach across to it. When she lifted it, turning it over in her hands, she was confronted by the image of an attractive woman in her mid-fifties—of the lines of strain around the face which Frankie had grown accustomed to see there was no sign.

The face was that of a vital, vivacious woman in the prime of life. She was in riding kit and held the reins of a fine black stallion in one hand.

Frankie studied the photograph for a moment or two and then looked across at Tristan, but his face was averted and the fine profile with which she was confronted was coldly enigmatic. Carefully she replaced the photograph in the desk.

'Get out, will you?' The brooding look in the dark eyes changed instantly to one of sparking anger.

'I'm supposed to come in again tomorrow morning—' faltered Frankie, now at a loss as to what to do.

'You'd better do so, then, hadn't you?' He lifted his head and she saw the full lips curve sardonically. 'Don't be late. You've got three weeks to prove your case. Then I return to the Far East and Mother either comes with me or goes somewhere where she can be properly cared for.' He dismissed her with a peremptory wave of the hand.

Frankie only realised how seething she was when she saw her knuckles white on the handle as she closed the door behind her. She drove recklessly as far as the main road before she managed to bring her senses to heel enough to give herself a stern warning about driving in such an emotional state.

Her anger, despite the busy and demanding activities that filled up the rest of the day, did not abate, and it was with gritted teeth that she stormed into the house that evening.

RANI WAS sympathetic when she heard what had happened, but she said, 'It must have been a shock to him, to hear of the accident, and to find not only his father dead, but his mother crippled, possibly for life.'

Frankie wasn't having that, however. It was her turn to cook, and she slammed about in the kitchen while Rani lounged in front of the gasfire and listened to her ranting on.

The food, when it finally got to the table, was roundly criticised.

'I'm sorry,' said Frankie, looking at the congealed mess on the plates. 'It was supposed to be risotto, but I just can't cook when I'm in this state, damn him!'

Rani picked politely and said she wasn't hungry anyway. 'It's not like you to get all steamed up about a little job, and a temporary one at that,' she observed. 'Where's this famed professional detachment of yours gone to?'

'But it's somehow more than a job, isn't it?' replied Frankie.

'Is it? How so?' demanded Rani sceptically as she smoothed back her straight black hair from a serene brow. Her mother was Indian and Rani had inherited the same straight black hair and olive skin. Her gentle brown eyes were puzzled.

Frankie paused for a moment.

The risotto didn't taste bad at all; it only looked horrible. She finished another mouthful before replying. 'I suppose I feel something for Lady Manning—the fact that she was a dancer of some promise, and for family reasons gave up her career. It touches a chord somehow. In those days it needed courage, I suppose, to defy convention. Though now,' she observed with a grin, 'it does seem a bit wet! Fancy giving up a promising career because one's lord and master requires one's total attention!'

'Men!' sighed Rani. 'They're like demanding babies sometimes—but women often use their demands as a means of opting out from fulfilling their own destinies . . . and maybe risking failure.' She shot Frankie a shrewd glance. 'What about you and your kid brother?' she asked bluntly.

Frankie put down her fork. Her face seemed suddenly pale as she registered the meaning behind Rani's words. 'Is that what you really think?' she whispered. 'That I'm using Davey as a cop-out?'

Rani avoided her glance. 'It could be seen like that,' she replied at last. 'Look, Frankie, I don't mean to be unkind, but if you were really as tough and professional as you say, nothing, but nothing, would have stood in your way two years ago. You would have taken that job with that dance company if the heavens had fallen.' She put out a hand to touch Frankie gently on the sleeve. 'But you were in shock over your mother's death. And,' she smiled, 'you would have had to be a pretty rotten type too—to go off leaving a young brother at a time like that to fend for himself.'

Frankie shook off her friend's hand and stood up suddenly. 'What you're saying, Rani, is that to be professional it's necessary to behave like a third-rate louse?'

'It sometimes seems like that, yes,' Rani agreed. 'That's why men are so good at it,' she grinned.

'And that's why women often don't make the grade, I suppose?' Frankie smiled. 'Because we're so much nicer?' She paused. 'Cold comfort, I must say!'

Despite the lightness of her reply Frankie felt herself grip the edge of the table with both hands. 'This is the second challenge I've had today.'

'How so?' asked Rani.

'Well, if what you say is true—it's a pretty poor prospect for us, isn't it? I want to be a top dancer—but I don't want to turn into a stone monster in the process.'

Rani grinned. 'Fat chance of that!' She knew Frankie was impulsively generous, innately warm-hearted, and she couldn't imagine anything changing that.

'So what it means is I'm going to have to show you that what you're saying is quite wrong. In other words, I'm jolly well going to have to prove that I haven't copped out.' Frankie raised her grey eyes; they were beginning to sparkle. 'Tell you what, Rani—I shall apply for the vacancy with Electra Dance Company for a start. I told Matty last week that I thought I wasn't ready—but you're right, my old love. I was probably just copping out! It would mean starting in Davey's last month at school—if I was successful, that is,' she added hastily.

'I wouldn't worry about him. He'll be hanging round waiting for exam results then anyway, and won't want his aged sister playing little mother, cramping his style. What's the second?'

'What?' Frankie already had a faraway look in her eyes that showed she was immersed in the possibilities of which dance sequences to use in the audition.

'The second challenge,' prompted Rani.

'Oh, yes—the second one.' Frankie looked slightly abashed. 'Well, we started off talking about *him,* didn't we? You tried to tell me not to judge him yet, if I understood you properly. So obviously it's to do with what the pig said to me.' She moved away from the table and stood beside the marble fireplace which irrelevantly surrounded the modern gasfire. 'He had the gall to question both my integrity and my professional judgement. I aim to set him right on both counts.'

'Good.' Rani got up. 'By the way, if you can come down to earth for a moment or two, maybe you could give me a hand with the washing up? Davey, since you ask, rang to say he'd be late at the computer club and wants his food to be kept for him.'

Frankie became brisk. 'I'll show Tristan de Vere Manning! And I'll show you too, Rani. It's got to be possible to be human *and* professional. Caring for Lady Manning is just one way of proving it...but it's a way that will make *him* eat his words!' she finished triumphantly.

CHAPTER TWO

MATTY WAS delighted next day when Frankie broke the news that she had decided to audition with Electra after all. He at once set her through a gruelling programme designed to bring her up to scratch.

'There's nothing like the challenge of an audition to concentrate the mind,' he told her. 'Although you might feel you've been working well, it's difficult for anybody to maintain that professional edge without either a performance or, at the least, an audition in the offing.'

Frankie soon learned what he meant. She found she was dancing with a flair and precision she never knew she had. It told her why Matty, the wily old professional, had been so willing to sink so much of his time and energy into her training so far. As she spun her now almost constantly aching limbs about the studio she made a vow that for Matty too she would show them all what she was made of.

Such long hours did she put in, when all other thoughts but dancing were erased from her mind, that it was with a jolt that she remembered her next session with Lady Manning. She was just running down the stone steps into the changing room after an early morning practice when she remembered what day it was.

'Oh no!' she spun to face Rani who was coming down behind her. 'I've got the Manning job at eleven and I haven't got a clean catsuit!'

She glanced down at the sweat-stained garment she had on. Her two others which she usually washed out overnight had been bundled up under the bath at the house because she had been too dog-tired to face washing them the previous night. While the red leotard and matching footless tights she now wore were suitable for practice in the studio, she liked to appear fresh and presentable when giving private lessons, the more so with Lady Manning, as their work brought them into such close physical contact.

She cast a quick eye over her friend. No, she took a size twelve and was five feet six if she was an inch. Frankie barely scraped the five foot mark and her figure-hugging suits were all size eight. She mentally went over a list of the rest of the students who would be in before she had to leave, in case any of them would by chance have a spare leotard with them, but contemporary dance, unlike classical ballet, attracted taller dancers and, as the smallest in the centre, she knew there would be no luck there either.

'You can borrow my spare all-in-one if you like,' offered Rani at once. 'You could roll up the legs and arms.'

'It would hang like a sack, though,' Frankie shrugged.

Just then two or three students came in for the ten o'clock session and when they heard Frankie's problem there was general sympathy, but nobody could come up with a solution.

'I'll get a good shower, then, and hope the effect isn't too overpowering!' she shrugged again.

'I'm sure you're exaggerating,' mocked Rani, holding her nose.

'Wear some of my French perfume if it's that bad.'

'And compound the olfactory distraction,' said somebody in a good imitation of Matty, and they all laughed.

Frankie came out of the shower glowing after finishing off with the taps turned full on to cold to close her pores.

One of the older women who had recently taken up dancing in her spare time now that the last of her children was at school came shyly over to Frankie. 'I heard what you were saying just now,' she began. 'I wonder if my daughter's leotard would fit you? She's only twelve, but she's quite well-developed.' She held out a tiny pale pink garment. 'She left it in my carry-all after her ballet lesson yesterday.'

Frankie took the little slip of material from the woman. It looked impossibly tiny, all crunched up just as the woman had brought it out of her bag, but when it was shaken out and stretched into shape it seemed almost big enough.

'You'd better slip it on first,' suggested the woman.

Frankie flicked a glance at her watch. 'I'm already late,' she replied. 'May I take it with me? If it's too small, I'll just have to wear my old one.'

The woman nodded agreeably, and Frankie made arrangements to give it back to her the next day.

IT WAS almost on the stroke of eleven as she drove up to the front of the house. She usually contrived to be early so that she could warm-up first, but today she would obviously have to forgo that necessity.

The drive, she noticed, was empty. No chauffeur-driven car. She wondered at the pretentiousness of Lady Manning's elder son. Such grand trappings didn't seem to fit with the casual, though in its final effect, elegant, mode of dress he adopted. She tried to imagine what sort of car would have seemed more appropriate, but couldn't think of anything. No wonder, she mused, chiding herself as she went rapidly up the steps, she hardly knew the man. Nor did she wish to!

She was just letting herself in as usual when she heard a door close on the first floor and even as she clicked her way across the hall to the practice room, she saw a figure appear at the top of the stairs.

There was no word of greeting as he made his way
briskly down the stairs, and Frankie, already with her hand
on the door-knob, stepped back as he drew level. Even
then, she expected some kind of acknowledgement and
had already brought the beginnings of a rather frosty smile
to her lips as she turned her head, but, to her stupefac-
tion, he passed within six inches of her without even
glancing in her direction.

She could, she explained afterwards to Rani, have put
out her foot and tripped him up without the slightest effort at all. At the time, however, she was too amazed to do
more than stare. Feudalism isn't dead yet, flashed the
thought after his retreating back. Only the kindness of
Lady Manning stayed the words from springing immediately to her lips.

She slipped out of her things as soon as she got into the
little dressing room Lady Manning had set aside for her
and pulled out the pink leotard.

It was no good dwelling on the hostility of her employer's elder son. He was best avoided as much as possible. At
least she knew where she stood.

The leotard was tiny indeed but, made of elasticated
material, it gave sufficiently for Frankie to be able to pull
it on over her hips and with a little wriggling she managed
to get her arms through the holes. Luckily it was sleeve-
less, for she doubted whether she would have been able to
get her arms into it otherwise, but the body part of it gave
just enough to enable her to bend and stretch freely. She
did a few cautious steps, arched her back as she went into
the crab, then bent forward in the opposite direction so
that her long hair swept the floor in front of her. The cuff
round the legs rode up a little, but there was no obvious
strain at the seams. She was pleased. The leotard was clean
and fresh, and apart from the single-tiered frill round the
hips, it looked quite workmanlike—though she looked

closer to twelve herself than to twenty. Her flesh-coloured footless tights completed her outfit.

Briskly she went back into the practice room, half expecting to find Lady Manning already waiting but, unusually, the large, airy room was still empty.

She did half a dozen calypso steps, dancing barefoot as always, which brought her up to one of the windows overlooking the garden. It was beginning to drizzle in that sad, English way of early summer that seems as if nature is reluctant to give up on winter quite yet. It made the room seem dank and cold, so she went over to the light-switch by the door, intending to switch them on, but just as she was about to bring the palm of her hand down over the four switches at once, she thought she heard voices raised in anger in another room.

She froze as she heard the door slam, cutting off the sound. A line of worry appeared between her brows, making the uptilted gamine little face look uncharacteristically solemn. At least she wasn't the only one to get on his wrong side, she thought grimly. Somebody else was taking the rough edge of his tongue too.

Remembering her vow to be professional and remain unmoved by irrelevant emotions in her work, she did a few springs into the centre of the room and started to work at one of her audition routines until her patient should appear. It was, after all, none of her concern what domestic arguments were being discussed so loudly and indiscreetly in the next room. As she danced, however, although her concentration was adequate, she knew that all her senses were alert to any other sound.

It was no surprise when she heard someone at the door, and immediately she brought herself to a position of rest, turning with a smile of welcome. The door, however, was flung open to reveal not Lady Manning but the one person she could well have done without seeing at all. Tristan stood there, giving her a cool up-and-down look that brought a blush of anger to her cheeks.

As he didn't deign to explain his presence, lounging in the doorway for a moment without even a greeting, she walked purposefully towards him, back erect, grey eyes chilly, her worst forebodings already sending shivers of anger and disappointment up and down her spine.

'Where is Lady Manning?' she demanded, already holding Tristan accountable for her absence.

He came inside the room, closing the door with a languid gesture that conveyed the fact that he had all the time in the world at his disposal. 'Lady Manning is in bed,' he told her with what seemed like a triumphant smile.

Frankie's involuntary gasp of concern escaped her before she could camouflage it in a deceptive cough.

He was quick to notice it. 'Don't worry—I'm not holding you personally responsible for her indisposition. She's a dogged lady at best and you certainly aren't going to be able to stop her if she insists you drive her into the ground with your...er...' he seemed to fumble for the appropriate word and when he settled for the mild 'exercises' what it lacked in bite was amply conveyed by the intonation he put into it.

Frankie bristled but resolutely schooled herself not to rise to the bait. She guessed he was the type who would take great pleasure in provoking her to lose her temper just so he could mock her for giving way to 'feminine' hysteria. She would not give him the satisfaction.

'I'm sorry to hear your mother's ill. Is it anything serious?' she asked, as unprovocatively as she knew how.

'Serious?' His eyes darkened. 'On top of what she's already suffering?' he demanded harshly. 'No. Compared to all that, it's a mere nothing.'

She expected him to stand aside then and dismiss her with an autocratic wave of the hand, but instead, he went on blocking the way, his expression unfriendly to say the least. She started to walk towards him again, but when he didn't move, she stopped a couple of paces in front of him, looking up, as he towered over her, with as much hauteur as she could muster.

'I'm extremely sorry to hear she's unwell. I suppose it means that I may as well go,' she suggested, giving him the chance to move aside, but, ignoring it, he gave a short laugh.

'Why the hurry? The lesson is booked. You can't have any pressing engagement for at least an hour.'

'You don't intend to keep me hanging about here for a full hour, do you?' she demanded in surprise.

'Who said anything about hanging about? And anyway,' he went on, before she could query his words, 'you're hired for an hour, so for an hour you'll stay. There's no reason why you shouldn't earn your fee, is there?'

'I wouldn't dream of asking for a fee if there's to be no lesson,' she replied curtly, with a toss of her head.

'That just goes to show how unbusinesslike you are,' he retorted. 'We should have let you know your services would not be required this morning, instead of dragging you all the way out here for nothing.'

'If you'd known I'm sure you would have,' she responded with a generosity she did not feel.

'I did know.'

Frankie lifted her chin at this admission. There was a watchful expression in his eyes that did nothing at all to reassure her.

'What do you mean?' she demanded.

Instead of answering he sauntered over to the window and stood there for a moment, looking thoughtfully out at the garden. If she had had any sense, Frankie later told Rani, she would have taken the opportunity to slip out through the door there and then.

That, if anything, had been her point of no return.

Instead she waited, motionless, for what Tristan would say next. When he did speak, his words took her completely by surprise.

'I want you to dance for me,' he said, quite seriously.

She stared at him to make sure he wasn't having her on. 'You want what?' she asked incredulously as he merely waited as if for her to break into a song and dance routine there and then.

'You heard...' he paused. 'Dance for me.' He went to sit on the arm of the chair.

She couldn't help noticing how silkily his tan gleamed against the beige cotton of his shirt with its casually half-rolled sleeves and open neck. Even with his back to the light she could see the expression, half mocking, half expectant, on his lean clean-cut face.

There was no fat or flab on him, she noted, yet again. The tight fawn cord trousers revealed that much to her observation.

'Mother tells me you've set your sights on becoming a professional dancer as soon as your young brother is out of school—so you can't tell me you're shy.'

His words roused her to the question of his strange request again. 'I'm certainly not shy—' she began.

But he broke in with a hard laugh. 'I can see that,' he cut in, meaningfully, letting his eyes travel lazily over the contours of her body so clearly revealed by the skimpy little borrowed leotard. 'Last time, I seem to remember, you wore something with a little more coverage, plus a pair of those rather inelegant woollen things to conceal your legs—'

'Necessary for a dancer to keep the calf muscles warm and flexible—' she broke in with a tilt of her chin. If he was going to start implying all kinds of things about her in that lazy, suggestive voice of his, then she would at least defend herself.

'Maybe—' he went on, 'but I note that you've now discarded them and plumped for a rather more revealing get-up!'

'And why,' she asked in a quietly controlled voice, 'should I bother to do that?'

His ready laugh had a knowing edge to it. 'You tell me, sweetheart.'

Frankie stood her ground. 'No!' she insisted. 'You're obviously the one with the ideas.' In more ways than one, she thought, trying to ignore the gleam in his eye.

'And you—you're just an innocent ickle girl with big grey eyes and a pwetty pink dwess on,' he mimicked. 'Come off it, darling. That air of sweet innocence doesn't match the allure of the rig-out. You leave nothing to the imagination, sweetie.'

As he spoke, Frankie glanced at herself in the wall mirror. During her warm-up the leotard, cut high at the thighs, had ridden up again and it did indeed reveal rather a lot of flesh and, covered though it was by the coloured tights, she could see how it must look to someone less used to the normal gear worn by dancers at work.

She shrugged. 'That's ignorance on your part, not my desire to give you a cheap thrill. This is ordinary dancing gear. I'm sorry if it bothers you.'

'It bothers me, sweetheart, as it was meant to do, yes?' He was about to get up.

She stepped back lightly. 'What a pity your days spent in business or high finance, or whatever it is you do, should have left you with such a prurient attitude to the human body,' she mocked. For a moment the wide, urchin smile which made her so eye-catching lit up her face, but it was gone almost at once. 'Now, if you don't mind, I really must get back. I have an audition next week and want to use every opportunity I can for practice.' She turned as if to leave, but before she had gone two paces, he was barring her way, moving with the speed and agility of a lynx.

He put one hand on her shoulder and she could tell from the way he did it that if she tried to shake it off it would suddenly become a less than polite grip to hold her prisoner.

'Prurient, am I?' he gleamed down at her.

It wasn't fair that he was so tall and masculine, and almost her employer to boot. Frankie stood still, eyes demurely down-cast.

'I said dance. Didn't you hear me, or did you hope I'd forgotten?'

She opened her mouth to protest, lifting her head as she did so, but the sudden touch of his fingers brushing a sensuous line down the side of her mouth in a sort of chiding caress dried the words in her throat.

'You could practise your audition piece if it's so important,' he told her, letting his hand drop abruptly to his side.

She felt her face burning in response to his touch. What on earth was wrong with her? She was used to being touched, it was her job. Physical contact held no embarrassment for her, did it?

She tried to avoid his eye. It was easy enough. He had moved away to the armchair, his back turned towards her, something odd in the sudden tense angle of his shoulders. Perhaps he's still angry with me? she realised. Maybe this is a test to see if I'm really good enough to help his mother? The realisation that this might be so overcame her doubts about dancing in front of him. She would show him she knew all aspects of her job! Resolutely she moved into the centre of the room.

When he was sitting down he looked across at her impatiently, and she explained, 'It might look a little odd, without the music.'

'What is the accompaniment?' he asked.

'The last part of *Pierrot Lunaire*—' she began.

'Schönberg,' he nodded.

She felt herself relax. So at least he wasn't a total philistine. He knew something about modern music.

As if to prove it he hummed a few bars—the strange, awkward, yet haunting arabesques of the music at once setting the scene for what was a moving little masterpiece on the old topic of unrequited love.

Frankie danced with charm and precision, and she knew she was moving well. The unaccustomed setting inspired her to discover new qualities in the movements which she sensitively explored. There was also a powerful sense of the attentiveness of her audience to which the performer in her couldn't help but respond.

As soon as she had finished the small extract, she swivelled to look across at Tristan. His brown eyes were fixed intently on her and when he caught her gaze on him he seemed to pull himself back into the present with a physical effort.

'The way you move is at times quite lyrical,' he murmured. 'How unexpected!'

To her immense chagrin he uncoiled abruptly from the chair and in a few rapid strides was at the door. He turned long enough only to say, 'Mother would like a brief word with you before you go. Oh, and please, sweetie, wear that thing again. It's quite delightful.' With that he was gone.

Frankie stood open-mouthed as his footsteps receded down the corridor. She couldn't have felt worse if he had thrown a bath tub full of dirty water over her. How dare he dismiss her dancing as if it had been no more than the sexy cavortings of some television disco dancer? She had poured out her very soul in her attempt to mirror the qualities of the work, and his only response, after his expression of surprise that she could dance at all, was to call her sweetie!

Frankie hated being patronised, and she probably came in for more of it than most women because she was so petite. Men seemed to think that because she was tiny she was a total dimwit, with no more ideas in her head than a baby doll. The pink leotard, of course, was just the sort of silly garment men like that liked to see girls wear. It fitted in with their prejudice that there was something fluffy and inconsequential about a girl who danced for a living.

She stamped angrily. It looked as if every encounter was going to end like this, with him getting under her skin, and deliberately, it seemed, trying to rub her up the wrong way. And why on earth had he charged off like that?

'How damned rude!' exclaimed Rani that evening.

Frankie's visit to Lady Manning's room had been brief though reassuring. A slight head cold after staying out in the garden with the nurse yesterday had made the effort required for the therapy quite out of the question. But she was, she told Frankie, getting on well with the foot exercises they had recently started and she felt very positive about her continued progress.

'Well, that's some consolation.' Rani stirred some honey into a mug of cocoa and shot a sidelong glance at her friend. 'I must say I don't care for the effect this bloke seems to have on you.'

'Bloke? That's hardly the word for—' Frankie bit her lip.

Rani picked up on her reaction, however, and was laughing wickedly. She hummed a tune meaningfully under her breath and murmured something provocative about 'the de Vere Manning' in a silly exaggerated voice.

For once Frankie didn't smile. 'You can be awfully facetious, Rani, when you choose,' she said, with a pompous expression on her face.

'From what you've just told me, you'd have to be a genius to see the funny side of his character. He sounds a proper prune to me.'

'At first you made excuses for him,' Frankie reminded her.

Rani leaned forward, cocoa mug in both hands. 'I was wrong, obviously. Now you make him sound totally unreasonable. Once you would have agreed with me if anybody had behaved like that, but now it seems as if you've passed the point of no return.'

Frankie looked up sharply, her eyes narrowing under level brows. 'The point of no return?' she repeated.

The trouble with Rani was, she knew her almost as well as she knew herself. It was uncanny, though, how the phrase exactly mirrored her own feelings that morning in the practice room at the Hall. She felt as if she had slid over an imperceptible boundary which divided safety and peace of mind from something she could as yet not even imagine.

'You've fallen for the man, you clot. What are you going to do about it?'

'IT WOULD be a most injudicious thing to do anything about it for several reasons, all of which are so obvious I don't have to enlarge on them.' It was Matty speaking. He was at his most avuncular. To give him his due, he had a natural talent for it. It wouldn't be the first time he had had to counsel some poor girl who had been hit by the infection of falling in love. By and large, the fever passed quickly, leaving little trace of the temporary havoc it had caused. He was a firm believer in the curative effects of hard work, and told Frankie so in no uncertain terms.

In the face of such certainty she could do nothing but nod her head in agreement. 'I suppose you're right.'

'I am—I am right. Take my word for it. You should have one thought and one thought only in your head at this moment—and we both know what that is.'

Frankie nodded again. She had taken her waistlength hair out of its usual neat bun and left it to trail fetchingly around her shoulders. It was a new look. Attractive though it was, this romantic, waif-like image worried Matty. He'd seen that before too—the sudden softening influence the love disease could have on even the toughest and most ambitious women. And not women only, either, he reminded himself with a wry grin at his sense of justice.

He sighed. 'So that's settled, then.' He threw a piercing look in Frankie's direction which was usually enough to stop any incipient slacking before it really got a hold on any of his students, but, this time, he might as well have looked at the wall. Frankie didn't even see him, though her huge eyes were wide open and turned in his direction.

'Frankie . . .' he sang, letting just the right note of exasperation into his voice, 'when you come back into the real world, I think we'll go over that second number again. *If* you don't mind.'

'What?—Oh! Oh yes, of course, Matty. Sorry.'

But though she appeared to be going through the motions of starting the dance, her mind, elsewhere, seemed to drain her movements of the essential vitality which makes the difference between exercise and true dance.

Matty did what he rarely did. He took his stick from a corner of the room and banged it imperiously on the floor. The sound brought the pianist to a halt and half a beat later Frankie, too, stopped and inclined her head towards him.

'And again!' he shouted.

Matty made her go straight back into the same sequence. He made her do it a dozen times so that when he finally released her from the tyranny of his instructions she flopped down in a heap as if someone had abruptly cut the strings of a dancing doll. She was too exhausted to speak.

Matty remained where he was by the piano and surveyed the artlessly elegant arrangement of limbs and torso in the middle of the floor, without any show of sympathy.

'Tomorrow morning at eight,' he barked, turning at once to leave.

'What?' Frankie was shocked enough to raise her head.

'Eight sharp. And don't keep me waiting. You need extra work, and if you want my help, you're going to get it!'

'With a vengeance!' Frankie was stung to retort.

'Well? Has a little real work changed your mind about becoming a dancer?' he jeered. 'Because believe me you're not a dancer yet. Perhaps you'd rather go back to being treated like a quite talented amateur?'

Frankie rose to the bait.

'You're a slave driver, Matty, and I always knew there was a callous streak underneath that suave exterior of yours. You don't put *me* off with threats, though. I'll be here tomorrow morning before you are!'

The challenge brought a smile to Matty's face, but he concealed it well, merely nodding curtly to her, then turning to speak to the pianist as if she had ceased to exist for him.

As, Frankie later mused, she probably had.

CHAPTER THREE

Davey had taken remarkably well to living with the two girls.

When Frankie had reluctantly come to see the inevitability of getting a lodger to help pay off the mortgage on the house, she had thought long and hard about the sort of person who would be most suitable. She took her role as head of the now tragically depleted family very seriously in the first months and worried incessantly that she might do the wrong thing for Davey.

How would he feel, at seventeen, growing up in a house full of women? On the other hand, it was hardly on to contemplate a male lodger. The house was too small, too intimate. Tongues, in the quiet residential suburb, would wag.

Frankie thought of advertising for an older woman, someone who could, albeit unwittingly, give a feeling of stability to the household, but when Matty—of course, it had to be Matty, as always—had offered to help out by making enquiries among the students, lodgings naturally being at a premium, she had left the matter like that for a while.

But the payments on the mortgage had to be kept up and the date on which they had to be paid came round with increasing rapidity, it seemed, and it was then, to everyone's eventual relief, that Rani had suggested moving in.

'It's Dad,' she had confided. 'He's becoming really horrible about my dancing these days. He wanted me to go on to university to read history, as you know, but I managed to persuade him to let me take a year off between school and university. He no doubt thinks that I'll continue where I left off.' She scowled for a moment. 'It's my own fault for coming top in history and politics. I can't help having a flair for that sort of thing. But what he won't realise is that I have no interest in them whatsoever.'

'That's tough. So what can you do?' asked Frankie, perturbed.

'I've tried to compromise by telling him I will go to university—but only if I can study performing arts.'

'What did he say?'

Rani shrugged. 'It's like that at the moment.' She balanced a hand in front of her. 'He's not sure whether it'll mean he's backed down or scored a point. I really hate all the arguments. Every mealtime turns into a full-scale battle, and poor Mum is stuck in the middle. She wants to back him up, but she knows how much I hate the thought of academic life.'

Rani looked so desolate for a moment that Frankie took her impulsively by the arm. 'So if you move in with Davey and me it'll allow things to cool down for a bit?'

'That's right,' replied Rani. 'We'd all have a breathing space, and if Dad saw I was really serious about what I'm doing, and could be made to see that a degree like the one I have in mind really does have some professional standing, then I'm sure everything will eventually work out.'

'It certainly won't work out if you're at each other's throats every day,' Frankie agreed. 'But won't he object to your leaving home? Surely he'll see that simply as a way of flouting his wishes?'

'I don't think so,' Rani answered. 'I've had a word with Mum and she thinks that, despite himself, he'd like to agree to what I want but feels that he can't back down when it's such a burning issue between us.'

Frankie couldn't conceal her pleasure. 'You can tell him you're being philanthropic too,' she said gleefully. 'You're saving Davey and me from the workhouse!'

She knew Rani's allowance would stretch to cover accommodations as, with her university professor father and her G.P. mother, her family was quite comfortably off.

When she broke the news to Davey, he had been typically sceptical like any self-respecting schoolboy. Although he had had almost a year, Frankie thought guiltily, of penny-pinching and seeing her ill-concealed worry each time the monthly bills arrived, he understandably scoffed at the idea of not one but two women in the house.

'There's a bright side, though,' he told her with a cheeky grin. 'I'll have a built-in excuse not to get washed ever again—what with two lots of soggy practice tights cluttering up the bathroom.'

'I wasn't aware, dear brother, that you needed an excuse—' She ducked as he threw a dishcloth with habitual accuracy. Fielding it neatly, she grinned back. 'You'll really have to watch your step from now on,' she told him, screwing the cloth up ready to take aim. 'Rani used to be fast bowler in the school cricket team!'

In fact, it helped, having someone they both knew well in the house. Friends since schooldays, there was little of that strain it takes to adjust to a stranger's foibles, and Rani fitted in perfectly.

She and Davey talked cricket most of the time—a topic that left Frankie cold—and it was a relief to have someone else around to help with the cooking and the domestic chores. All the jobs were divided three ways—Davey, under Rani's spasmodic instruction, turning out quite passably good meals now and then.

'He really tries hard now,' Frankie told Rani. 'I suppose he doesn't want to lose face in front of you.'

'It adds to one's status among the schoolboys fraternity to be a cricket freak,' Rani grinned. 'I've something to thank Dad for at least!'

There was no sound from either bedroom as Frankie went downstairs at six-thirty that morning. She had told Matty she would be in before him, and she fully intended to be there well before he arrived.

His disparaging remarks about her dancing had jolted her out of her complacency and she was determined to let nothing—and no one—interfere with her schedule from now on.

She made herself a drink of decaffeinated coffee and toasted two slices of wholemeal bread. She would have to wake Davey before she left, she told herself maternally. Even though they tried to live on an equal basis of sharing she still kept a watchful eye on him, checking that he ate a proper breakfast before school.

As she ate she plotted in her mind how she would organise the day's work ahead of her. Luckily she only had to teach two ninety-minute sessions at the centre today.

The first one was a beginners' class in tap dancing—something of an experiment, this one, she grinned to herself. Matty had managed to cash in on a sudden upsurge of interest among housewives who, no doubt remembering their childhood and wanting something relaxing but energetic to do in their spare time, had flocked to the class. By its nature it was a happy class and Frankie felt she got far more from it than she could put in. It was good to see the students discovering muscles they hadn't used since schooldays, and acquiring a greater sense of well-being in the process.

Her other class was tougher, a second level jazz dance group, but again, by the very nature of the music, it was a fun class.

Frankie smiled to herself. All this left an hour in the morning for her extra lesson with Matty and, from half-past three, the rest of the day was her own. She would take time to fit in a sauna after the afternoon session to set her up for the unbroken practice she intended to do that would take her well into the evening.

She checked the rota on the kitchen notice board. Yes, it was Davey's turn to cook tonight. Her turn to do the shopping. Well, that was no problem as the dance centre was conveniently situated in a little street just off the market square itself.

Now almost seven o'clock, it was time to be setting off. She went to the bottom of the stairs and called up. There was no time to skylark now. The wet sponge treatment, Davey, in his cosy bed, would be pleased to know, would have to be missed.

'Davey!' she called 'Listen! I'll do the shopping—' there was a muffled response. 'Will you ask Rani to pick it up from the centre so you've got it for this evening's meal? I shan't be back until about ten. OK? Davey! Are you listening?'

His door opened abruptly and the shock-haired boy stumbled frantically on to the first floor landing.

'What time is it?' he demanded, already half way to the bathroom.

'Cool it, kid,' she mocked. 'I'm leaving early, that's all!'

She heard the muffled exclamation as he looked at his watch.

'You mean you've woken me up for nothing?' he protested.

'I only called once quietly. If there'd been no sound at all I'd have written you a note. Must fly, though. Don't forget to tell Rani, will you?' Tactfully she had not tried to wake her.

Rani had crept up to her attic room on the second floor at a quite disreputable hour the night before after having what she had announced as her farewell dinner with her latest boyfriend. It had been a stormy and, if the farewell had indeed taken place, short-lived relationship.

Rani's current scepticism about men, Frankie suspected, was much influenced by the antics of Joel, who also, unluckily, was a dancer in the same jazz class as Rani. From the stories of what he got up to in the way of emotional blackmail, he seemed remarkably immature to Frankie, as, in fact, did most of the boys at the centre. There wasn't one over twenty-one, and boys, she supposed, when she supposed anything at all, were exactly what they were. Rani, however, had fallen for Joel's ethereal good looks.

Frankie threw on a patterned quilted jacket over bright peacock blue trousers, picked up her hold-all into which she had already packed her practice clothes, and let herself out of the house.

As she let the front gate click behind her she mentally chalked up a point for herself. She had successfully got through the first part of the day without a single rankling thought about... She smiled grimly, not even admitting his name to her thoughts, and walked briskly into town.

SHE HAD her own key to the centre and marked up another point when she discovered that, even if she wouldn't have time for a proper workout, she had at least managed to arrive before Matty.

When he did get in a few minutes before eight, she didn't bother to conceal her glee at being one up on him.

'Hi, Matty!' She called, surveying him with her head upside down between her legs. 'What kept you?'

He concealed a smile and came briskly into the studio.

'Right. As you've obviously done your warmup, we'll commence at once!' he called without further preamble. 'From section D in *Pierrot,* if you please!'

It had started to rain by the time Frankie had showered and changed into street clothes after giving her tap lesson that day. Not the sort of weather in which to go shopping, but given the strictness of her self-imposed schedule, it was the only period in the day when she could allow herself the luxury of thinking about anything other than dancing.

In fact, it was quite pleasant at first, after being cooped up indoors all morning, to feel the fine drizzle issuing from low-lying clouds. They almost seemed to touch the top of the Minster dominating the town, but when, only half way through the list of purchases that had to be made, it started to pour down in a dull, relentless way that suggested there would be no early let-up, she gave a sigh of irritation.

Should she go on, traipsing up and down the avenues of produce, being dripped on from the overflow from the tarpaulins slung between the stalls, or should she indulge in a ten-minute break in a nearby coffee shop? Her sense of discipline was such that even a short break like that seemed to leave a hole in her schedule.

She had just decided that she was taking things a bit too far, feeling guilty over such a little thing, when she felt a push from behind as she hovered under an awning on the edge of the market where a crowd of bedraggled shoppers like herself were huddling indecisively out of the rain.

'Excuse me. I—oh! It's you!' There was an insolence in the man's exclamation that made her hackles rise almost before she had realised who had made the remark.

Steadily she raised her glance to meet his without any attempt to conceal her dislike. Sexily attractive he might be, but she wasn't going to give him the satisfaction of seeing how his proximity affected her. Rani must be out of her mind if she thought she could fall for a man like this!

She didn't bother to answer him, her grey eyes barely registered the fact that she knew him. He seemed, she observed with satisfaction, quite put out at her obvious disdain.

'You're so tiny I didn't see you there. Did I hurt you?' he asked, bending his head to duck under the awning and stand next to her.

She lifted one thin shoulder, dismissing him. 'Hardly. I'm not made of glass.'

'You mean, you don't regard yourself as transparent?' he mocked, scarcely opening his lips so that the people passing around them wouldn't hear.

Momentarily thrown off balance by his bantering attack, Frankie edged away, looking for a break in the traffic so that she could dash across the road, out of harm's way. The coffee shop looked inviting now, and she would rather break her routine for ten minutes than spend a second longer than necessary with this arrogant man.

She ducked round a stream of water pouring off a corner of the tarpaulin and managed to dash between the rear bumper of a Cortina and the front of a delivery van. The driver of the van honked his horn, more to acknowledge her appearance than as a warning, and as he called out cheekily from his half-open window, Frankie turned to glower back from the pavement. She was just in time to catch a glimpse of Tristan walking nonchalantly round the back of the slowing van, and before she could disappear into the coffee house, he had loped along beside her, proprietorially taking her by the elbow, pushing her, without a by-your-leave, into the shop.

'Hey, what are you doing?' she protested weakly, accidentally banging him about the legs with her heavy shopping bags.

He took them from her, and when the manageress came up, he said, 'Table for two,' and pushed Frankie firmly ahead of him, without giving her any answer.

She could have refused to go on, but the curious stares of the other customers and the pungent enticement of freshly ground coffee were too much, so she sat down with an expression of deliberate hostility to glower at him across the stiff white cloth. She would have her drink as she had intended, then leave as soon as possible.

In no hurry, it seemed, to strike up a conversation, Tristan regarded her enigmatically for a moment or two.

Despite her outward calm, Frankie's thoughts were racing. If this was a battle of wills, she would play it to the end. It must be obvious even to him, she was thinking, that they could have nothing to say to each other. She didn't even want an explanation of his cryptic remark about her apparent state of transparency! She glowered silently at the rain as it dripped resolutely from the curved eave of the much tarted-up medieval building in which the café was housed.

'Fascinating, the way rain falls, isn't it? I'm sure an Einstein or a Newton could build a theory of the universe on it.'

His words made her glance travel from the window to his face. What she thought of a remark like that was evident in the set of her slim shoulders and the slight angle at which she held her head.

Her wide grey eyes were expressionless.

'No make-up today? I seem to have caught you out,' he resumed with deliberate provocation.

Her glance flickered over him without changing. It was true, she wore make-up when going up to the Hall, but not when practising. Today she had been rushed anyway. She was trying to pare life down to its essentials. Without conceit she knew that she looked all right without make-up—

the van driver had just acknowledged that fact—but she couldn't see what concern it was of the man in front of her.

'And back to the figure-concealing garb too,' he observed meaningfully.

'Surely you don't expect me to do my shopping in a borrowed pink leotard?' she drawled. 'Why not hang around till summer and perhaps I'll oblige then?' The sarcasm rolled off him.

'That's too long to wait as far as I'm concerned,' he replied at once. 'What I want, I want now. And that applies to you.'

She pretended to misunderstand, though his audacity took her breath away. 'Oh, but I'm quite willing to wait for what *I* want,' she answered with gravity.

'You know what I mean—' he broke in, but just then, to Frankie's relief, the waitress brought their pot of coffee and the hot buttered scones she supposed Tristan must have ordered.

She pretended to concentrate on spreading strawberry jam on a scone and thanked her lucky stars she had no need to watch her figure.

'As I was saying—' he started as soon as the waitress was again out of earshot.

'I can't say I'm at all interested if you were saying what I think you were saying...' she broke in, but his quiet laughter drowned out whatever she had been going to add and she allowed her words to trail off, convinced now that he was the type who never listened to anyone else, especially girls.

He was beyond the pale!

His expression, however, was serious when he spoke. He leaned forward, his lean face shadowed, with the light behind it. 'I feel it's time to get to know you a little better. I'd decided to ask you out to dinner when you next came up the Hall, but it was stroke of luck seeing you just now—'

'And cheaper,' she quipped before she could stop herself. Tristan raised his eyebrows. Frankie had the grace to colour. 'Well—it is, anyway,' she muttered lamely.

'Don't worry, you'll still get your meal.'

She gripped the edge of the table. 'I didn't mean that,' she said in a low voice. Everything about him made her feel cheap. She couldn't help being defensive with him, looking for slights and insults where they might not even exist.

'It's neither here nor there what you meant,' he was saying, with a quizzical tilt to his head. 'I was going to say—it's a stroke of luck that we've bumped into each other, because it means we can fix a date to suit us both now. There isn't time to have a proper talk this morning.'

'You're right!' The cheek of him! He hadn't got time— well, neither had she. Would *he* even consider questioning that!

'And,' he added, with a slight smile that was wholly infuriating, 'you look so awfully bedraggled, it's not only instructive for me to see you as you naturally are, underneath all the glamour, it also gives you a chance to dry out!'

'Thank you very much,' she replied sarcastically, 'but I happened to be coming here anyway. I didn't need *your* invitation!' Glamour, he had said. Her lips tightened. Was it some kind of backhanded insult? She watched him carefully.

'At least I made sure you did have a drink,' he went on coolly. 'You don't look to me as if you're taking enough care of yourself.'

'What on earth's it got to do with you what I do?' she exploded, cheeks crimson with anger. The effrontery of the man! Her expression told him plainly what she thought of him.

He went on calmly, 'That shopping bag you were struggling with looks as if it's got enough provisions in it to feed an army. Your kid brother must have an appetite like a young horse.'

'There are three of us, actually,' Frankie replied as bitingly as she could. He raised one eyebrow fractionally so that she added, just to bring the point home, 'I share the house with someone else.'

When he stiffened she realised that, as she hoped he would, he had jumped immediately to the conclusion that the third person was a lover.

She smiled at him. Let him think what he liked. It would do him good to realise that he wasn't the only eligible male in town. Or—and it was her turn to stiffen—was he? She assumed he was still unmarried—but only because of his come-hither attitude. He might—and her eyes narrowed—be a philandering married man for all she knew.

'What a lot goes on behind those enormous grey eyes of yours,' he remarked conversationally.

'What a pity you can't tune in to it,' she retorted, 'you might learn something.' She gulped a mouthful of coffee and burned her tongue for her lack of caution.

'Listen, Frankie, why don't we call a truce? Meet me for dinner this evening and you can tell me about this therapy of yours.'

'I'm afraid it's impossible,' she replied sweetly. 'First, I'm too busy—'

'Boyfriend?'

She ignored the question. 'Second, I don't want to. I don't think there's anything I can say that would penetrate your obvious prejudice against me.'

'Prejudice?' he asked incredulously. 'I'm anything but prejudiced against you, sweetheart.'

'That,' she exclaimed triumphantly, 'is the clearest demonstration of prejudice there could be—sweetheart!' she repeated scathingly. 'I am not your sweetheart and I object strongly to having my professional status belittled by such a belittling term.'

'Oh, no! Women's Lib rears its head . . .' he began.

'And what would you suggest, from the heights of your automatically privileged position of male superiority? That we all return to the kitchen and the bedroom?'

'From my privileged position sitting opposite you, sweetheart, I would say "yes" to the latter, and leave the former to my chef.'

Tristan's eyes sparkled as he gave her an inviting look that left no doubt as to the nature of the invitation.

Frankie's impulse was to pick up the tablecloth and dump the whole lot, cups, coffee pot and all, over his insufferable head, but she somehow restrained herself. As in the practice room she should at least have got up there and then but she found she could not leave well alone. There was something so intolerably arrogant in his expression that she could not concede defeat. She would have to make him see that sexual innuendo didn't work with her.

She managed to bring a cold smile to her face. 'If I worked in an office and we had the same employer-employee relationship,' she told him coolly, 'I could no doubt make out a case for sexual harassment against you.'

'Hey, wait! This is outside working hours. Surely the normal male/female roles are legitimate now?'

'So you imagine harassment is legitimate behaviour, do you?' she demanded scornfully. 'The way you play it, it seems more like jungle warfare! I can't say I'm interested.' She had the pleasure of seeing him look slightly nonplussed.

'I've never known anyone turn a compliment away before. I suppose it's your boyfriend. He'd object to your having dinner with the son of your employer?'

'Don't be ridiculous!' she blurted out.

When she opened her mouth to continue, he added heavily, '"No man tells me what to do"—no, I didn't think they would.'

'Precisely,' she glared at him.

He hesitated for a moment, and she thought she had managed to silence him, but she was wrong.

He looked across at her with a crooked smile that did nothing to camouflage the determination in his eyes.

'We're going to meet, Frankie, and we're going to meet soon. We're going to meet on my terms too. And we're going to have a long talk.' He leaned forward, resting the leather elbows of his tweed jacket on the table in front of him. 'Do you hear me?'

'I hear you. How could I help it—bellowing like that!' She pretended to look offended. 'But just because I, and half the café, can hear you, it doesn't mean I say "yes"— we have nothing to say to each other.'

'We have plenty. You'll see.' He glanced at his watch. 'I have to go now, but I can give you a lift somewhere if you like. I'm going——'

'You must be joking,' she replied rudely. 'I'd rather walk, thanks.' She got up. By rights she should have come out of the encounter the victor. After all, she'd declined his dinner invitation unequivocally, but in some obscure way she felt she'd lost.

Maybe it was his unshakable self-confidence that made her feel like that. Or maybe it was simply that she knew he hadn't given up. And that whatever she said to him, however much she tried to put him down, in some peculiar way, she never quite hit the mark. It was like shadow boxing. Tristan was always somewhere a little out of reach of her attack—as if the role he was playing was a deliberate attempt to hide his true self from her.

'You try to be obnoxious on purpose, don't you?' she sneered, gathering her things together.

'Thank you,' his eyes sparkled, 'that seems to mean that I could be quite nice if I tried!'

His smile burned her flesh with its radiance. She longed to be able to do something that would wipe it entirely from off his face for good.

Speechless, she made her way to the cashier's desk, fumbling in her shoulder bag as she did so for some change, but he was already by her side, and when he saw what she was doing, he shook his head.

'It may be against your principles of equality and all that, but I insist on paying. After all, you're here at my invitation. No!' he remonstrated as she opened her mouth to argue. Then he turned to the cashier, bringing out a five-pound note as he did so.

Frankie didn't wait for him to take his change. She gave a curt thank you and walked swiftly out into the street without a further word.

To SAY that her routine of good intentions had been spoiled would be to exaggerate. When she got back with her errands completed she went at once into a sequence of exercises that were tough enough to wipe Tristan from her thoughts for at least an hour. She had a light salad lunch in the snack bar at the centre, and made sure that the next hour and a half's teaching successfully prevented her from thinking about anything but the work in hand.

Only when she found herself with time to unwind in the privacy of the sauna did she find her thoughts circling back again towards the morning's encounter.

Pouring a couple of ladles of cold water on to the hot coals, she lay full length on the top bench, her long brown hair freed for the first time that day from its restraining clip. How dared he say she looked bedraggled! She would wash her hair after this, though, she mused, drifting off into a peaceful state of half slumber, half wakefulness. Then for some more practice.

A tanned clean-cut face leered at her in her dreamy state, making the muscles of her neck tense when they should have been relaxed.

This is ridiculous, she told herself. I have a normal sex drive, so why am I startled out of my wits by the strength of what I feel about him? He's a very attractive man. There's a sort of magnetic, animal attraction about him that any girl would find hard to resist. So why don't I acknowledge this by giving him the little flattering looks he so obviously expects? Why do I have to be so prickly, so damned touchy, all the time? Jumping down his throat just because he makes a pass at me? He's obviously a man who likes little games in order to boost his ego. So what? It's no skin off my nose to play games like that, if only to smooth the path. So long as he realises that that's as far as I want to go... She shivered, turning, uncomfortable on the yellow towel spread over the wooden slats.

Something in her was fighting tooth and nail against playing such a game with him. She saw herself from his point of view—that was, from the point of view of a spoiled, aristocratic male who was used to clicking his fingers to have whatever he had a whim for fall into his grasp.

She would represent the latest little plaything, brought to the Hall for him by his mother, an inconsequential toy playing at doing a professional job of curing his mother where official medical people had failed. Someone wrongheaded, therefore. Not to be taken seriously. A doll-like figure. A toy. Someone with whom he could while away his rather dull three weeks in the bleak north Yorkshire countryside. That was how he saw her, pink leotard and all, and there was nothing she could do against such prejudice but ride with it... for the sake of Lady Manning.

Frankie sighed. It was going to be impossible to go on working with his mother in the same house as him knowing that all the time there was a chance of coming face to face with him. She would have to accept his offer of a truce—just so long as he realised there was going to be nothing personal in her change of attitude.

She wriggled over on to her stomach, her skin gleaming moistly as the dry heat at last began to do its work. Now, she told herself sternly, she was going to get on with thinking about the audition next week.

BY THE time the last notes of the record died away Frankie was already walking over to switch it off. It had been a gruelling session. The silence that suddenly wrapped her round told her that everyone else had gone home. The last class finished at nine-thirty, and though people sometimes congregated around the drinks dispenser in the foyer, tonight the bad weather must have sent them all scurrying for home. The studio looked eerie now as she went round switching off the lights. The vast mirrors which covered the walls from floor level to a height of ten feet threw back an image of her diminutive figure, lonely in the unnatural stillness of the deserted studio.

She would have to check the other practice rooms too, as she had promised Matty, just to make sure that all lights were extinguished. She ran lightly up the normally bustling stairs to the first floor, then down two flights to the silent basement changing rooms. She would have a soak in the bath at home, then treat herself to a leisurely meal. It was to be hoped young Davey had come up with something edible tonight—she was famished!

She put on her jacket, gave the changing rooms the once-over, picked up a pair of tights someone had dropped, then went out, closing the doors behind her.

She had just reached the top of the steps leading into the foyer, walking slowly because it suddenly hit her how she had been on the go for over twelve hours, when her blood froze.

There was a dark figure standing just by the door leading into studio one. It was a man. His back was turned as he looked at something on one of the noticeboards in the entrance, so Frankie couldn't see his face, but there was enough light to recognise that it was no one from the centre, not with that height and mature physique. It was no boy.

She shivered, glad that the takings had been safely banked by Matty earlier in the evening, then she gasped.

The man had heard the soft fall of her footsteps, and was swivelling to face her. He smiled dangerously and began to move towards her.

CHAPTER FOUR

As HE came nearer, moving through the shadows cast by the single light from the reception cubicle, his face seemed almost satanic in the intensity of its expression.

Frankie shivered and drew back. He had seen her, and his eyes gleamed, picking out her still figure from the shadows without difficulty. She saw that he was wearing something dark that only added to his air of menace, but he was smiling.

'Well, finished now?' he demanded throatily. 'You certainly took long enough!'

She tried to still the sudden rapid beating of her pulses as he drew near enough to lean down over her with one hand resting nonchalantly against the wall by her head. When she tried to move out from under him he caught hold of her by the upper arm.

Remembering her decision to try to humour him for the sake of Lady Manning, she didn't brush him off as she felt like doing, as all her instincts told her to do. Instead she endured the violent, contradictory emotions his touch aroused in her with a pretense of indifference.

'What do you mean?' she asked, keeping her voice level.

'I arrived at what I hoped would be a suitable time to have dinner. I told you this morning I wanted you to dine with me, remember?'

'And I told you I didn't want to, remember?' she wanted to retort, but again she played it down and merely asked, quite calmly with a slight widening of her grey eyes, 'You mean you've been waiting for me?'

'Yes,' he admitted grimly. 'This drinks dispenser is poor company, I must say.'

'More fool you,' she broke in, unable to help herself.

'That's better,' he approved. 'For a moment I thought you'd lost your sassyness through too much hard work.' He grinned broadly at her and proceeded to push her on ahead towards the exit.

'Hold on a minute!' she cried out. 'You're not still hoping I'll say "yes", are you? I've already told you, it would be a waste of time talking—we're on opposite sides of the fence.'

'And would you still say "no" if Mother had invited you to dinner?'

'At this time of night?' Frankie looked at him in astonishment.

He didn't answer.

Perhaps they usually ate late, she hazarded, with a searching glance at him. It was unlikely, but possible. How could she refuse in the circumstances? Damn him—he must have talked his mother into inviting her over during the afternoon.

When she finally raised her eyes to his, he smiled, reading her capitulation in them.

'I've parked just around the corner. Come on.'

'I have to lock up first.'

Taking her time, her thoughts once again in turmoil, Frankie carefully went round checking all the doors. Only when she was good and ready did she go over to where Tristan waited, smiling slightly, as if unaware that she had been playing some game with him.

It was when she drew level that he asked laconically, 'Er—what about the windows? Don't you think you should double-check?'

Her chin rose. Without answering she allowed him to
lead her outside. It was still raining with a heavy dull insistence. But she had to stop once more in order to double
lock the main doors. He held his big black umbrella over
her head while she fumbled about with the keys. The
thundering of the rain on it was like the thundering of her
heartbeats whenever he accidentally brushed against her.

As she straightened he murmured, 'Good, well done!'
and put a hand underneath her elbow. 'I shall know who
to come to if I ever go into the prison business.'

'You'd do pretty well in that game as it is,' she extri-
cated her arm pointedly.

He laughed, but made no attempt to take hold of it
again.

When they rounded the corner Frankie expected to see
the silver-grey limousine, complete perhaps with chauffeur, but instead there was only a rather old-looking
though sporty MG, its hood up against the rain.

Tristan led her over to it and unlocked the passenger's
door.

Frankie didn't know a great deal about vintage cars, but
she knew this was one. Davey had been through the car
craze and at one time his bedroom wall had been plastered with pictures of cars such as this, so when she slipped
into the passenger seat, she was at once impressed by the
immaculate care that had been bestowed on it. The genuine hand-carved oak of the dashboard gleamed with a well-
polished look and all the metal trim glowed as if it had just
come from the hands of the makers.

As Tristan let himself into the driver's seat she nestled
back in the rich dark leather of the passenger seat, but was
unable to resist asking, 'So what happened to the chauffeur? Is this his night off?'

Tristan chuckled. 'He wasn't mine. He was sent by the
government whose guest I've been, in order to give me an

emergency lift home from the airport—' he broke off. Then, as if considering something, he said, half turning towards her, 'If I seemed rather harsh in my attitude when we first met it was because I was somewhat shocked to see the state Mother was in. I only learned of the accident and Father's death a few days before that. News, unfortunately, doesn't travel fast in the region where I was working, and it had taken two months to reach me. I'd simply come straight back, and walked in to find all that waiting for me.'

There was a hardness in his voice and in the light of the street lamp filtering through the rain-washed windscreen, Frankie could see there was no softening of apology in his face.

He spoke as if she should have known how he was feeling.

Defensively she said, 'I didn't know who you were. You seemed to just loom up, shouting and being beastly. I only learned that you were Lady Manning's son in passing, if you remember.'

'I see.' He turned, his eyes gleaming wickedly. 'I was right, it is time we had a talk.'

The engine gunned into life before she could reply and in a moment they were on the edge of town approaching the roundabout where the road turned off towards the Hall, but to Frankie's consternation Tristan took the next turning and they were soon roaring along a narrow country lane that didn't even have any street lights.

She sat upright. 'Wait a minute! This isn't the right road—' she laughed, thinking he had made a mistake, but instead he chuckled and merely accelerated, carrying them faster into the tunnel of light created by the twin headlamps.

Frankie gripped his arm. 'Stop, Tristan! Stop at once!'

'Calm down. I told you we were going to have dinner. Even at this time of night I know somewhere where we can expect something worth eating.'

'But you said your mother had invited me...' she burst out.

'Correction, I said, "What would you say if Mother had invited you?" I didn't say she actually had—though, of course, I'm sure she will, as soon as this therapy of yours begins to work and she feels well enough.'

'Why, you—you...!' Frankie struggled against the urge to slam on the handbrake and kicked herself for allowing him to trick her so easily. 'Of all the underhand things to do—you're unbelievable!'

'It was the only way I could think of on the spur of the moment, bar kidnapping you, of course. You can't blame me!'

But she did blame him, and she told him so in no uncertain terms, all her good resolutions of playing it cool deserting her in one onslaught of rage.

'You could have taken "no" to mean "no"!', she screamed at him. 'I might just as well be a mindless doll if you think you have a right to ride roughshod over anything I say!' she stormed.

His quiet chuckle in response merely added to her feeling of helplessness. Short of opening the car door—an eventuality that apparently crossed his mind too, for he reached over to lock it—she had no alternative but to endure being his temporary captive. She stopped complaining when she saw it was having no visible effect on him and, setting her mouth in a straight, unforgiving line, she lapsed into moody silence.

In less than fifteen minutes he was bringing the car to rest between two others parked outside a low-roofed timbered building. The rain was coming down in such buckets it was impossible to see where they were. A single light shone above what looked like an inn sign.

Tristan turned to her. 'Wait here. I'll go and see if they've got another umbrella they can lend us.'

'Don't bother. I'm not afraid of a drop of rain.' Frankie fumbled at the door lock. Better to get the encounter over with as soon as possible than sit here in this horrible proximity with the sound of the drumming rain locking them into a dangerously private world of their own. 'You don't have to treat me like a china doll,' she grumbled resentfully.

She was having no luck with the door lock and Tristan leaned across to open it. She could smell the muskiness of his aftershave as it enveloped them in a subtle haze of perfume. It only served to make her flinch back in the passenger seat as if to avoid the slightest physical contact with him.

Her involuntary movement did not escape his notice. He shot a surprised look at her, but by then the door was open and she took the opportunity to scramble hurriedly out. Head bent against the rain, she dashed across the forecourt into the shelter of the porch, without looking back.

Tristan was a moment or two locking up and when he joined her his hair was dripping soddenly in flat black locks over his forehead. Evidently he thought that if she could do without the umbrella, so could he. 'I'd forgotten it could rain like this in England,' he said lightly.

She was still, however, tight-lipped, and didn't attempt to bounce the conversational ball back. He wasn't getting round her like that!

Unperturbed, he ducked his head to lead the way through a pair of double doors that gave straight on to a low-ceilinged lounge bar. There were only a couple of tweed-jacketed farming types at the bar, yarning with the publican, and a scattering of other guests ranged about an open fire.

The landlord greeted Tristan as if he was an old friend, and when the question of a meal was broached he couldn't do enough for them. They were shown into a cosy dining room beyond the lounge and their drinks brought to them while they looked at the menu.

'His wife's an excellent cook and makes all the pies and quiches and so on herself,' Tristan told Frankie. 'This is one of my favourite haunts when I'm home.'

Frankie studied the menu without looking up. She wasn't going to make conversation. Kidnapped she might be, but at least she could offer some passive resistance to his blandishments!

A quick look at the menu made her realise how hungry she was, and as the warmth from the blazing log fire began to seep into her tired limbs, she had a sneaking feeling that she was quite enjoying being dined so unexpectedly. She wasn't going to let Tristan know that, though, was she?

'I won't have much,' she murmured, reading the rest of the menu rapidly.

'Watching your figure?' he jibed.

'I can leave that to you,' she came back, not missing the way his eyes had strayed appreciatively over her body as he had helped her off with her jacket.

'I thought that was the name of the game?' he came back with a silky smile.

Frankie cut him short by saying, 'I'll have the venison pie, but no potatoes.'

'And for starters?'

She shook her head. 'I've been on the go since seven this morning and tomorrow will be the same. I'd like to get back home as soon as possible.'

He didn't argue, merely raising his eyebrows a fraction as if he was surprised that she should waste her time putting in so many hours for something so unimportant. She braved out his glance, and when he started to talk she gave him the minimum amount of attention she could, pointedly looking away over his shoulder as if far more interested in the patterning on the oak panels behind him.

It was only when he mentioned the treatment being given his mother that she leaned forward with more interest.

'For six weeks after recovering from the immediate effects of the accident, she did nothing but lie in bed, grieving, maybe, for your father. I saw her then. She would hardly turn her head when the G.P. came into the room. He had heard of therapy such as the kind I have been trained in.'

'Why did you train as a therapist? I thought you wanted to be a performer?'

'I did—I do,' she corrected, 'but my mother died after a short illness a couple of years ago, and it was in the aftermath of that...' she shrugged. 'It seemed a good thing to do at the time. It meant I could also continue my training with Matty—he's the director of the dance centre,' she explained in response to the question in his eyes. 'It was an opportunity to widen my experience.'

'With an eye to the future?'

It was her turn to look quizzical.

'I mean, when you're too old to dance in public,' he explained. 'A dancer's life is short, isn't it? Like any athlete's.'

'Athlete!' she burst out. 'So you see dance as a branch of athletics, do you?' She couldn't disguise the note of disparagement in her voice.

'It has similarities,' he insisted.

Frankie made an exclamation of disagreement. 'We're miles apart, aren't we?' She wanted to explain that through dance the inner searchings of the soul could be expressed, but Tristan was giving her one of his heart-stopping smiles that seemed to turn her limbs to jelly. His expression suggested nothing so much as a sheer animality, so that her words trailed inadequately away and she had to let her glance drop to hide what was in her mind.

When he at last broke the silence that had fallen over them both, his voice was husky with open desire. 'I know we can do something about those miles between us, Frankie...' he began.

It was a good job the waitress arrived with the food just then, because she could never had found a follow-up to a moment like that. Anything she could have blurted out would have got her into even deeper water just then.

Despite the antagonism he aroused in her his words had set her pulses racing, and she felt that if she dropped her guard for a minute she would find herself on a slippery path of no return. She was furious with herself, too, for the ease with which Tristan had tricked a response from her.

When he started to talk to her about her interests in music she answered only stiltedly, nerves prickly with tension for when he would inevitably make another remark like the last one. In order to turn the conversation away from herself she asked him what sort of government work he was involved in, expecting him to mutter something about the Diplomatic Service or something like that, and was surprised to see him open his eyes as if mystified by her question.

'I thought you knew my particular area,' he started off. 'English country landowner, I at first assumed, but—'

'Yes. There's that as well now...' A shadow darkened his features for a moment and he gave an almost imperceptible frown. 'As the eldest son, I naturally inherit the house and the estate. I'm expected to farm it.' He paused. 'If there was any justice, my younger brother would get it. He's the farmer in the family now, but he's already well established in Africa. Mother would be heart-broken if I refused to take it on, but...' he shrugged, 'who knows?' His expression was bleak for a moment. Then he continued. 'I'm a musicologist,' he told her, watching her expression. 'I've just spent a year as a guest of the Indonesian government, making a permanent taped record of island music. They were flattered when I asked permission to enter the country and came up with all kinds of help, including financial backing and the car and chauffeur you saw.' He laughed. 'I don't usually travel in such style!'

Frankie's eyes had widened at all this. Encouraged, he continued, 'The music varies considerably in style, instrumentation and so forth from island to island, which isn't surprising when you realise that the islands cover several thousand square miles of ocean and some are so isolated as to take several days to reach by boat.'

She couldn't disguise her interest. Damn the man—he actually seemed worth knowing! As a dancer she was interested in the ritual dances of other cultures.

'The reason I was so difficult to contact by the authorities after the accident was that I hadn't bothered too much about keeping in touch with the mainland, never dreaming that anything like this would happen—and I'm afraid I succumbed to the temptation to go native. There's something magnetic about the sheer timelessness of being in a place without cars, television, even radio in the sense we know it...'

'I see.' Frankie smiled thinly. Slowly she was beginning to build up a quite different picture of Tristan de Vere Manning, gentleman farmer... A faraway look had come into his eyes, and at the risk of learning things about him that would hurt, she probed a little further.

'The people,' she breathed, not daring to look at him in case he should read something in her eyes best hidden, 'what are they like?'

'Beautiful,' he replied at once, 'even to Western eyes. Though I'm not sure what they think about us.' He laughed aloud. 'What are you trying to discover, Frankie?'

She blushed.

He took her hand suddenly and without warning where it lay loosely on the table. 'On the one side you suggest I have a prurient interest in the female form—with a nasty puritanical embarrassment about physical things—and on the other you obviously suspect that I was over there living the life of Riley with a dozen native women to satisfy my every need. Which is it to be, then? Which are you going to believe is the real me?'

Frankie burned all over with confusion at having revealed so much of her inner thoughts. It seemed to confirm Tristan's earlier jibe that she was transparent. Vainly she tried to extricate her fingers from where they were interlaced so tantalisingly with his own, but all she succeeded in doing was to make him utter a throaty chuckle that brought the flush of anger to the very roots of her hair.

'Do you seriously think it matters to me one way or the other what you're like?' she defended herself. 'Just because I ask an innocent question about a country I've never been to, you twist it so that it seems as if I'm poking and prying into your private life. Believe me, it's of no interest to me whatsoever.'

His fingers registered a response to the vehemence of her words and she found it easy to slide her own shaking fingers from their prison beneath his.

She finished off the rest of her venison pie, allowing that it tasted like ashes in her mouth, but she noted with satisfaction that for once he looked as if her words had struck home. Gone was the habitual teasing glint in his eyes, and his words when he at last picked up the scattered strands of their conversation had lost that bantering edge that had so far kept her on her guard.

She refused a pudding, and when the waitress came with the bill and Tristan pulled out a bundle of credit cards, she said, in a low, determined tone, 'How much do I owe?'

He waved the question aside. 'This was my idea.' He was unsmiling.

Frankie didn't argue. She knew he could afford it more easily than she could, and she hadn't wanted his damned invitation anyway. She wondered how they had managed to get off the topic of Lady Manning's treatment so quickly when that had, apparently, been his main reason for wanting to have dinner with her. They had only skated over it, and now they were about to get up and leave, it looked as if the matter was closed. She would certainly not let herself be put in the position of repeating *this* experience.

Excusing herself for a moment, she went to the ladies' and surveyed her face, still flushed with annoyance, in the mirror over the washbasin. Her features, despite the unaccustomed heightening of colour, were rather drawn, and she was angry with herself for not being more firm and insisting on going straight home after practice to the hot bath and early night she had promised herself. So much for good resolutions! she chided herself bitterly. It was a poor start to the build-up to the audition next week. She deserved to flunk it if this was the best she could do.

When she came out Tristan was leaning nonchalantly against the bar, talking to the landlord. The other customers had already left, but Frankie noticed two full glasses in front of the men.

'What about a nightcap?' Tristan enquired as soon as she approached, but she demurred, saying something about its probably being after hours, but the landlord laughed and insisted on offering whatever she wanted. Feeling that she might as well join them, as she would have to wait for Tristan to finish his drink anyway, she sat down on one of the bar stools, resigned now to the disintegration of all her plans and good intentions.

Something of her impatience must have conveyed itself to Tristan, for he did not linger longer than was necessary and within twenty minutes they were standing in the porch, once again faced by the relentlessly falling sheets of rain.

'Wait here,' he ordered. 'I'll unlock the door first, then you can dash straight in.'

Without waiting for a reply he plunged off through the downpour, fumbled no longer than was necessary with the door lock and then, to her surprise, plunged back again to where she stood poised in the doorway. In a trice he had whipped off his jacket and draped it round her shoulders and, holding the umbrella over her, curtly ordered her to run back to the car.

By the time they were both sitting down with the doors closed and the rain pounding mercilessly on the thin fabric hood, his shirt was soaked through and Frankie, relatively dry, was protesting, too late, that he shouldn't have done that.

'I know,' he told her wryly, 'you're not frightened of a drop of rain.'

She rubbed the back of her hand over her wet cheek, and shuddered when she felt his hands come out in the dark to smooth her soaking hair back from her brow.

'Don't do that,' she managed to croak, already like a drowning woman in the overwhelming excitement his touch aroused.

But he did do it, gently touching her face with one finger, again and again smoothing out the tension, at first carefully, as if afraid of her reaction, then with more urgency, allowing his fingers to dictate their own message and exact a trembling response from her.

He caressed the taut skin over her cheekbones, sensitively seeking out the line of her jaw and the tenderness of her lips with his fingers, but though she tilted her head back, and felt her lips part in an ecstasy of yearning for the touch of his lips, he did not kiss her, instead he stroked and caressed her, taunting, teasing, deliberately withholding the contact she was in a fever to experience. With a last full-handed movement that brought her hair tumbling from its clip he let both his hands lose themselves in the rippling tresses before turning with a muffled groan to start the car.

As if in a dream Frankie felt the car pulling away, and saw the light above the inn sign go out at the same moment like some kind of portent. Then they were locked in the intimate dark of the rain-soaked night.

The sporty little car slithered through the driving curtain of water for a mile or two before it bumped over what seemed like the beginnings of a cart track and came to a sudden halt. Then what Frankie had begun to yearn for with every fibre happened, and she felt herself being held in the strong circle of Tristan's arms and, as his muscled body crushed against her own yielding one, his lips came down sweetly on to her own at last.

When he eventually released her she could feel his eyes boring into hers in the darkness, and as if to compensate for the loss of sight his lips began a thorough exploration of her face, touching her eyes, blazing a pathway of deli-

cious magic over her brow, trailing teasingly over her
cheekbones and along her jaw, until he reached her neck,
and then he went on, searching out the knowledge of her
body's secret places, so that she felt as if she was being
carried on a warm cloud.

He pushed aside her concealing jersey to reveal her bare
midriff and the neat, taut, unashamed beauty of her
breasts, and she moaned as his tongue licked them to
quivering peaks of ecstasy. Her body arched against him,
fighting the restrictions in the confined space of the little
sports car but stretching and expanding despite it to the
burning rhythm of his touch.

Even when she felt the belt on her jeans slither free and
the heat of his caresses extend to her belly, she let her body
open and raise itself to allow him to reach the secret fires
hidden there.

He was beginning to murmur her name over and over in
a hypnotic kind of way and she was being driven to the
height of wanting when something incongruous began to
bring her back to reality.

'Tristan,' she whispered, 'there's something outside!'

She stilled his head firmly between her two hands.

'Darling, don't stop me now . . .'

'Listen!' she hissed. Then her body froze. There was a
light flickering and swaying in the darkness and it was
coming towards them.

Frantically she tried to push him off, pulling up her jeans
at the same time.

The light—even he saw it now through his bleared
eyes—flashed harshly into the car, illuminating the disarray of limbs and loosened clothing in a brief glare of light.
A face appeared, blurred by rain and the condensation that
covered the windows of the car, and Frankie saw someone
tap rapidly on the glass.

Tristan pulled himself together sufficiently to wipe the glass clear with the back of his hand.

Frankie ran her fingers shakily through the tousled mop of her hair and tried to look as if they had merely been discussing the state of the economy, as a gruff voice from outside said, 'Sorry to disturb you, sir...'

Tristan wound down the window, as Frankie tried to stifle an hysterical giggle.

The man came straight to the point. 'The river's burst its banks further up. You'll have to get off this road as quick as you can. The police are coming along to put up flood barriers and divert traffic. Not...' he added as an afterthought, 'that we're expecting much in that way before tomorrow morning.' He coughed bronchitically. 'You'll have to take the Anderby road back to the by-pass. That'll be your safest bet.'

'All right. Thank you.' Tristan seemed incapable of saying anything else.

'Good night, sir. Good night, ma'am.'

The old man, sou'wester funnelling water down the back of the shiny black waterproofs he was wearing, touched his fingers to the peak before moving off into the night.

Tristan wound up the window and rapidly switched on the engine without looking at Frankie. She had cringed back in her seat when the man looked in through the window, and was now in a state of semi-shock.

What on *earth* had come over her? Had she gone completely mad? To behave like some cheap tart having quick sex in a stranger's car... for no matter how quickly their bodies had established an intimacy, they were in reality nothing more than strangers.

She began to tremble. She felt cold and sick. 'Thank God he came!'

She felt Tristan react and the engine stalled. He swore quietly and started it up again.

'What do you mean?' He was tight-lipped, staring straight ahead.

'I mean just that. I don't know what came over me. That venison pie was more potent than I guessed!' She tried to make a joke out of it, but her voice shook with emotion.

Surely he couldn't believe she made a habit of behaving like this? She phrased the question, with stiff lips. It sounded trite. It was a stock line, she realised, used a thousand times as an excuse to escape responsibility.

Tristan gave her a look which showed her plainly what he thought of such a cop-out. His words confirmed it. 'At least have the courage to be what you are,' he retorted harshly.

And what am I? Frankie thought miserably, too ashamed to frame the words. She turned accusingly on him, 'And what are you?' she demanded. 'Trapping me into coming out with you in the first place. Driving me out here, a virtual captive in your car. Then—then...' The words choked her throat.

'Then trying to give you what you've wanted since our paths first crossed?' he finished drily.

Tears of humiliation pricked behind her eyes. He seemed to know her better than she knew herself. Certainly she had needed little encouragement to unleash such a torrent of desire. She squirmed with humiliation.

'Take me home. I want to forget this night ever happened.'

She lapsed into a deep silence which he did not try to break, and after a few miles they began to see the lights of the main road ahead of them.

A couple of police cars, blue lights flashing a warning, were re-routing cars at the intersection. Tristan slowed to pass through the barrier, and when once more they were back on the main road into town Frankie breathed a sigh of relief. It was as if they managed to elude the clutches of some more than human predator of the emotions.

'Where to?' The curt voice reinforced her return to an everyday world.

She gave him directions, using no more words than were necessary. After her outburst the atmosphere had become frozen between them. The only sound was the monotonous regular swishing back and forth of the windscreen wipers above the whine of the speeding engine.

Tristan scarcely looked at her as he brought the car to a halt in front of her house. There was a light in Rani's attic room which he was quick to notice.

'Someone seems to be waiting up for you. It's a good thing we're not later than we already are.'

Frankie couldn't answer the sarcasm in his tones. Wretchedly she struggled with the catch of the door, and he had to reach across once more to open it for her. Their bodies touched, but it was like the inadvertent brushing together of strangers, as his eyes flickered over her without expression.

'Good night.' The words were uttered in a cold, flat tone that was entirely dismissive of her and everything she wanted to be. It made her bend her head, hiding behind the thick fall of rich brown hair, as she climbed out into the rain.

'Don't forget your bag.' Tristan reached into the back of the car and passed the bag out to her. As her fingers closed over to take it she felt him hold on to it for a fraction of a second, and his eyes were like two dark unforgiving slits as they met hers. She saw his lips open in a sneering smile.

'Pleasant dreams, sweetheart.'

Snatching the bag, Frankie muttered something indecipherable and went as hurriedly as she could, without actually running, towards the gate. Even before she had

managed to open it, the car was sliding away, the sheets of
rain closing behind it like the pages of a book.

Not caring now whether she got wet or not, she plod-
ded dully up the path, let herself in and threw her bag
down in a corner of the unlit hall with a spasm made of
rage and despair.

It was after twelve, and the house was shrouded in total
silence. Rani would be reading, perhaps. If she crept quietly up to her room, she could hug her shame to herself,
undisturbed till morning.

CHAPTER FIVE

THE NEXT few days sped by in an exhausting haze of preparation for the audition. Frankie had never worked so hard in her life, yet, paradoxically, she had never felt so physically fit. Her body began to attain a peak of physical conditioning that strengthened and suppled her muscles as never before. What was more, it became addictive, the early-morning work-out before anyone else arrived at the studios, and she could scarcely drag herself away at night; only the thought of an early start the next morning made her return home for the rest she needed in order to carry on with the same energy the next day.

Matty stayed behind one night to do the books in his little office below the stairs and came up as she was in the middle of her final workout for the day.

He didn't say anything, but he watched her thoughtfully for a few minutes as she put her body through its paces.

After she had changed into street clothes and was just about to go past his office on her way out, he called her in.

'You'll be here tomorrow, will you, Frankie?' he asked casually.

'Naturally—why?'

'Oh, nothing,' he gave her one of his quick smiles. 'I wasn't quite sure whether you'd be visiting Lady Manning in the morning.'

'Yes,' she shuddered inwardly. 'She's got over her cold now. I have to be back here for that lunchtime session, though. Then I've got the whole afternoon free for some serious work—unless you have anything for me?' she queried with a lift of her head. Sometimes she stood in for other teachers.

Matty shook his head. 'I'd like to see you go through the *Pierrot* sequence some time. Did you intend to work on it tomorrow?'

'I don't want it to get stale,' she hesitated, 'but if you want to see it...'

'Good, that's settled. About three, shall we say? Carry on as if I'm not there. I shall probably be wandering in and out with a few visitors. Oh, and Frankie, by the way—don't forget to eat plenty of protein!' He smiled and turned back to his ledger. 'Night, Matty!' she called, as she carried on up the stairs to the exit.

She took a bus home, had a quick shower and washed her hair and was eating the remains of a beef casserole someone had left for her in the oven when Davey came in.

'Hey, I haven't seen you all week, Frankie. How's it going?' He plumped down beside her, near the fire.

She looked up briefly. 'So-so. Three days to go.'

'Think you'll get it?'

'Might.'

'Hope so. All the lads in the Upper Sixth are rooting for you.'

'Davey! You haven't spread it around, have you?' Frankie was appalled.

'Why not?' he queried. 'You don't imagine I'm going to keep quiet about having a dancer for a sister, do you?'

'But what if they don't choose me? We'll both look so stupid!'

Davey shrugged. 'I haven't even considered that possibility.' He looked confident. 'Of course they'll choose you, Frankie. They know what they're doing, don't they?'

His faith in her was so touching she hugged him impulsively, crushing his gangling body to hers with a rush of affection. She realised she had been taking him very much for granted lately—what with the audition and…her eyes closed momentarily.

'Rani thinks you're a certainty as well,' he added, forestalling her rapid descent into the fruitless self-searching which her total commitment to work had been able to keep at bay.

'I'll have to get a place with them, then, won't I? I can't let so many people down all at once!'

Frankie got up to take her plate through into the kitchen. 'I'm having another early night, Davey,' she explained, and was already at the door when he gave a start.

'Oh, hang on a minute. I knew there was something… There was a phone call for you earlier.' He furrowed his brow. 'It was an odd name. I've written it on the pad. De—something or other.'

Frankie froze. 'De Vere Manning?'

'That's it!' Davey had moved over to the telephone pad. 'Is it work?'

She shot him a quizzical glance. 'What did he say?'

'He wouldn't leave a message. Just said to say he'd called.'

'Very helpful,' Frankie shrugged, trying to make light of it, trying to disown the sudden feeling that had swept over her as if to turn her limbs to jelly. 'I hope it doesn't mean Lady M. is cutting her session with me tomorrow morning,' she frowned.

'Oh, it's *that* job. I thought it was a new boyfriend,' Davey laughed.

'Goodnight, Davey,' Frankie said firmly.

She managed to wash her dishes and get up to her room without betraying any sign that his information had disturbed her, but once in the privacy of her room, she flung herself down on the bed and stared up at the ceiling with large unseeing eyes.

What was the meaning of his phone call? If it wasn't to cancel tomorrow's session, then why had he rung? On the other hand, if he had wanted to cancel it, he would have said so. That made it sound like a social call, but what could they possibly have to say to each other after that last stormy meeting? They had reached an impasse, and Frankie could see no way out.

She had tried to rationalise her feelings since that night, and had come to the conclusion that for some mysterious reason to do with body chemistry or something like that, Tristan had unwittingly triggered a physical response from her which was totally divorced from her true thoughts and wishes.

The situation would not have got out of control if he had not been the sort of man to regard her as fair game but his persuasive manner had been hard to resist after their conversation over a good meal and a drink. He had consciously exerted his charm on her—and she had succumbed!

She tried to make allowances—his wealthy background, his undoubted good looks, all of which encouraged him to think well of himself and to take for granted that he could have whatever he wanted merely by putting out a hand to take it—but she could not forgive the unfair advantage to which he had put these natural assets. She was employed by his mother, and in a caring, almost a nursing capacity—not as some good-time girl, put on the payroll for merely decorative and recreational purposes! She accepted part of the blame—appearing in the rather suggestive attire of the dance studio in what was, after all, a rather formal environment, the elegant eighteenth-century family country seat. The effect must have been incongruous to say the least. On the other hand, she had made her feelings perfectly plain, and Tristan had had no cause to talk to her—about wanting her and so on—in the way he had done. Or to look at her in the way he had done, right from the first.

She bristled. All right, she argued for the hundredth time, I should have been warned and, as a consequence, should have kept my distance. Instead of—even now the memory of it made her cheeks blaze—confirming his first impressions by practically throwing herself all over him without any sign of inhibition!

She quickly undressed and got into bed. She would be ice tomorrow. She would convince him that it had all been a ghastly mistake. As she drifted off to sleep, the only chink in her resolve was a little voice crying in the dark. It said she loved him, didn't she? Loved him...love, love.

It was as positive as it was unwelcome.

NEXT MORNING Lady Manning greeted Frankie with renewed enthusiasm.

'I *did* miss you so,' she told her. 'You inspire me to walk again, Frankie, and without your encouragement it would be so desperately easy to give in to pessimism once more.'

'Oh, but I hope you get plenty of encouragement from everyone else?' Frankie asked, opening her eyes wide in consternation.

'Naturally, my dear. Tristan is an absolute brick. But it's you who holds the key.' She gripped the side of the wheelchair as if in an effort to rise. 'Without your sixth sense I would exhaust myself, struggling to move these wretched limbs, but you seem to know exactly what to do with them.'

'It's just a question of knowing how the muscles interact,' Frankie replied modestly.

Lady Manning gave her a penetrating glance. 'Never undersell yourself, my dear. You have a rare talent, believe me. Now,' she said, raising her proud chin defiantly, 'I intend to stand up today. I spent the whole night dreaming about it, and it's high time I did it.'

Her courage and determination were so strong that she had almost managed to raise herself, but when she was nearing exhaustion and Frankie advised her to rest, her ambition was still unfulfilled.

'Tomorrow, perhaps?' Her eyes were bright with the unshed tears of her exertions.

'You *will* do it. It's just a question of when, now, isn't it?' Frankie reassured her. She wrapped the fluffy Stewart tartan rug around her patient's knees to make her comfortable before she left. 'Promise me you won't overdo it when I'm gone?' she asked her earnestly. 'We mustn't be impatient. It would be wrong to push too hard and undo all the progress we've achieved so far.'

Lady Manning promised to do as she was instructed.

'Good, then I'll see you at ten o'clock tomorrow morning.'

Frankie let herself out without seeing Tristan, and as she made her way to her car she wondered where he was. She fiddled around for a minute or two before driving off, but even when she lost sight of the big grey house around the bend in the drive, there had been no sign of him.

She heaved a somewhat gloomy sigh of relief and turned her thoughts to the day ahead.

THE MUSIC from the record player filled the echoing studio with the plaintive tones of the *Pierrot* piece.

Frankie's hesitation about dancing it today was due, as she had explained to Matty the previous night, to her fear that it would become stale, but there was another reason too, which she had not confided.

Now she gave herself up unrestrainedly to the lament it was—inhabiting the body of the poet-clown as if she knew no other, expressing in every tender movement of her body the yearning the character felt for his unattainable love, the moon.

All the techniques which the discipline of her training had brought within her grasp came to her aid as she strove to express the depth of his emotional longing. She knew that afterwards she would feel purged, as if, by some alchemy of artistic transformation, her own feelings of longing for what was out of reach would be brought to a point of rest. So involved was she, once the music caught hold of her, that she was quite oblivious to the fact that she was being observed. If, in the periphery of her awareness, she was conscious of a door opening and closing and opening and closing again, she put it down to Matty, who had warned her he would be in and out that afternoon.

As the last notes died, Frankie felt her feelings die too, and she afterwards lay for a long time stretched out on the floor, drained, lifeless, without feeling.

Then she did become aware of a presence, and her head turned as the door clicked. Looking up, she was surprised to see Matty with a small, neat, balding gentleman, who walked with a surprisingly light gait but who, from the look of his suit and polished hide briefcase, was the man who came to look over the books from time to time.

Frankie half rose, but Matty waved her to rest.

'Continue if you wish. Don't let us disturb you.' He turned to the man and something passed between them.

'We'll be back!' he called over to her and, together, he and the stranger went out again.

Her brief rest over anyhow, Frankie switched to an abrupt change of mood. She needed to dance wildly after the restrained lyricism of *Pierrot,* and her second audition piece was in perfect contrast to the first.

A brief showstopper, it was designed to show off her speed and sharpness of attack to best advantage, and when the music rang out her body seemed to become a Catherine wheel of sparkling trills and swoops and turns and leaps that aptly evoked the title—*Fireworks*—of the piece itself.

She danced with a sparkling sense of gusto and wit, and finished to the sound of spontaneous applause. Swivelling, she was just in time to see Matty shepherding the accountant outside again, and she grinned to herself. Audience reaction was what she yearned for, and even a single pair of hands was better than no hands at all!

Jauntily she made her way up to the café. She knew she was going to be nervous on the day, but her qualms were slowly being overtaken by an ever-growing self-confidence. Almost for the first time she felt herself convinced that soon, at long last, she would attain her rightful place among the ranks of the professionals of the dancing world.

HER BUOYANCY lasted all through the rest of the day and into the next morning. Rushing from an early workout to what Davey had called the Manning job, she couldn't help singing as she rattled along the country lanes to the Hall.

The rainy weather of the earlier part of the week had even given way to bright skies washed with summer blue and dotted with a few cottonwool clouds, and it was only when the grey house came into view that a slight tremor reminded her that sooner or later she would inevitably encounter Tristan de Vere Manning once more.

Brushing the thought aside, she sprinted up the steps and let herself in. Lady Manning greeted her at once.

'Today's the day, my dear,' she said confidently, pushing on ahead into the practice room.

'Well, we'll take it easy and see what happens,' Frankie demurred, she knew too much confidence might only mean that despair at failure would be all the greater. Her warning was well judged. Diligent and persevering as she was, Lady Manning's ability to stand even a moment unaided resolutely evaded her.

'I shan't give up!' she warned Frankie stoutly. 'Don't imagine I'm going to give up.'

'I'm sure there's no need even to think of it,' Frankie encouraged. 'You're on the verge of doing it. There's nothing wrong with your legs themselves now, it's a question of confidence more than anything.' She patted the tartan rug into place. 'Have a little rest and I'll see you for a few minutes more before I leave.'

Lady Manning folded her hands on her lap. 'You're a good girl, Frankie.' She closed her eyes, the purple shadows of recent illness deep in their hollows. 'I'll just sit by the window a while. This room reminds me of you and your teaching now. I find the atmosphere most encouraging.'

Frankie changed and went down to the kitchen. Cook had left some hot cheese scones for her and she helped herself from the coffee pot that stood warming on the Aga. The vast old kitchen was warm and peaceful, and the striped kitchen tabby came to wind itself around her ankles.

'Hello, old puss,' she murmured, picking up the purring bundle of fur. She was holding her in one hand and her coffee cup in the other when the door flew open, and with a shudder her gaze travelled to see Tristan there, a sardonic smile playing around his lips.

He looked abnormally dishevelled, his usually immaculate dark hair, which he wore rather long, tousled now as if he had been running his fingers through it once too often. The neck of his blue and white checked sports shirt was open and the sleeves of the navy blue cable-knit sweater he had on were rolled to the elbows. He wore green gumboots to give just a hint of the country landowner, but his deep, even tan was not the sort produced in the soggy wilds of the English countryside. It seemed incongruous in the cosy indoors atmosphere of the kitchen.

'Good—I thought you'd already left,' he said, omitting any preliminary greetings. 'Come upstairs.'

'I beg your pardon?' said Frankie faintly, scarcely recovering from the sudden shock of his unheralded appearance.

He smiled thinly. 'Didn't you get my message?'

'Message?' She raised her finely arched brows.

'I rang you the other evening.'

'Oh, that—yes, I got that. The fact that you rang.'

'Why didn't you ring me back to see what it was about?' he demanded.

'You didn't ask me to,' she responded, taking a sip of coffee.

'Oh, I have to give instructions, do I?' he replied grimly. 'Funny, I credited you with some initiative.'

Frankie stared at him. 'It never occurred to me to ring you,' she stated simply. 'Why should I?'

His only reply was to give her a searching look, but the perfunctory smile that accomplished it failed to reach his eyes. 'Come on up. Bring your coffee. I want a word.'

'Won't it do here?' She looked round the comfortable kitchen.

'My coffee's getting cold upstairs,' he explained impatiently. 'I only came down because I thought I heard you leaving. Come on, stop being awkward!'

Frankie bent to let the cat jump down and picked up the plate with her half-eaten scone on it, then, without a word, she warily followed him out. He paused for a moment to remove his gumboots, then he was leading the way up the wide, red-carpeted stairway.

She was very conscious of the self-confident figure striding athletically along just in front of her. Even in ordinary casual clothes he exuded a kind of powerful sexuality that was almost palpable. She felt as if her body had become spellbound by the man's mere presence. And he hadn't even touched her yet!

He led the way briskly into a small pleasantly furnished first floor room overlooking the yew gardens. It evidently did duty as his work room, for there was a large drawing board by the window, like one of those architects use that can have their angle of tilt adjusted, but when Frankie glanced at the sheets of paper clipped to it, she saw it was music manuscript, with notes partially filled in and a good deal of blank spaces as if he was in the middle of writing something down, and on a nearby shelf-system was a great mass of tapes, some cassettes and some old-fashioned reel-to-reel tape, and there were two solid-looking tape recorders and a light, shoulder-carried model that looked like the very latest in precision recording equipment.

She moved uneasily among the tools of his trade as if unwilling to be brought into such propinquity with the things used by someone with whom she could never hope to achieve that closeness she yearned for. She was also wary of what he might be about to say to her.

She waited with an air of nervousness that made her move about with unaccustomed awkwardness. She even knocked over a neatly stacked pile of magazines when Tristan abruptly motioned her to a chair.

'I'm sorry.' She made as if to pick them up, but he told her to leave them, in an offhand sort of voice that made her wonder what was coming next.

He came to sit opposite her in a canvas-backed director's chair that, deliberately or not, put him in a more dominant position, a good six inches above her, so that she had to lean back to look up at him, and the light from the window fell full on her face, revealing, she was sure, every nuance of her desire for him.

'Well?' he began, cocking his head questioningly to one side.

She blushed furiously. 'Well what?' she responded defensively.

'Well what?' He rose with the force of his exclamation. 'What do you mean "well what?"—how is she? When will she walk? What's more to the point—*will* she walk?' His face was thunderous.

Frankie almost yelped as he bent forward and gripped her fiercely by the shoulder. She wanted to swoon into his arms there and then but, remembering ice, she fought back the traitorous response of her limbs and regarded him stonily from beneath thick dark lashes.

'She will walk. And soon. That's a foregone conclusion, isn't it? What she needs at the moment is patient encouragement.'

Her blood was thundering in her temples. Was this coldly fierce man the one who had aroused her body to such extremes of sensuality only a few nights before? He was looking at her as if her body was completely unfamiliar to him, like a stranger, as impersonally as that. He had given a slight, deprecating lift to his shoulder as if whatever she could say now was beside the point.

'You may as well know, I'm getting a specialist up from London,' he told her bluntly.

She nodded. 'Good.'

'You don't mind?' His look was speculative.

'Of course not. Any help at all is for the best—just so long as he doesn't undermine her confidence.'

'You don't feel any professional jealousy?' he asked sardonically. 'After all, it might put your treatment in the shade if he gets some spectacular results.'

'I shall only feel delighted when your mother actually walks again, by whatever means,' she told him coldly. 'Surely you don't imagine I could feel otherwise?' She gave a hard laugh. 'I scarcely think feelings of petty competitiveness have a place in this sort of work, do you?' She gave him a level glance at which he had the grace to look momentarily abashed.

'Good.' He flexed his shoulders and went to stand over by the window.

'May I go now?' Frankie rose as calmly as she knew how. Just a few paces, and she could be outside the room and the danger would be over.

Tristan swivelled with a speed that caught her unawares.

'Just like that?' he murmured softly. In two strides he was towering over her, and she felt the warmth of his body against her own.

'No!' Her head jerked to evade his lips as they came down. She felt him reach for her around the waist, but with practised suppleness she twisted out of his grasp and in one movement was at the door.

'No!' she blurted again, feeling along the panelling for the knob. 'I'm not here for that! I don't want you!'

He hesitated for a moment and in the hiatus she had the door open and had slipped through it before he could stop her.

Every nerve was alive to the sound of pursuit, and at the top of the stairs she shot a darting glance back over her shoulder to see if he was coming.

'Wait, Frankie! Come back here!' he shouted.

Keeping her voice low, she said to him as he appeared in the doorway, 'I don't want to talk. That night in the car was just a terrible mistake. I've nothing more to say to you!'

He lunged at her as she spoke and, turning, she made a step towards the top of the stairs. But in the turmoil of her emotions she didn't notice that the fat tabby from downstairs had followed her and had been patiently sitting on the top step, waiting for her to come down again. With a cry she felt her feet twist from under her, and then she was falling, falling—bumping sickeningly on every step, too late remembering to coil herself to lessen the impact of each hard step as she smacked into them.

She came to a jolting stop half way down, all the breath knocked from her body.

Distantly, a cry had come from somewhere down in the entrance hall, and it had brought her head jerking up automatically.

Lady Manning, stricken-faced, was standing up in front of her wheelchair, both hands reaching out helplessly before her.

'Help her, someone! Help her!' Frankie heard her cry, then she saw as in a dream as Lady Manning seemed to make one tottering step forward before sinking slowly and clumsily back into the chair.

For a moment the two women had stared at each other, their roles abruptly reversed, then Frankie was desperately trying to struggle to her feet, aware only of a shooting pain in her right knee that sent her grappling for the banister rail with a sharp cry of agony.

Tristan was suddenly towering over her, his two strong arms lifting her tenderly like a broken doll. 'I'll take care,' he murmured. 'There may be broken bones.'

Frankie was hysterical. 'My leg! My leg!' she was shouting. 'I've broken my leg—I know I have! Oh, Tristan, be careful, I've broken my leg!' She thumped helplessly at Tristan's face as he bent over her, shrieking her pain with tears unrestrainedly cascading down her cheeks as, ignoring her as best he could, he carried her down the stairs.

Near the bottom step he staggered a little as she hit him hysterically in the mouth, and the softness of his lips on her bunched fist momentarily checked her wild flailing,

but before he had got her any further she was sobbing uncontrollably again, pounding at him to let her go in case he
did more damage.

'Shut up!' he ordered through clenched teeth as she
clung round his neck.

His voice was so curt that Frankie held in her fears and,
scarcely aware of the bruising over the rest of her body, she
slid out of his arms and gently lowered herself on to the
bottom step to run expert fingers over her right leg.

'It seems all right—oh, please God, please, let it be all
right—' She reached for his arm. 'Help me up.'

As if she was scarcely aware of the consternation her
momentary bout of hysteria had caused in Lady Manning, she leaned heavily on Tristan's arm and gingerly
tested her weight in the right leg. White-hot pain shot
through her body and she almost passed out with the unexpected shock. Tristan tightened his grasp.

'Easy, sweetheart, easy.'

'Take her into the drawing room, Tristan.' Lady Manning, invalid though she was, resumed her role as mistress
in charge. 'There's brandy in the cabinet.'

Frankie felt herself being lifted once more in Tristan's
strong capable arms and taken through into a part of the
house she had never seen before. Through the tangled
mane of her long brown hair she had only an indistinct
impression of a wide, cool, high-ceilinged room, with pale
green curtains framing a pair of french windows, and lav-
ish furniture ranged around the walls giving off the subdued lustre of years of french polishing.

Tristan placed her with unexpected gentleness amidst a
heap of soft cushions on a figured velvet chesterfield, then
turned to one of the cabinets which stood by the windows. She heard the clink of a glass and he was back in a
moment, forcing a heavy crystal brandy glass into her
hand.

'Here!' The glass was cold in her hand. 'It's shock more than anything. You'll probably find it's just a slight sprain,' he attested.

Frankie scrubbed the trailing strands of her hair out of her eyes and looked at him reproachfully. Tears welled up and trickled slowly down her pale cheeks.

'You don't understand,' she whispered, hysteria drained completely now. 'I can't put any weight on my leg—and I have an audition in two days' time...'

Her words trailed away again into a heartbroken sob. Tristan stroked her hand, but all she could do was close her eyes and cry like a little child.

'Poor girl,' Lady Manning came in soundlessly in the wheelchair, 'she's set such store by joining a professional company at last. It doesn't seem fair.'

Tristan went on stroking her hand. 'It might just be a sprain. I think she's suffering from shock, more than anything else.'

Frankie sipped the brandy without joining in their speculation. Despite herself sobs still shook at intervals all through her. She knew, she just knew, her knee was utterly jinxed. She had felt it go even as she fell, and it had taken her whole weight as she pitched down the stairs. Even if it had suffered only slight damage, there would not be time for it to regain its essential flexibility for the exacting turns she would have to put it through during the audition.

'It's all gone to waste,' she sobbed, 'I'll never get another chance.'

'Don't be silly,' Tristan chided her severely. 'Time enough to say that when the doctor gets here and gives an opinion. And it's not the end of the world—you can audition with other companies.'

She heard Lady Manning go out, saying something about some bone liniment, when she turned on him, her eyes blazing through the tears.

'I'll never get another chance to audition with this particular company again,' she shouted hoarsely, 'but how could you understand that! It was your stupid fault that this happened, lungeing at me like that, harassing me with your horrible sexual advances!'

She pushed his hand off hers.

'I hate you, Tristan. I wish I'd never met you!'

He stood up abruptly. 'It'd be just as fair to blame the cat,' he told her, tight-lipped. 'It was the cat you tripped over. Or,' he added harshly, 'take your own share of the blame!'

'Mine?' Frankie looked at him, astounded. 'So it was my own fault, was it, that you came chasing after me like a satyr?'

'Certainly!' he replied emphatically. 'If you hadn't run off none of this would have happened!' His eyes were gleaming dangerously and she looked at him in amazement.

'It's about time somebody made you listen,' he told her fiercely. 'Who do you think you're fooling with this prudish act, this pose of outraged virginity? You don't fool me! You know about your body's natural needs as well as anyone, so why don't you just accept your sexuality and enjoy it?'

'How dare you speak to me like that!' she almost screamed, trying to push him out of arm's reach, but he had her wrists in a vice-like grip that made a mockery of her puny attempts to get away from him.

'I hate you! You're a loathsome brute, a bully, and just because I can't get up and walk away you think it gives you the right to talk to me how you wish!'

'Believe me, Frankie,' his voice held a sudden savage note, 'this is *not* how I want to talk to you.'

He brought both of her wrists to his lips and touched them slowly and provokingly, allowing the tip of his tongue to flick over their backs, leaving a slow trail of kisses all the way round to the insides of her wrists where the pulses betrayed her by their erratic response.

'Let me go,' she whispered in a fever of helpless anger. She tried vainly to snatch away her hands.

'Don't hold out on me, Frankie. You know it's not going to do any good.' He dragged her close up against him so that his lips were on a level with her own. His eyes were bright with unconcealed desire, but the stark fear of what it would be like when he said goodbye, as he inevitably would, gave her the strength to resist.

'I'm not the type who goes in for one-off flings with any old passing stranger. Sorry to disappoint you,' she told him in clipped tones.

'Oh dear, what's this?' he laughed softly. 'A rather amateur attempt at emotional blackmail? I thought better of you, Frankie, I really did!'

Despite the bantering tone there was a steely glint in his eyes as he spoke, and she shivered unaccountably at what it meant.

'Think what you like about me,' she muttered, looking up with a quick sigh of relief as she heard Lady Manning's wheelchair out in the corridor.

Tristan reluctantly bit off what he was going to say and let her hands slide free from his grasp, so that by the time Lady Manning had pushed her chair back into the room, he was sitting nonchalantly beside Frankie on the chesterfield with a good two feet between them. Only the slight compression of his lips into a grim line of disapproval showed that anything at all disturbing had taken place between them.

Lady Manning handed the bottle of white liniment over to Frankie with a bright smile.

'I can see you're looking better already,' she beamed, 'and now perhaps you can both put out the banners for me!'

Frankie managed an answering smile. 'It was wonderful,' she replied with a warmth that was heartfelt. 'You said you'd stand today—and you did!' She shot a look at Tristan. 'Even you must admit, Tristan, that my therapy has its moments!'

CHAPTER SIX

WIT AND humour were the last qualities she would ascribe
to her present mood, Frankie told herself as, several hours
later, she lay with her leg propped up on a pile of cushions
in the little sitting-room at home, and the doctor's words,
intended to reassure her, plunged her into a paroxysm of
despair and grief.

She had set such store by the audition that to have the
chance of success whipped away from her in such a way
was unfair in the extreme. If she had faced the test and
failed she would have accepted it with a good grace and
simply redoubled her efforts. But not even to be given the
chance seemed to be a rotten trick for fate to play on her.

The next day or two saw a steady stream of visitors. She
could have got by on the wave of sympathy it unleashed if
it hadn't been for the fact that, paradoxical though it
seemed, Tristan's rather noticeable absence depressed her
spirits profoundly.

He hasn't even bothered to ring, she told herself savagely. And, of course, why should he? She had made it
clear what she thought of him and he, too clearly wanting
only a brief affair, could have no use for her while she was
laid up like a semi-invalid. She hated him with a ferocity
that was hard to conceal.

Matty, bless him, made a point of calling regularly each
day, and he was with her now, looking at her rather quizzically through the square-framed glasses he wore outside
the studio. His stylish silver-grey waterproof jacket was

flung over the back of a chair where he had dropped it as he came in.

They had known each other long enough not to stand on ceremony with each other, and he had even made it his first job to go straight through to the kitchen and fix them both a cup of coffee. He seemed quite at home now, with his blue shirt sleeves rolled to the elbows, his coffee on the floor beside him as he sat at Frankie's feet with her ankle resting across his knees while he gently massaged the muscles of her calf.

It might have seemed an intimate act to an outsider, but its intention was purely practical, and Frankie sighed as she felt the tension ease bit by bit and the vitality begin to flow back again into her poor leg. Her knee had swollen to twice its normal size, and any hope that she would be fit enough for the audition had quickly been scotched, but the swelling, and together with it, the constant pain, had begun to subside at last, and the burning question now was how soon would she be fit enough to dance again.

'I don't think you should consider doing anything much too soon,' he told her, fingers constantly busy at their work. 'I've managed to rearrange classes so that we can get on without you until the end of term. I don't want you doing any permanent damage to yourself.'

Frankie looked disgruntled, but what Matty was doing to her leg was so nice she turned what had started out as a sigh into a gasp of pleasure. 'Yes, just there! That's great ... You are clever, Matty, how do you *know?*'

'I'm an artist of touch,' he grinned, 'at least that's what I've been told ...' Then he sighed. 'Long ago ...'

'Poor old man,' she mocked, stroking his prickly crew-cut with its little points of grey peppered all over it.

He grinned wolfishly. 'Apart from all that I like doing it I'm interested in bodies,' he added drily.

At that moment Frankie nearly jumped out of her skin as without any warning at all the sitting-room door flew open and Tristan stood there, a savage smile on his face. The ferocity of his appearance, coupled with its almost cataclysmic suddenness, made Matty start back with a surprised gasp.

'Still the invalid, then?' drawled Tristan, sweeping into the room and almost trampling poor Matty in the process. He glowered down at Frankie so that she felt herself straighten up as best she could in such a position.

'As you see,' she replied with an accomplished coolness that surprised even herself.

'I'm sorry I didn't warn you I was coming. I didn't want to ring as I could imagine you stumbling to the phone and doing more damage in the process,' he almost snarled. 'But I should have realised, however, you'd be in good hands.'

'Yes,' she agreed pleasantly. 'Let me introduce you.'

Matty had gone back to kneading her calf like the professional he was, but when Frankie said, 'Meet Tristan de Vere Manning, Matty,' he stuck out a hand.

'And,' she went on, turning coldly to the man towering above her, 'this is Matthew Hansard.'

'I know—director of the dance centre,' butted in Tristan, ignoring the proffered hand. 'Your other employer,' he added meaningfully, swinging round to stare down at Frankie with a strange look in his eyes.

She couldn't exclaim that she didn't know what he meant, his meaning was palpably clear. She felt Matty's touch slacken.

'Well, Frankie, I suppose I'd better be getting back...' he began, but Frankie involuntarily caught hold of him by the arm.

'Please don't go just yet, Matty, I wanted to talk to you about—' She searched her mind, but Tristan, looking down at her, successfully deprived her of all ideas.

'—about things,' she finished lamely.

Matty stood uncertainly between them both, but seeing the stricken look in her wide grey eyes he sat himself down again and Frankie had the satisfaction of seeing Tristan's expression turn to a look of unmistakable chagrin.

She knew how it must have looked to him, but it was his own fault for barging in. Didn't the man have even the elements of good manners? Did he always go about bursting into private houses as if he owned them?

She gave him a cold glance. 'I'm sure that whatever Tristan has to say won't take long,' she said pointedly. 'Well?' Her clear grey eyes swept over him as if he had been of no more consequence than one of the chairs on the other side of the room.

Tristan's eyes glinted and, despite herself, Frankie felt a fluttering in her stomach as she saw his lips draw back in a brief smile that was designed to charm the birds off the trees.

All except *this* bird, she told herself, gripping the edge of the rug which lay loosely across her knees.

Matty felt her body tense and held her calf for a moment without moving. She felt his eyes on her. He guessed that something was up and was unsure whether she really wanted him to stay after all.

Oh, please stay, Matty, she whispered to herself, willing him to get the message. The thought of being trapped here alone with Tristan, especially in his present mood, was a thought too frightening to contemplate.

Tristan had lowered himself down on to the sofa beside her with a deliberation that suggested he had all the time in the world at his disposal. He was smiling genially now at her and Matty, as if they were both old friends.

'Well, how is she then, Matty?' he asked familiarly. 'She seems quite lively.'

'Yes, she's lively enough,' Matty agreed wickedly. He started to work on her foot.

Frankie tried to catch his eye, but he kept his head bent as if concentrating on what he was doing. The pig, she thought, surely he's not going to let Tristan get away with this?

'How long do you think she's going to be here in this state?' Tristan went on, conversationally.

'A week, maybe. But we're going to have our time cut out keeping her off her feet after another day or two. She'll start trying to walk again before she should and she'll finish up doing more harm than good,' Matty replied, separating her toes and working on each one individually with his firm sensitive fingers.

'She'll need watching then—closely, would you say?' Tristan rejoined.

'Absolutely. She's—'

'Hey, cut that out!' Frankie broke in. 'I'm not deaf and dumb—merely crippled. You don't have to talk about me as if I can't hear you!' She glared at Matty. The disloyalty of the man made her gasp. It was always the same with men—get two of them in one room and it was 'all boys together'!

Tristan looked down at her. He was sitting unreasonably close, almost squashing her against the head of the sofa so that she could actually feel the warmth of his body running down the length of her own and there was nowhere she could move out of his way.

He seemed to grin at her, delighting in her obvious discomfort and the fact that he had her trapped.

'She's very headstrong—were you going to say?' he murmured directing his question at Matty but letting his glance linger over Frankie so that she had to turn her head and gaze stonily out of the window to avoid the laser-like beam of his eyes.

'Very definitely,' Matty agreed. 'It's a good quality in a performing artist, mind you.'

'Thank you,' Frankie interrupted with an icy glance in his direction. She would have this out with Matty as soon as they were alone. Now she had to be content with the signs of body language to get her displeasure across.

Matty got the message loud and clear. But to her consternation she felt him draw his hand down her foot in a gesture that meant the massage was complete and then she watched with horror as he rose elegantly to his feet.

'I have a dance centre to run—' he began.

But Frankie cut in, not attempting to hide the urgency in her voice. 'Don't go, Matty, please!' she cried out, almost starting out of her seat. Her tone made Matty swing back, nonplussed, to look down at her for a moment. The look he gave her seemed to say that he realised she wasn't joking after all, but his gaze took in also the grinning man by her side. She could see his inner conflict as he tried to understand the situation. Then the businessman took over and he looked at his watch. 'Well—' he hesitated.

'I'm free for the rest of the morning. So don't worry— she won't be left alone. I'll see that she behaves.' Tristan correctly interpreted Matty's hesitation.

Matty gave Frankie a look that plainly asked if this was what she wanted, and Frankie gazed back at him with a stricken face.

'Please, Matty, don't go just yet,' she whispered.

'No, stay for another couple of minutes or so,' Tristan encouraged. 'I want to ask you one or two things about her.'

He settled back even more comfortably, now totally in charge of the situation, and Frankie squirmed with rage.

The man was totally insensitive! Couldn't he tell he wasn't wanted?

Matty perched elegantly on the edge of the armchair opposite. 'Ten minutes I can spare, certainly, then I must get back.'

'How do you fix lunch for yourself?' Tristan turned to her.

'Rani's coming back,' she told him triumphantly. He wouldn't be able to get rid of Rani so easily.

He lowered his glance as if considering this next obstacle. Heavens, she thought, is the man intending to inflict himself on me for the whole day? Hasn't he anything better to do?

He was already turning back to Matty. 'How soon do you think she'll be able to travel?' he asked unexpectedly.

'Travel? *I'm* not going anywhere!' Frankie squeaked.

Matty was looking thoughtful. 'By what means?' he asked cautiously. 'Air, land or sea?'

'Mainly air.'

Frankie gave a gasp. 'I'm not being wheeled on and off planes!' she exploded. 'Just what is all this?'

She might as well not have bothered to utter a word for Tristan totally ignored her. 'I was thinking perhaps in a couple of weeks' time,' he went on, looking at Matty with his lazy smile. 'Mother's keen to continue with her,' he paused to allow the merest hint of irony into his voice—'with her therapy—though,' he laughed, 'I hope it won't include the treatment given in the last session, effective though it was.'

Matty knew what he meant. Both men laughed. Frankie merely fumed, glowering at Matty with all the venom she could muster. What a stab in the back this was, and no mistake!

'She's able to get up on her feet quite easily now,' he informed Frankie pleasantly as if the convulsive clutching at the edge of the rug had nothing whatsoever to do with him. 'She'll be ready to take a few steps by the end of the week.'

'I hope your specialist from London will be duly impressed!' she couldn't help spitting out.

But Tristan had already turned back to Matty. 'As I was saying, Mother is keen to continue, but when I came back I'd already made up my mind to take her back with me for a few weeks in the sun. A change of scene will do her the world of good. Although she manages to put a brave face on it she's taken the shock of Father's death badly—as, of course, one would expect. They were very close.' He addressed this last remark to Frankie as if it was something she might have wished to question. 'It means,' he continued without giving either of them a chance to interrupt, 'that Frankie will have to come too...'

'It means nothing of the sort!' Frankie exclaimed weakly.

'...as it would be foolish to stop treatment which is so obviously efficacious, as I'm sure you'll agree,' he smiled blandly down at her. 'I'm assuming,' he turned to Matty, 'that she'll be no use to you for the next few weeks?'

Matty, traitorously, nodded, and Frankie was appalled to see her last hope of any help from him fast disappear in the encouraging smile he gave her.

'I think a few weeks in the sun would be just the ticket,' he observed jauntily.

'But what about work?' wailed Frankie, already feeling that her own wishes were the very least of anyone's concern. 'I need to audition—I need to get back into form again. I won't get work if I'm not *here!*'

If she could have stood up and knocked their two heads together she would have. Instead she had to be content merely with bunching her fists and giving them equal looks of reproach and disgust.

'She's very excitable this morning,' remarked Tristan in a deliberately provoking tone.

Frankie smiled sweetly. 'Anyone would be excitable,' she told him acerbically, 'to find that they were being packed off to God knows what package sunshine holiday resort against their will. Perverse though it may seem, I'm not into surf, sea and...' She bit her tongue.

'Sex?' he raised an eyebrow.

'...and all that,' she corrected with asperity. 'There are far more interesting and worthwhile things on offer. Dancing with a professional company is one of them as far as I'm concerned—in case you didn't know.' She paused for breath.

'But you're obviously going to make a poor showing at any audition in the state you'll be in over the next few weeks,' he broke in with cruel accuracy. He turned to Matty for support.

'Matty! You're on my side, aren't you?' she couldn't help blurting.

The time for diplomacy had passed. This was open warfare and it was time the fact was acknowledged!

Matty, on the horns of a dilemma if ever a man was, stood up, a small frown creasing his brow. He shot a look in her direction that was nothing if not the look of a hounded man. 'I'm sorry, Frankie. I'd like to be able to say what you want me to say, but I really do think that in the circumstances you'd be a fool not to take the chance of a short break, if it's a serious offer?' He gave a brief questioning look at Tristan.

'It's a serious offer all right. She'll be paid, and well, for her services. All she'll have to do is continue to inspire Mother the way she seems to have done over the last few weeks. She'll be a sort of companion to her, that's all. I have business to complete out there and would rather Mother was with someone she knows and trusts while I'm absent than with a bunch of complete strangers. Of course, the housekeeper could come along—she's an old and trusted friend, but she's getting on in years and it would be obviously more sense to have someone younger and more active along.'

And more amenable to your attentions—you hope! Frankie added bitterly, but in silence.

Now she saw it all. Beneath the bantering tone of the conversation, she saw the full sickening truth of it. He'd said he was going to have her and, miles from home, he imagined she was going to fall into his bed without a struggle—employed by his mother during the day as nurse-companion, employed by the son at night as—she grasped the edge of the rug till her knuckles showed white.

'I am not going,' she stated in a flat voice drained of emotion. 'You two can stand there discussing it for the rest of the day. I don't care. I am not going anywhere, and that's that.'

Pointedly she picked up a magazine from the table beside the sofa. The words danced meaninglessly before her eyes, but she didn't care. It shut out the two men and she would go on shutting Tristan de Vere Manning out for as long as she had the strength to resist. She saw a muscular brown hand come down to grasp the edge of the paper and instinctively she tugged back. There was a tearing sound and the page ripped in two.

'Damn you! Will you go away!' she almost shouted. 'Leave me alone! Can't you tell when you're not wanted?'

'She's bound to be a little upset,' Matty had the nerve to say, and while she struggled for the words which would adequately express her effrontery at his bare-faced betrayal, she heard Tristan smilingly excuse himself.

'Now that's settled I may as well go,' he was saying. 'Can I give you a lift anywhere?' he turned to Matty.

Frankie watched woodenly as Matty shook his head.

'My motor's outside,' he explained. 'It's been good meeting you at last. I'd heard a lot about you,' she heard him saying affably. 'We'll no doubt meet again before very long.'

Tristan smiled cheerfully at Frankie.

'Ciao, sweetheart!' he called. Then he was gone.

Frankie screamed once, a long pent-up fury finding momentary release as the front door closed behind him.

'As for you, Matthew Hansard—I'd never have believed it if I hadn't seen it with my own eyes! At first I thought you hadn't understood how utterly repelled by him I am. Then you allowed him to turn the tables—no, not allowed—actively egged him on! Saying I needed a holiday! How dare you! And I always thought you were my friend! How wrong can you be? Why couldn't you have pretended to be my lover or something? That would have taken the wind out of his sails. The conceited oaf! I don't know who I hate the most at this minute! Betrayed by one I trusted! You're unspeakable! And as for him—I think—'

'Listen, before you really do fly through the roof, I want to say one thing—'

'Ha! Think you can talk your way out of this one? No way!' She folded her hands grimly in her lap.

'Frankie, first thing—much as I care for you—lovers? As you say, no way. He's not a fool. You've got a perceptive and intelligent man there—even if he seems to take a delight in rubbing you up the wrong way. Second, you could do much worse than go off for a few weeks at this time of the year. Auditions don't get under way until the schools break up for the summer. If you come back with a nice tan, plus a mended knee, you're going to be a knockout, and I mean that. Besides, I don't think you're going to have to face a round of auditions.' He looked out of the window, avoiding her glance.

Frankie couldn't tell what he was thinking because the actor in him could school any emotion from his face. 'Don't soft-soap me!' she said sharply, watching to see how he reacted.

He merely smiled enigmatically and went over to the door. 'You should be feeling pretty pleased with yourself,' he told her. 'A free holiday somewhere exotic and a man like that after you! You've got it made, baby!' His American accent was convincing and made him seem like some wheeling-dealing impresario.

'Anybody would think you were going to get a cut of the action!' she fumed.

'I should be so lucky!' he gave a little back kick, slung his jacket over his shoulder and strolled out of the room.

'I hate you, Matthew Hansard!' she shrieked helplessly as she heard the front door open.

'See you soon!' he called out. Then the door slammed and she twisted in a fury to watch him stepping jauntily down the garden path towards his car.

WHEN RANI came in with some lunch, Frankie told her all about her morning and was satisfied that at least Rani sympathised.

'He's so pigheaded, it just doesn't get through to him that I don't want him,' she fumed.

'It sounds as if he's used to having things swing his way all right,' observed Rani.

'Well, he'll have to get unused to it,' rejoined Frankie vehemently.

'You could go on this working holiday,' her friend suggested, 'but make sure your bedroom door is always locked! Why shouldn't you go and help the old lady and get yourself a glamorous tan for your pains? I think it's the least you deserve for the time and attention you've devoted to her. And why should she be deprived of your help just because of her sex maniac of a son?' As usual Rani took a pragmatic view of the situation. 'Your judgment is a bit clouded by emotion at the moment,' she pointed out. 'I'm sure it wouldn't be beyond you to convince him that he leaves you cold. Then you can all settle back to enjoying yourselves.'

'If only it were true!' Frankie admitted mournfully. 'If only he did leave me cold!'

'Better still then!' exclaimed Rani, grinning mischievously. 'Why not go out there and just have a good time!'

'I couldn't bear it—knowing that I was just a lay for him.' Frankie's heart-shaped face was pale and a slow tear trickled down her cheek when Rani went out into the kitchen. She wasn't a prude, but she did draw the line at lovemaking without love. It just wasn't for her.

Shortly after her mother had died she had a brief affair with a young schoolteacher. Its ending had coincided with the ending of the period of mourning and she realised that what had seemed like love had only been an emotional reaction to her mother's death. The young man had been upset, but she couldn't pretend she cared when she didn't. It had been more honest to end it than carry on out of a sort of habit. Since then there had been no one else and she had devoted all her time to Davey and to dancing.

No one had had the effect on her that Tristan did. It was one of life's ironies that after so long a time the man she fell for should be socially out of reach—as well as being a self-confessed philanderer. That made him doubly offside.

She dabbed at her face. Why did life have to be so complicated? Why did she have to become all emotional about a swine like him? Perhaps she was run-down. Maybe she should have taken more notice when Matty had said 'eat more protein'.

She sighed and ran a finger thoughtfully round the pattern on the rug. She could do with some sun. And it wasn't every day someone came along with the offer of a free holiday.

She was in this indecisive frame of mind now that her anger had somewhat abated when the telephone rang.

Rani hurried through to answer it. 'For you!' She uncoiled the flex and brought the phone over. It was Lady Manning.

She came straight to the point. 'Tristan tells me that he broached the idea of your coming away with us for two or three weeks when he goes back to Indonesia,' she began. 'I'm so pleased about it. It means we won't have to interrupt the therapy, and I do feel that a change of scene is just what I need at the moment. Tristan tells me that luckily he met your boss and managed to square things with him too—'

'He's very good at squaring people,' Frankie interrupted before she could stop herself. Squaring them and putting them into little boxes where he could use them when and how he wished, she thought tartly. Well, not me, buster, not me! 'I'm awfully sorry, Lady Manning,' she began, 'I think Tristan misunderstood. I told him I couldn't leave for three weeks at this time. He doesn't seem to realise I have a career to plan.'

'Oh dear! I gathered from what he said that Mr Hansard was agreeable. Indeed, I rather gathered that he had actually encouraged you to have a break.'

'Mr Hansard must have misunderstood my wishes too,' Frankie replied gloomily, wishing the disappointment in Lady Manning's voice wasn't so apparent. She heard a pause at the other end of the line.

'I do seem to have got hold of the wrong story rather, don't I?' she heard Lady Manning say quietly. 'Of course I would never have let Tristan approach you if I'd realised it was going to cause any embarrassment. I *am* sorry, my dear. I'd allowed myself to begin rather to look forward to it. All those strangers—' she broke off.

Frankie felt about two inches high. 'I'm sorry,' she almost whispered. She gripped the phone tightly in her hand. Then she surprised herself, for she heard herself saying, 'It came as a shock—maybe I was rather rash to say no out of hand like that. Maybe I could have a chance to think it over for a day or two?'

She regretted her words as soon as they were out. What possible excuse could she have for raising Lady Manning's hopes like this? It was totally irresponsible.

Lady Manning had already brightened. 'Frankie, that would be wonderful. Tristan does rather pressure people once he gets an idea. You're right not to give in to him straight away. Oh, I do hope you'll think about it *very* carefully.'

When she replaced the receiver, Frankie smiled grimly to herself. She would think about it carefully, all right. She would think about it so much she would be obsessed by it. But what possible conclusion could she come to? She could just see a locked bedroom door putting Tristan de Vere Manning off. It would need a moated castle and an army of armour-clad infantry to do that.

Hell, hell, hell, she thought, and all I really want to do is dance.

Rani left the phone on the floor next to the invalid before she went back to her classes.

'At least you won't trip over the flex, will you, or are you going to start hobbling about the minute my back is turned?' she demanded.

'Oh, stop mother-henning over me, will you?' snapped Frankie, sorry almost at once for being so tetchy. She gave a lugubrious smile. 'I'm going to practise the can-can the minute you're out of the way. I thought you knew that.'

'O.K. Just don't smash the furniture. See you later!'

Unperturbed, Rani let herself out and Frankie settled back to an undisturbed afternoon of reading. But the phone went almost as soon as she picked up her book.

'Yes?' she was short.

'Still fuming?' came a husky voice with a note of amusement in it.

'Oh, it's you!' She didn't disguise her disapproval.

'Yes, it's me, sweetheart. I'm just ringing to see if I can hurry you into making a decision. Mother says you want a couple of days in which to think about it.'

'She also says I'm right not to give in to you,' she responded tartly.

'If my memory is correct—which it usually is—' she could hear the grin in his voice '—what she actually said was, "You're right not to give in to him *straight away*".'

'You're incorrigible! You mean you were actually listening in to a private conversation?'

'Mother knew I was on the extension. She wanted to hand you over to me straight away to discuss the practical details like jabs and passports.'

'That will hardly be necessary. I wasn't aware that travellers to London crossed any national frontiers, and I certainly don't intend to go any further than that in the near future.'

'She's going to be desperately disappointed,' he told her, his voice quite serious now. 'Do think again, Frankie. I wouldn't have asked you if I hadn't thought it important.'

'This is emotional blackmail!' she snarled, suddenly trapped now, feeling the gates of the cage clanging shut around her.

'You shouldn't have tried to get such spectacular results if you didn't want to be bothered to take responsibility for what you've done.' His words made him sound smug, but she couldn't fail to detect the sincerity of his observation at that point.

Even after a curt goodbye and the reiteration that she would think things over, she replaced the receiver in the knowledge that her answer would be, had inevitably to be, yes.

She cursed herself for a fool even—as she put it to Rani later that day—even as she placed her head in the noose. But what else could she do? There was no blocking her ears to the sound of disappointment in Lady Manning's voice when she feared she was going to decline the invitation, and what sort of a person could walk out on someone in need?

Only a third-rate louse, she thought, as she recalled an earlier conversation when she and Rani had been discussing the sacrifices made for ambition's sake.

All it meant for her career was that she would work extra hard as soon as she was fit enough and that anything that could be helpful she would seize with both hands.

Matty wants me bronzed and beautiful at auditions, and so I shall be, she resolved pugnaciously.

SHE WAS back on her feet as soon as Matty had predicted, and the days before their departure passed with miraculous speed.

To her consternation Tristan insisted on giving her a cheque in advance so that she could buy herself some suitable clothes and she smiled maliciously, as, despite her protestations, he forced her to accept it. But she gasped when she saw the amount. 'Aren't you afraid I'll do a bunk?' she asked him.

He smiled slyly. 'Try it, sweetheart, just try it. You don't imagine a day would pass before I was in hot pursuit, do you?'

She shuddered. Despite his bantering she was always aware of the steel inside the velvet glove. Nevertheless she drew the line at having him actually come with her to choose something. 'I'd rather have Matty choose my clothes than you, thanks very much.'

'Yes, I'm sure he'll make a better job of it too,' he conceded. Then his eyes glinted. 'I nearly fell for your little trick that day I came round to see you after your accident,' he told her.

'What trick?' she demanded.

'That ploy of trying to make me think Matty was a lover of yours. I was fooled at first, seeing him handling your foot like that.'

'So, you were fooled. What makes you think you're not fooled by thinking he's *not* my lover?'

'Matty?' His eyebrows shot up in such a way that there was no need for words. 'Let him persuade you to get something beautiful,' he continued. 'And Frankie, bring that little pink bit of nonsense too, there's an angel!'

She wanted to bring her hand up and slap that insufferable grin off his face, but instead she merely turned with an icy scowl, swinging her long hair deliberately in his face. 'And you!' she retorted rudely before stalking off.

Rani was right—it would be locked doors all the way!

CHAPTER SEVEN

LADY MANNING had fallen asleep as soon as the plane took off on the last leg of their journey.

Almost as if he had been waiting for it Tristan leaned over and took one of Frankie's hands in his own. She tried to get it free without any of the other passengers noticing, but he only increased the pressure.

'I can't wait until we touch down,' he murmured suggestively in her ear.

'Well, you'll just have to, won't you?' she replied sweetly, 'like everyone else... I suppose you're keen to get back to your work,' she went on blandly, ignoring the overt invitation in his tone of voice.

'Oh, very,' he averred with a serious expression. 'Back to my jungle love paradise.'

He stroked her hand and, tired from the long journey, Frankie found she had to struggle not to let her lids close drowsily over her eyes.

'Put your head on my shoulder,' he suggested, moving so that she could do so.

'I'm not tired,' she protested.

She came round abruptly when she felt a light kiss on her forehead, and she snapped open her eyes to find herself looking straight up into Tristan's hateful, laughing brown ones.

'Don't do that when I'm asleep!' she ground out, blushing to the roots of her hair and looking round to see if any of the other passengers had noticed. Lady Manning, fortunately, was still sleeping peacefully.

'Why not?' he asked teasingly. 'Are you worried you'll miss all the fun?' His eyes glinted with amusement as Frankie lifted her head sharply from where it had been pillowed on his shoulder.

What on earth had possessed her to go off to sleep on his shoulder like that? There was no wonder he had got the wrong idea! He would get a rude awakening once they landed.

'It's not fun for me—it's harassment of the worst sort,' she told him primly.

Tristan replaced her hand inside his own when she withdrew it and, turning to her for once with a serious expression, he said, 'Frankie, if I really believed you meant that I would be the last person to take advantage of you, believe me. I despise the pathetic sort of male who takes advantage of a woman just because he happens to be in a position of authority over her. I find that sort of thing utterly abhorrent. I thought you knew me better than that. But,' and his eyes told her that he was entirely serious, 'the language of our bodies tells me otherwise. Do you expect me to pretend there's no attraction between us? Why are you afraid of it?'

She lowered her eyelashes so that they fanned out on her cheeks. 'Who said I was afraid?' she answered stiffly. 'I just don't see any future in it, that's all.'

He looked at her thoughtfully. 'You mean you know marriage isn't on the cards, is that it?'

She shot him a baleful glance. 'It's not marriage I want,' she laughed, 'that's the last thing I want, thanks!'

'Yet you don't seem to want an affair either,' he pursued.

She rubbed a hand confusedly over her face. 'Oh, why don't you just leave me alone?' she almost snarled.

'If I could understand perhaps I would. It's just that you don't seem to know what you do want, yet you ignore the blatant demands of your body—'

'You talk as if I'm two separate entities!' she interrupted with a toss of her head.

'There seems to be a split,' he reminded her, 'that's presumably why you're so confused. Oh, Frankie, why not just listen to the promptings of your inner self and forget all the judgments and the calculations, the pros and cons? There are always arguments against enjoying ourselves— it's our puritan heritage. Give pleasure a chance for once. Say yes to the sheer joy of finding someone who wants you, body and soul.'

She was trembling now, feeling the tremors rise up her body in wave after wave. 'I can't,' she told him in a croak. 'Please leave me alone, Tristan. You yourself have said there's no future in it, so let's leave it at that.'

'I can't marry you, if that's what you mean. I'm not the marrying type,' he answered shortly. 'And anyway, nobody uses emotional blackmail on me.'

'No, of course not,' she replied through clenched teeth. 'You're too adept at using it yourself to become a victim of it.'

'And what's that supposed to mean?'

'Ha!' she gave a hard, derisory laugh. 'You know as well as I do. You've really had your own way for far too long, Tristan. This latest bit of gentle persuasion,' she went on sarcastically, 'has only come about because you realise that for once you're not going to get your own way. Tough on you!'

This time she withdrew her hand firmly from his and reached for a magazine. 'Now if you don't mind...' She gave a quick glance from beneath her lashes, surprised to find him silent for once. His hateful brown eyes were on her like two bright beams.

'So that's the state of play, is it?' His own laugh matched her own in hardness while his eyes mentally undressed her. 'Well, all I can say is, it's going to be a lonely three weeks for you, sweetheart. Still, that's your choice.' He himself picked up a paper. 'Don't worry,' he murmured as a stewardess walked by, 'only another three quarters of an hour before we land, then as far as I'm concerned, you're on your own.'

IT WASN'T long before the first signs that they were nearing their destination began to appear. First Frankie glimpsed some of the thousand islands, rich green against the deep blue of the sea, that jewelled the coast of the main island of Java, and then the orange-tiled roofs of Djakarta itself came into view, a city smaller than she had expected, surrounded by lush green fields and woodland, and the glistening rice paddies. Java, she knew, was the most heavily populated of Indonesia's more than thirteen thousand islands, as well as being one of the biggest, and, no sign of conversation being forthcoming from Tristan, she chatted exclusively to Lady Manning as they recalled snatches of information they had culled from the guide books Tristan had thrust into their hands at the airport.

He was so obviously in love with the country that Frankie was not surprised now when he was forced to overcome some of his self-restraint in order to point out some of the sights visible from the air, to his mother.

Somehow or other he managed to make Frankie feel like an eavesdropper. But Lady Manning, whether she was aware of it or not, brought her into the conversation at every opportunity. It allowed the coldness between Frankie and Tristan to go apparently without notice.

'It would be a lifetime's work, documenting the musical heritage of such a vast region,' remarked Lady Manning. 'Do you intend that, Tristan?'

He gave a small noncommittal shrug. 'There are worse things to devote oneself to, don't you think?'

'Two hundred acres in Yorkshire being one of them, no doubt,' she retorted with uncharacteristic bluntness.

Frankie turned back to the guide book. For an instant she had felt she was witness to some family bone of contention, but the moment passed before she was allowed to consider what it meant.

'It says here,' she read from the guide book, 'that the islands stretch some two thousand five hundred miles from Sumatra to West Irian, uniting the Indian and Pacific Oceans and Australia with South-East Asia.'

Frankie was awestruck, and looked wide-eyed at her two companions.

'Don't worry, my dear. I'm sure he won't try to drag us over the whole two thousand five hundred in the three weeks we have at our disposal, will you, Tristan?' Lady Manning laughed. 'I think Djakarta and a week or so in Bali will be quite enough, and that other place where you said we'd be staying, but I'm blessed if I can ever remember the name of it.'

'Pelabutan Ratu,' Tristan replied promptly. 'It's four hours' drive from Djakarta, out on the south coast. There's a decent toll road all the way. The Institute are sending a car for us after breakfast tomorrow, but we'll stay overnight in the capital. I won't tell you it's beautiful because it's not,' he added, still avoiding Frankie's glance. 'There's been too much rather haphazard industrial development since the President was deposed and foreign investors were encouraged, but there are some good hotels and it will give you a chance,' here he looked directly at his mother, 'to get a good night's rest.'

He touched her briefly on the back of the hand. 'You'll have a chance to recuperate by the sea for a few days while

I conclude some business in Djakarta. Then we'll take a domestic flight to Bali.'

'It all sounds terribly exciting, and I'm pleased to say, after my nap, I feel quite energetic.' Lady Manning began to gather her things together.

SOON THEY were undergoing the slow business of going through Customs.

Though Halim International Airport was the main gateway to the country, Frankie was struck by the leisurely pace at which officialdom conducted its business. There was a cheerful, easy atmosphere, and the man who helped them out to the car that was to take them the nine miles into the city was smiling cheerfully as he chatted to Tristan.

It was a shock to hear Tristan conversing in the lilting accents of the place, and Frankie was impressed by this new dimension to his character.

'So you're not just a pretty face,' she was tempted to quip as he got into the car beside her.

The pressure of his thigh seemed to sear her flesh, but she assumed it was accidental that he was pressing up so close to her, as he merely gave her a cool stare in reply before turning to attend to his mother.

Be like that! thought Frankie, turning to look out of the window. There was so much to see that was different and strange that she almost forgot him as the car sped along.

He was right about the city—it was ugly and sprawling on the outskirts, although in the centre were many modern hotels and the delightful Dutch-style buildings that were what remained from the days of Dutch colonialism. The air was soporific with the scent of exotic spices and it enveloped her senses with a power that lulled her into a mood of unexpected serenity. She almost felt she could forgive Tristan for his blatant expression of desire for her and the cavalier manner which now marked his attitude towards her.

Lady Manning was taken straight up to her suite as soon as they arrived and, pleading their indulgence, begged to be excused dinner with them that evening.

'I don't eat as much as I used to and I'm sure you two will want to go off to one of these restaurants in the old town where, so you tell me, Tristan, they serve twenty-five-course meals! I'm hardly up to that myself, but you two mustn't deprive yourselves because of me!'

She made it clear when they protested that she really meant it, and Frankie felt a slight plunge in her spirits when she realised it would mean spending a whole evening in the company of Tristan.

She needn't have worried, however. Tristan picked up on her dismay at once. 'We've been invited out to a restaurant by a colleague of mine—a musician with the court gamelan. I told him we'd be pretty well drained by the flight and that it would have to be early to bed for us tonight—' he couldn't help letting a meaningful gleam come into his eyes, but Frankie remained stony. 'He'll quite understand the situation,' he added then.

She felt his eyes sear through her. 'I'm sure he will,' she murmured. Especially if you have anything to do with it, she added to herself.

In the event, she was whisked off in a car with him at ten o'clock when Lady Manning was already sound asleep. It was a relief to find that, all through dinner, she was sandwiched between a chubby, smiling little man, whose one word of English seemed to be 'good day' and a similarly chubby dark-haired lady who seemed to be his wife.

Tristan, somewhat aloof, sat opposite, and only once all evening did their feet accidentally touch beneath the table. Frankie instantly drew hers in under her chair, and apart from a couple of occasions when their hands touched inadvertently as they helped themselves from the array of little dishes that lay in profusion across the red lacquer table that separated them both, there was little other contact between them.

Tristan spoke in their own language to the couple and only briefly bothered to translate for her now and then. She would probably have been bored and upset at so blatantly being excluded by him from the conversation if the Indonesian couple hadn't paid her the greatest and most courteous attention possible. The wife tried to explain the different dishes and Frankie struggled gamely with an attempt to remember the different names. To be honest, they all began to sound the same after a while.

She followed the woman's example and put a little of each dish on to her plate—placing them separately and in an agreeable pattern that took their bright colours into consideration.

Tristan, on the few occasions when he said anything to her at all, explained in a bored, off-hand sort of voice that for Indonesians colour and texture were as important in a meal as taste. 'They're more cultured and civilised than we in the West, perhaps.' He turned back to the musician as if all the shortcomings of Western civilisation were entirely her fault. Frankie rewarded him with a sour look that had no visible effect on him.

Left to her own devices somewhat, she decided to enjoy the scrumptious and unfamiliar tastes despite Tristan's deliberate coldness.

'It's such pretty food,' she remarked to no one in particular, but her words seemed to be swallowed up by the animated conversation of the two men.

What a bore he is, she thought moodily to herself, observing his aquiline features from between uncharacteristically slitted eyes.

She managed to pick out the word 'gamelan' from what they were saying and remembered from somewhere that it was the name for the traditional gong orchestras of the country. Deliberately she intruded into the conversation by asking Tristan pointedly if she would be allowed to hear some some time.

'You're *allowed* to, of course,' he answered sarcastically. 'You can do what you like so long as you take good care of Mother. You're not a prisoner.'

She smiled sweetly. 'It sure as hell feels like it.' She went on smiling, knowing that the couple couldn't tell what she was saying. 'And you sure as hell are one of the biggest bores in town right now.' She gave him a brilliant smile and the couple sat back, smiling too, presumably thinking they were witnessing a lovers' interlude of mutual endearments.

Tristan of course had cottoned on to the game. He smiled back. 'And you're a pain in the neck, sweetie, with all this touch-me-not rubbish. You know you want me, and sooner or later you're going to come to me willingly.'

Despite the fact that they couldn't tell what he was saying to her, Frankie felt the colour rise to her cheeks.

'Damn you, buster, I'm not sitting here to be insulted by you! I'm going for a stroll while you finish your no doubt fascinating conversation.'

She rose, still smiling, and he didn't try to stop her. She hesitated for a moment, appalled by her own impulsiveness. She had no desire to stroll around the streets of an unfamiliar foreign city at midnight without an escort! He must know that. But seeing the challenging glint in his eye she couldn't back out without looking like a fool. With gestures and shrugs of explanation to the two Indonesians she collected her things together.

There was a smile even now fixed to her face. As she passed his chair a hard bronze hand caught her by the waist and for a moment she felt relieved at the thought that he would forcibly refuse to let her go. Instead he merely pressed her wrist to his lips.

'Don't get lost,' he murmured. 'I'm tired and I don't feel like staying up half the night searching for a headstrong little madam who really only deserves a good spanking.'

Snatching her hand away, Frankie gave him a gesture that told him plainly she would rather be on her own anywhere than be here with him.

Damn him! she thought as she stalked furiously out of the restaurant. He's the most unchivalrous pig I've ever come across! Even a casual acquaintance would feel some slight protectiveness towards a woman in this situation. She was doubly angry because it was all her own stupid fault for giving in to a sense of pique at being ignored all evening by him. Now she would have to pay the penalty for her bravado.

Not quite sure what to expect, she stepped out into the night. The street was thronged with people, dark-skinned, curly-haired and, she noticed, with wide, open, friendly faces and round laughing eyes that caught her glance and grinned broadly in greeting, then moved on. It was so unlike the pale uptight expressions of Londoners hurrying for their midnight taxis. Here nobody seemed to be in any particular hurry and Frankie let herself be carried along on the warm friendly tide of humanity.

She found she merged in almost unnoticed, her tininess being an asset where nobody seemed to be much over five foot four and her long dark hair was matched by the common sight of the other women, whose hair hung long and sleek to their waists. Inexplicably, she felt immediately at home and couldn't help returning the smiles she received with a sense of joy.

It was beautiful, a dark sky scattered with a million stars, the sparkling happy faces of the crowd, the glitter from the many restaurants that spilled out across the pavement. The sense of freedom was intoxicating.

It was a shock then to find herself suddenly gripped tightly around the waist. When she swivelled she found two hatefully familiar brown eyes glowering down into her own. Impulsively she put out her hand.

'Don't spoil it, Tristan. It's so beautiful. I adore it. I adored the food and your two friends and now this, the lovely crowds in the warm night. It's all so happy and carefree. I could imagine living here!'

His answer was a blank stare that transmitted nothing to her about his inner feelings. He merely gripped her more firmly around the waist.

'It's easy to get carried away in the euphoria of the moment,' he told her in clipped tones, turning her round bodily to face the way she had just come. 'That's how people like you get into situations they can't handle.'

There was an obvious meaning behind his words which was not lost on her. 'I'm fully aware of the dangers of euphoria,' she told him primly. 'I thought you knew that, at least.'

There was a flicker of a smile around his lips when he looked down at her. 'Come on, they're waiting to say goodbye—very disappointed that we won't spend the night carousing with them. I promised that we'd make up for it on our way home.'

He walked her slowly back, drifting with her through the crowds, with his arm still resting lightly around her waist.

'WAS IT a pleasant evening, my dear?' asked Lady Manning at breakfast the next morning.

Frankie felt she was watching her face carefully for a reply. She nodded vigorously and launched at once into a detailed description of the meal to hide the embarrassment she felt at having to censor what she really wanted to say about Tristan. As far as Lady Manning suspected, she and her son were on the best of terms.

Frankie guessed it would be upsetting for her in her present condition to learn that she had inflicted on her someone whose presence was deeply abhorrent to her. At least, this was what she was still telling herself. And last night had not done anything to make her change her opinion about him one bit.

Plainly Lady Manning was proud of, if a little puzzled by, her eldest son. He had obviously been considered the potential black sheep of the family, Frankie had concluded, and from chance remarks she had gathered that he and his landowner father had not had much in common. Whether their differences had ever flared into an all-out confrontation was something she did not know—but having felt the brunt of Tristan's sudden blaze of temper herself, she would not have been surprised if something of the sort hadn't taken place in the past.

She could also see how inappropriate the career chosen by his heir would seem to the sort of man she imagined the late Lord Manning to have been—now, in the exotic location where his career had taken root and begun to blossom, she could see why Lady Manning claimed that Tristan took after her, with her love of artistic things, and she saw that it was the antithesis of all those cool English virtues no doubt fully endorsed by a staunch member of the class which traditionally was supposed to embody them.

Not that Tristan wasn't cool, she thought morosely, as the car with its native driver whisked them in air-conditioned comfort along the twisting white toll road across the western end of the island. He was cool all right. He had been cool last night, when, after leaving the restaurant, he had escorted her silently back to the hotel, then

wished her a curt good night outside her room. No need
for locked doors!

She sighed. That, she reminded herself, was exactly what
she wanted, wasn't it?

They stopped for lunch at the little town of Bogor which
nestled in the foothills of the Puncak mountains whose
remote purple flanks had been visible ever since they had
left Djakarta soon after breakfast.

It had been a pleasant drive—Tristan's icy coolness ex-
cepted—taking them across flat plains with the variation
of rice paddies and dense green forest.

Every little village they went through seemed to have its
roosters in wicker cages hanging under the thatched eaves
of the houses, and she heard Tristan tell his mother, not
without a sly gleam, that cock-fighting was the equivalent
of fox-hunting out here, though the government had at
least had the sensitivity to pass a law banning it.

'I'm sure Father would have regarded that as the first
sign of degeneracy,' he remarked.

Lady Manning for once merely pursed her lips and
Frankie gazed out of the window to pretend that she had
not heard the exchange.

Tristan this morning seemed nervous and on edge, and
when the meal took slightly longer than anticipated he
could not conceal his impatience.

'It's not laziness on their part,' he explained for the
hundredth time, 'they merely regard time differently from
you in the West.' Frankie noticed the disclaimer in his
choice of pronoun. So did Lady Manning. She put a hand
on his arm. 'I'm enjoying myself enormously, darling. You
know I've always been keen on travel. If everything was
exactly like it is at home there'd be no point in leaving
one's own fireside.'

Frankie was surprised to notice something like relief
show itself briefly in his eyes for a moment, then it was

gone and he was leading them out to the car again. He and the driver manhandled the collapsible wheelchair into the boot and they set off on the last leg of the journey.

WHEN THEY reached Pelabutan Ratu they drove alongside the manicured undulations of the golf course before making a sharp right turn that brought them out on to a main road again. The place was frantic with traffic at this time of day and they had to thread their way at a snail's pace until they came to a large white-painted mansion built in the colonial style, set back from the road behind an expanse of immaculate green lawn dotted with tall oak trees.

Tristan turned to look at the two women. His mother's face was already showing signs of fatigue, but she patted him on the arm. 'It's lovely, Tristan,' she breathed, reading the need for approval in his face. 'I'll appreciate it properly when I've had a short rest.' She turned to Frankie. 'Help me when we get inside for a few minutes, Frankie, then you can get Tristan to show you around the place.'

Once again Frankie was faced with the problem of how to avoid Tristan, but again he came to the rescue as if able to read her mind. 'I'll see you both settled in, then I have 'phone calls to make and a hundred other things to attend to.' He didn't look at all apologetic when he glanced in Frankie's direction and went on to tell her, 'I shall be very busy for the next day and may even have to go back to the capital for a while. But at the end of the week I'll have some spare time before we move on. I'll show you around then if you like.'

'I'm sure it won't be necessary,' Frankie responded, trying not to let her voice sound too sharp. 'By that time we'll have had a chance to explore every nook and cranny ourselves.' She deliberately included Lady Manning as she wanted it to be quite clear she regarded her own presence with them very definitely as Lady Manning's companion—and no one else's...

This seemed to amuse Tristan, for he hid a smile as he bent to hoist Lady Manning out of the car and into the waiting wheelchair.

But Tristan was true to his word. Now they were satisfactorily quartered—in a house which turned out to belong to a man who was a prominent local businessman, educated in Europe—Tristan was barely seen at all. He had said Frankie would be on her own as soon as they arrived, and he was right.

Except for Lady Manning, who, in fact continuing what now turned out to be walking practice, as her condition improved visibly day by day, spent much of her time in the lush gardens of the white mansion, Frankie scarcely saw anyone else.

Their hostess, for the businessman had married a Frenchwoman some thirty years ago, was closer to Lady Manning's generation than her own, and Frankie diplomatically left the two women to chatter away in French as often as she could.

She devoted her time to solitary walks around the grounds, to swimming from the busy little beach—made busy, she noted, by prolific family groups, jolly with round-faced offspring—and to the sunbathing which in Rani's eyes should have been the prime purpose of her journey.

She began to regain the glowing fitness which had had its edges dulled by the weeks when she had had to forgo her daily workout, and, in the cool of early morning, or again, in late afternoon when the rains usually came to cool things down again, she took to dancing in the empty ballroom at the back of the house.

The rain was still shimmering down the long windows that ran the length of the ballroom as she donned her leotard that afternoon and let herself quietly into the high-domed, echoing room.

It was impressive with its white and gold-painted roof trusses and the glimmer of ornate filigree work around its walls, austere in its lack of furnishings, yet with a touch of unmistakable magic in the exotic richness of its decor. Frankie felt inspired and thought for the hundredth time how lucky she was to be able to practise in such a beautiful setting. The rain made a mysterious swishing sound, locking her into a private world of fantasy where anything might happen.

She danced joyfully, thoughtfully, lyrically, letting herself follow the ebb and flow of feeling as it moved her. Briefly she danced snatches from the *Pierrot* piece, improvising around its central theme as the note of yearning nostalgia set up by the melancholy fall of rain took hold of her.

She was not so far lost in her own inner world, however, that she didn't hear the big white and gold double doors at the far end of the room open slowly and, admitting one person, slowly swing shut again.

There was a little silence in which she completed her movement and came to rest in the middle of the floor, her head on one side in order to observe the intruder.

Tristan, wearing a short, dark kaftan in place of his usual shirt, and a pair of loose white cotton trousers, his strong feet bare, stepped forward. His brown eyes, alight with the old attention he had always given her, openly ripped the skimpy peacock-blue leotard from her suddenly tingling body. She felt his eyes touch her as deliberately as if he had reached out with his two hands to caress her, and with a little stifled gasp, she stepped back as if to move out of range.

There were invisible currents flowing between them that seemed to bring her flesh to a peak of trembling awareness without his so much as laying a finger on her.

Again she stepped back, putting up a hand as if to ward him off.

She watched, mesmerised, as he slowly began to prowl across the expanse of polished floor, its high gloss throwing back the reflection of his white trousers, making him look as if he was floating on a cloud of unearthly light.

She felt his approach as a scorching sensation on her flesh and she knew her cheeks were suddenly flaming to expose her innermost feelings to his mocking gaze.

The rain fell, locking them in together behind its wall of sound. In that one moment Frankie knew that all her reservations were immediately overturned.

Tristan didn't utter a word when he reached her. Simply, gently, she felt his arms come out and fold her to him and with the same deliberate calm, their lips drew together. Then for a long moment there was nothing but the irresistible flames of passion, warming them from the same source, drawing them inextricably closer, and the slow melting of flesh on flesh.

Somewhere beyond the moment, in a kind of void, she became aware that the rain had stopped and a little later, from the far recesses of the mansion, dimly echoed the gong that told them dinner would soon be ready.

There was something incongruous in the way they were drawn towards it, entwined in each other's arms and, still without a word having been spoken, halting at the high door leading out to the corridor. Reluctantly their limbs moved apart, only to come together again for one last embrace. Then apart, only to return once more.

The gong clashed louder now as one of the servants marched up and down outside, crashing the covered wooden mallet on to the brass dome to send the sound echoing and re-echoing throughout the house. Its sudden proximity in the corridor outside separated them abruptly and finally.

Tristan held the door. Frankie ran shakily back to where she had left her wrap, then they both stepped out on to the rich red carpet of the corridor into what now seemed to Frankie to be another stranger and more unpredictable world. Everything seemed changed, glowing with greater clarity. Her body shook against Tristan's as he briefly pulled her close to him behind the flower-printed uniformed back of the boy with the gong. 'Later, sweetheart, but not too late,' his voice was husky with desire, then he sent her on her way with a gentle push in the small of her back.

She changed for dinner in a haze of breathless confusion. Her fingers shook as she tied up her hair in a loose chignon and slid the silver metal clip into place.

It was crazy! She had no resistance to the man. He could take her with an ease that was indecent.

She gave a sharp intake of breath, staring at the unexpected brightness of her eyes in the mirror on her dressing-table. People would only have to glance at her to know that she was in a fever of desire for someone. How her eyes would continually seek him out in the crowd would tell them as clearly as if shouted from the rooftops who that someone was. And then what? Tongues would wag. The religious beliefs were strong here—Buddhist or Moslem, licentiousness of any sort was frowned on. Even ethics of dress were strict. Bare arms, even, Tristan had warned, bare legs, met with disapproval by all but the most progressive of the tourist trade operators.

Then there was Lady Manning herself. Frankie shuddered. There must be a way of hiding the signs of such a blatant consuming desire from the eyes of the world?

She dropped her glance. When she looked back at her reflection she saw only the seductive flare of her dark lashes opening to reveal eyes large with yearning. Her body undulated despite her attempts to move steadily and stiffly. When the gong sounded for the last time, she snatched up a thin wrap—a somewhat half-hearted hope that it would be defence against his power—and tried to bring her limbs sufficiently under control to allow her to move with a brisk air down the stairs to the dining-room.

She took a deep breath before entering.

Everyone else was already seated. Tristan, she noted, searching despite herself along the parallel rows of heads, had changed into a white cotton evening jacket and a formal shirt with miraculous speed. He had the air of a man who has taken time over his appearance.

She knew it couldn't be true and the flicker of irony in her glance as she took her seat, mercifully at a safe distance from him, told him that she admired his efficiency.

More practised than I, no doubt, she thought drily, avoiding his glance as she felt those wicked, lively eyes seek her out for a secret, provocative exchange.

CHAPTER EIGHT

THE MEAL, traditionally, was to be lingered over far into the scented tropical night and it was well into the early hours when the party finally began to break up.

The gamelan had accompanied the meal with its hypnotically repeated phrases and intricate rhythmic counterpoint, weaving an incantation of sound that effectively completed the spell which had begun to be cast over Frankie from the first magical moment of Tristan's unexpected appearance in the ballroom. Her senses felt drugged with the exotic tastes and sounds and scents of the night, and when Tristan came to her and discreetly took her by the arm, he put a finger mysteriously to his lips.

Then she was willingly allowing herself to be led towards the moonlit garden where the exotic tropical blooms filled the air with their perfume. Tristan seemed familiar enough with the garden. Frankie found herself being led along a narrow walk between high sweet-smelling hedges of hibiscus. He held her in his arms as soon as they were hidden from the sight of the house, bringing his lips searchingly on to hers, his voice smoky with unleashed desire.

As if torn between kissing her now and hurrying with the urgency of his passions to somewhere more secluded he would stop every two paces to trail kisses over her face, then, half-carrying her, would hurry on down the narrow path that came out eventually by the side of a wooden pagoda at the side of a small ornamental lake.

The door creaked slightly as he pushed it roughly open, and even before they were inside, their bodies had thrown themselves into another feverish embrace.

Frankie stumbled slightly in the velvet blackness that greeted them as the door closed but, never letting her go for a moment, Tristan somehow found a way to light an oil lamp standing in an alcove by the far wall.

Frankie dared not allow herself to question how often he had used the pagoda at this time of night.

His face, when he turned to look at her, was burnished to a soft bronze by the flickering light and its expression stopped all her niggling rationalisations. She moved without thought into the irresistible circle of his embrace. As he ran a finger tantalisingly under the strap of her plain white dress, she shuddered with pleasure. He made the ties of her dress snake free almost of their own accord to reveal the fresh tan that ended modestly in an even line above her breasts. Then he bent his dark head to kiss the untouched pale flesh where it gleamed with a pearly sheen in the lamp's glow. She swayed on limbs from which all resistance had fled long ago, so that it was without surprise that in one sinuous rippling movement she found herself lying on a heavily embroidered native rug that covered part of the floor.

With a little slicking sound, her white dress slithered away to reveal her body at last to his burning glance.

His own clothes vanished in the same expert fashion and she gazed in adoration at the beauty of Tristan's limbs and the evidence of his impetuous desire for her.

Words became irrelevant now as their bodies burned for each other and came together suddenly in a volcano of pent-up desire.

Frankie cried aloud as Tristan's mouth enveloped hers and he rushed to claim possession of her, urging her to a sudden extreme that became a prolonged and ecstatic cry.

Each movement of his body seemed to bring her to a peak beyond which no mortal could fly, yet still he transported her ever further until the last vestige of her control was gone and she could only cling sobbing to him, crying out his name, riding the summit of her ecstasy until finally she shrieked out her pleasure in one long dying fall.

The silence of the night was broken only by the gentle warbling of some distant night bird, and the darkness seemed to welcome them into its breathing secret stillness as if to conceal lovers was its reason for being.

Tristan ran his warm hands over her limbs, tangled her hair and kissed her eyes over and over again.

Soon she felt his body quicken with desire once more and her body opened languidly to him, joying in the unhurried ease with which he took her now the excess of their fever for each other had abated.

It was shortly before dawn, at that time when the birds of the garden are beginning to break into full-throated song as if to chase away the reluctant lingering of the night, that Tristan roused her from a light slumber to caress her for the last time. There seemed no end to the varied nuances of his touch, and she felt herself responding with no lessening of ardour to the unabated urgency of his desire.

She felt drugged and sleepy when they finally let themselves out into the racket of birdsong, and Tristan held her close to him as they made their way lingeringly back between the morning-fresh hibiscus.

His lips found hers once, warmly, with a gentle passion as he turned her face up to his when they reached the gilded portico of the guest wing.

'I have to go to Djakarta in the morning—this morning, that is.' His voice was hushed as he gave a brief glance at the shuttered windows. 'I'm not sure when I shall be back.'

Frankie clung to him in a sudden, desperate sorrow. It was cruel to have him wrenched away even for a moment.

'Please, don't stay away long, my darling,' she whispered, drowning in the dark power of his eyes hooded under their finely arched brows.

He stroked her hair as she nestled against him. 'I would take you with me but for the fact that you're needed here,' he told her. He kissed her once more, deeply and arousingly. 'Go up before you tempt me again now. It's hardly worth my while going to bed, but you can get some sleep.'

Reluctantly she slipped through the door, and before it closed, she turned once to catch a last glimpse of him, a white-clad figure with a cap of tousled black hair, caught there in a blaze of sunlight as he raised one hand in a hurried farewell.

She stepped out of her creased white dress and let it lay where it dropped while she had a slow, dreamy shower. Glistening wet, she came back into her bedroom and picked up the dress, holding it for a moment to her face, so that she could breathe in the scents of his body which still lingered in it.

Every thought and memory of him seemed ineffably sweet and dear, and she felt her body aroused at the memories that the dress recalled. A minute without Tristan seemed an eternity and she struggled to cope with the prospect of a day or two without the magic of his touch. Beyond that day or two stretched an unlimited prospect of bliss to which she stubbornly refused to admit a single doubt.

She lay in the cool white sheets but sought sleep in vain. Sleep was as remote from her now as it had been through most of the night. Her whole mind was afire with the memory of him and she moaned softly, tossing on the bed, half alert to the idea of seeking him out for one last snatched embrace.

The sun was already beginning to pierce the shutters and soon she heard the sounds deep within the mansion as it was prepared for a new day, and one by one the sleepers were roused from their beds.

THE NEXT day and the next dragged. Everything seemed to act as an irritant and a distraction. Frankie felt impatient with Lady Manning's slowness and tried desperately to control herself; she couldn't eat and had to hide her loss of appetite in case she offended her hostess. She tried to dance, but such sensuous movements of her body seemed pointless without Tristan's presence beside her. She tried to escape by reading, but nothing held her attention for more than five minutes, and she tried sightseeing, dutifully trundling Lady Manning around, armed with half a library of guide books under her arm, but with no real interest than if she had been in her own back garden at home.

In contrast to her inner disarray her face glowed in the sunny climate, acquiring an effortless tan, and her hair shone with the healthy conditioning of so much sun.

She went shopping with Lady Manning one day and her interest was aroused by the bright lengths of batik that the native women wore wrapped around their hips, and on an impulse she bought some jewel bright lengths—only, even then, he was in her mind when she did it, and in her fantasy, she played with the idea of how Tristan would slowly and excitingly unwind the silky cloth from around her naked body.

But still he didn't return.

The day for their planned departure to Bali came. Lady Manning greeted Frankie at breakfast with the news that Tristan had sent a message. They were to take an interior flight by Garuda Airways from Kemayoran Airport the next day. Servants sent by their host and hostess would help them at the Java end of the journey. Tristan himself would be waiting in Bali.

'He flew there direct from Djakarta,' Lady Manning told her.

Frankie felt a prickle of apprehension. Why had he not hurried back to her as he had promised?

She had no time to dwell on her misgivings. There was some packing to be done and last-minute obligations that saw her swiftly through the day. Time, it seemed, now passed with increasing tempo as mentally she hurried towards their meeting.

Kemayoran was a small congested airport handling only internal flights to the other islands, and she was relieved when she saw the servants put in charge handle everything with assurance if not with any visible air of efficiency. At least they had plenty of time to get themselves settled for the brief hop across the channel.

Frankie was in a fever of anguish to see Tristan again—his face, his welcoming smile, most of all his welcoming embrace. At last the coastline of Bali came into view, the island a jewel set in the glittering setting of a sea the colour of hyacinths.

She was wearing a gauzy skirt in blues and greys shot with silvery thread and long enough to take account of the dictate against the showing of too much unadorned flesh, and a tight matching bodice with long, narrow sleeves bought in one of the bazaars. It had a hundred little buttons fastening it up the front, and there had been an element of deliberation in her choice as she envisaged the strong brown fingers fumbling at them as a huskily masculine voice swore softly with impatience at his own clumsy haste.

There were masses of people waiting below in the bright sunlight—women, butterfly-bright in batik print sarongs of many varied patterns, and men in white. Feverishly she scanned them for the tall figure of her expectations, and with a shudder she saw him detach himself from a group nearest the airport building and come striding out to watch their plane touch down.

It was chaos in the rush to disembark, and Lady Manning waited until last when her wheelchair could be assembled without too much inconvenience to the other passengers. She needed it less and less now and urged Frankie to let her surprise Tristan by walking down the gangway on her arm, but Frankie shivered at the disapproval she would see flick over Tristan's face at any unnecessary risk, and she managed to persuade the old lady to be patient and wait for everyone to leave. Heavens, she thought, it's difficult enough to be patient. She could barely restrain herself from throwing herself straight off the plane into Tristan's arms. Then she took a firm hold of herself. She was mad if she expected such a greeting in full view of everyone. Discretion would be the name of the game until—she frowned.

There was a shadow lying distantly on some horizon whose existence she refused to believe in. She didn't know what was going to happen to them. It didn't matter. She refused to think about it.

Tristan was hurrying towards them now. His glossy black hair hovered close enough to be touched as she bent to kiss his mother warmly on the cheek.

Frankie stood at the bottom of the gangway, loving him for the care he bestowed on his mother in helping her without impatience or fuss into the waiting car, then she followed after them, drinking in his every movement, longing for the moment when their eyes would meet. He strode athletically round to the driver's seat, swinging the door open before looking back over his shoulder to where she came up with a couple of bags—moving towards him across the interminable white desert of the tarmac. It

seemed an endless time before he had bothered to look
back to see if she was following them.

Even now he had turned away again, bending to say
something to his mother inside the car, straightening up
again, drumming impatiently on the roof with the fingers
of one hand. Then he raised his head and their eyes met.
His gaze swept over her once, then away.

'What's the matter?' he called. 'Bags too heavy?'

Frankie nodded when he looked briefly back again, and
rested the two bags for a moment in order to flex her fingers. He drummed again on the roof of the car, while she
picked up the bags and struggled on with them. When she
drew level he said quickly, 'You should always travel light.
That's the first rule.'

Before she could think of a suitable retort, he had coiled
himself into the driver's seat and switched on the engine.

She looked aghast at the clean-cut profile that was
framed in the open window. 'So what am I supposed to do
with these?' she demanded in a choky voice.

Lady Manning tapped him on the shoulder. 'They're
heavier than they look, Tristan. Help her put them in the
boot, do!'

Tristan unfolded his long length and climbed out of the
car with ill-concealed impatience, picking up both cases
without so much as a glance in her direction. He slammed
them both into the boot, shut it, and climbed back into the
car.

Frankie was conscious of Lady Manning's pursed lips as
she miserably went round the car to take her place beside
her. The endless streets seemed to flash past in a blur of
meaningless shapes and colours as Frankie resolutely kept
her gaze fixed on the view beyond the window.

With her whole body rigid with tension she watched
Tristan bring the car to an eventual halt in front of a long,
wooden, single-storey building that sprawled in a vague L-

shape round a dusty tree-shaded compound where a group of interested children ran in a higgledy-piggledy crowd beside the car.

A buxom, pleasant-faced woman in a flowered sarong came down the steps from out of the house at the sound of the car. Seeing who it was, she turned to call to someone in the shadowed depths of the house and a couple of boys came out to help with the luggage.

'This is my headquarters, Mother,' Tristan turned slightly so that Frankie could see the familiar muscles in the back of his neck ripple with the movement.

'I don't spend much time here as my work takes me off all over the islands, but you'll be comfortable here and certainly well fed.' He laughed softly at some private memory, then abruptly climbed out of the car into the brilliant sunlight of the compound.

She heard him speak rapidly to the woman, then Lady Manning's chair was being unloaded and Lady Manning herself, with a sudden spark of independence, slid her legs out and raised herself with an effort so that she was standing upright against the support of the car. Tristan came back and took her arm protectively and began to lead her with painful slowness towards the house. Unnoticed, Frankie followed stiffly behind.

The incident at the airport was because he had been worried about his mother's condition after the flight, she told herself. Now he had ignored her because once again, and quite rightly, his first responsibility was to the invalid. When she was comfortably settled and they were at last alone, then—then he would turn to her and give her at last the welcome for which she burned.

She was in a fever of anticipation.

After helping unload the car of the hand luggage and generally making herself the useful companion she was paid to be, and then later, after being shown her pretty room at the back of the house, she took a moment to freshen herself up. She brushed her hair loose from its chignon, till it fell like gleaming satin around her shoulders, then she left her room and made her way across to the spacious sitting room which took up the shorter length of the two arms of the L-shape. A glance round the comfortably furnished room with its one or two pieces of European furniture and gaudy piles of cushions ranged with haphazard grace on the simple polished wood floor showed her that no one was yet down.

She moved nervously across the floor towards the verandah, every nerve alert to the sound of his approach, but when at last she turned with a gasp of relief at the sound of soft footsteps entering the room she was disappointed to find only the housekeeper there.

'Oh, I thought it was Tristan,' she blurted without thinking.

'Tristan?' the woman looked puzzled.

Thinking that probably she didn't speak English, anyway, but that she might as well try again, Frankie repeated the question.

The woman turned with a smile. 'Lord Manning is already down, I believe.' Her English was perfect.

'Not Lord Manning,' corrected Frankie without thinking. 'Lord Manning died a short time ago. I mean ...'

Just then she turned to see Tristan looming behind her. He had evidently been standing out on the verandah and had overheard the exchange.

'I may be moribund, but I'm not pushing up the daisies quite yet!' he remarked coolly, brushing past her as he came straight on into the room.

Frankie gave a gasp, both at her own stupidity and at the lack of warmth in his manner. It was the first time she had heard Tristan addressed by his newly acquired title. She had never even thought of him as Lord Manning; the idea hadn't even entered her head. How gauche she must seem!

The older woman was smiling enigmatically at them both.

'I won't have anything now—I have to leave soon. Miss Redpath will no doubt want something to eat, however. Serve her in here if she wishes.'

He was already making off towards the inner door when Frankie, throwing discretion to the winds, called out in a shaky voice, 'Tristan! Wait!'

When he stopped she faltered with a sudden impulse of pain. There wasn't even a hint of friendliness in his face when he turned to her.

Her hands twisted nervously in front of her. 'You haven't even said a proper hello yet...' she blurted, feeling foolish beneath the older woman's watchful eyes.

With a nod Tristan dismissed the housekeeper and spun to face her with anything but a welcome on his face.

'Well, what is it?' he glowered impatiently, giving a quick glance at his watch.

Frankie felt her blood run cold. 'Don't you remember when we said goodbye—'

'Well?'

Her breath caught convulsively in her throat. 'Well?' she whispered, reaching out a hand helplessly towards him.

He stepped closer but was careful to avoid her touch.

'Frankie, this is a different time and a different place. We couldn't afford to be as indiscreet here as we were in Pelabutan. It just isn't on... Besides, I'm about to leave for one of the outer islands—'

'To your jungle love paradise?' she asked bitterly, recalling his bantering words on the plane coming over.

'It's already well past the hour when I should have left,' he went on, ignoring her. 'Your flight was, as was not totally unexpected, a hell of a sight behind the scheduled time.'

'But Tristan—' She hesitated, tears pricking her eyelids, then she let her hands fall and turned away. What could she say to him? He had made no promises, had not even said he loved her. And what would Lord Manning want with her, that wouldn't bring only pain? Her blood ran cold. What was there left of that night but a memory?

'I'll be back in a day or two,' he informed her. 'In the meantime I've arranged for you and Mother to visit the artists' colony at Ubud and you might find a visit to the dancing school of some interest. It can be arranged if you wish.' His face had no expression in it. 'Look, sweetheart,' he brushed her shoulder with one hand, as if to touch her more intimately would harm him, 'take care of Mother. She's doing marvellously with your help.' With that he swivelled on his heel, and then all that was left was just the faint aroma of spice to remind her of his presence.

THE HEAT and the dust didn't bother Frankie.

She positively thrived in the climate, though, of course, like everyone else, she kept in the shade at midday and took shelter when the late afternoon rains came.

Their visit to the artists' colony would have been a delightfully fascinating experience in any other circumstances, but despite the visual pleasure she took from browsing round the big modern gallery there and ambling round the colourful open markets with their exotic wares for sale, the inner pain at Tristan's abrupt rejection of her gnawed with an insistence she could not escape. Her thoughts fluttered this way and that like butterflies trapped in a glass jar, but whichever way they flew they battered themselves senselessly against the cruel truth of Tristan's change of heart.

In the bustling market she insisted on Lady Manning remaining safely in her wheelchair. To anyone watching she must have appeared to be quite happy, pushing the old woman along the busy avenues, haggling over the chased silver work and leather wares which were specialties of the region. In reality it all passed before her eyes in a nightmare blur of meaningless images.

Day after day she saw herself going through the motions of normal reactions, while inside the pain grew unbearably. True to his word, Tristan arranged for her to visit the nearby school of music and dancing, and while Lady Manning rested, she spent what would have been an intriguing morning watching the different classes in progress.

Her heart ached as she went through the motions of talking to the two women who showed her over the school. In a blur of pain she told them that yes, she too was a dancer. They invited her back again after that first visit, and despite the feeling that nothing in the whole world would ever matter again to her, she accepted. Surely, she thought frantically to herself, if I keep myself busy this terrible sense of loss will gradually go away?

Sharing a love of dancing with the teachers and pupils of the school was the nearest she came to forgetting her heartache. It showed that the world didn't begin and end with Tristan—it only felt like it.

PREPARATIONS WERE under way for a special performance of the *legong* at the New Moon Festival. This was one of the traditional dances Frankie had been looking forward to seeing since she had first accepted the invitation to come to Bali. She knew that the costumes and make-up for it were exquisite. Now, though, she could scarcely bring herself to attend.

Lady Manning was standing erect on the verandah with mail from England in her hand when Frankie happened to mention the performance.

'Of course we must go!' the older woman exclaimed, handing a couple of letters to Frankie at the same moment. 'Though I must say you don't sound terribly enthusiastic, my dear.' She gave her a sharp look. 'It should be quite delightful, by all accounts. What a pity we can't have Tristan with us. Still, he seems to have set himself some deadlines for completing this present phase of work, so perhaps I shouldn't complain.'

Frankie slit open the envelope with Davey's familiar scrawl across it. He gave her all the latest news and she scanned it briefly to make sure he was getting on all right.

The other one was in an unfamiliar green envelope, and as Lady Manning chattered about the *legong* she flicked through the contents of the typewritten letter inside, scarcely taking in what it was telling her. She crumpled it up absentmindedly in her pocket until she had time to mull over its contents in the privacy of her own room.

Contrary to his mother's expectations Tristan did in fact turn up at the house a few days later—just as they were getting ready to leave for the performance.

'I couldn't miss an event like this,' he told them as he breezed into the house that evening. He scarcely glanced at Frankie. She watched with dismay as the lithe figure came towards them.

Lady Manning was holding on to her, gamely attempting to walk out to the car, and Frankie gave a startled exclamation, her fingers tightening involuntarily before she managed to regain her composure in time to greet the new arrival with a wary 'hello.'

'Dear boy, this is wonderful!' cried Lady Manning. 'We're just off to the square now. Do hurry.'

'Where's Singh? Isn't he going with you?' demanded Tristan, drawing his brows together as he referred to one of the elderly administrators who had kindly driven them around in his car once or twice.

'Of course,' replied Lady Manning, 'but he'll be far too busy to make a proper job of it. I gather this is going to be something of a beanfeast.'

'You're right, and as I said, that's why I'm back.' His glance brushed Frankie's face lightly but with no apparent feeling. 'If you can wait five minutes I'll go up and have a quick shower and then we can all go together.'

Lady Manning plumped down on a rattan chair by the door.

'Don't look so distraught, child,' she reproved Frankie gently as soon as Tristan had gone. 'You look as if you've seen a ghost!'

I have, thought Frankie bringing a rueful smile to her face—the ghost of my lost love.

She shrugged and would have tried to make some excuse if Lady Manning hadn't said quietly, 'They're all children, my dear, reaching out for the latest toy. They're not worth our tears. I say this even though he's my own son. He has always been wilful and needs to be curbed.' She patted the back of Frankie's hand. 'That style of dress suits you. You're petite enough to be able to get away with it. I've seen the heads turning for you, you know.'

Frankie blushed and stupidly she felt tears well into her eyes. She got up abruptly and paced the entrance hall for a moment.

She was wearing a sarong, one of her purchases in the market at Ubud, its saffron shade perfectly setting off her deep even tan, and the maid had shown her how to put a single white hibiscus, native fashion, in her straight brown hair. For once she had made up her mind to forget Tristan. She had intended to make a gala occasion of the event. But now the oblivion for which she craved was in one full swoop denied her.

She stopped abruptly beside the outer door and swung to face Lady Manning. 'Do you think we're going to be late?' she managed to ask in a voice that sounded almost normal.

Lady Manning called loudly and one of the boys popped out from behind a door. A few minutes later Tristan, showered, and it seemed, freshly shaved, and wearing a loose cotton kurta over a pair of clean white trousers, came out to take his mother by the arm.

No apologies for making them late, noticed Frankie grimly, as she took the old lady's other arm and they helped her carefully down the steps to the waiting car—and no sign that he even notices my existence!

THE *LEGONG* was a dance for three women.

Frankie had already met the dancers during her visits to the school, but now they were transformed from their ordinary workaday apparel into exotic birds of paradise. Each was ornately decked in the traditional jewelled headdress and glittering collars that emphasised their slender necks and swanlike bearing.

Their dancing was characterised by quick body movements and darting glances of the eyes which were heavily emphasised by black kohl and sequins. Their dance told the story of a cruel king who tried to woo an unwilling princess.

Frankie gave a darting look from beneath feathery lashes to gauge Tristan's thoughts. He turned his head at that precise moment and a fleeting smile flickered over his face.

Frankie dropped her glance in confusion.

'So you've been having lessons too,' he murmured, squeezing her arm with a suddenness that took her by surprise. Someone came to talk to Lady Manning and he took the opportunity to come closer.

'L-lessons?' she faltered, blinking rapidly as his lips hovered just above hers.

'The eyes...' he drawled smokily, 'so expressive—and I like that colour for you, too.' He brushed her forehead slowly with his lips.

She couldn't help stepping back with a wary little frown on her face, though it hurt to propel herself out of range of the magnetism of his touch.

'What's the matter?' he breathed. 'Are you still mad at me?'

'I didn't know I was *mad* at you,' she replied defensively. She was confused now. What game was he playing with her?

'Not mad? What, then?' He gazed intently into her eyes as if to extract an answer from her.

But a single dancer had begun to solo across the stage. Frankie turned her head as the bamboo pipes took up the melody and Tristan hummed a brief snatch of the intricate patterns of the tune before turning to smile down at her again. He put one arm lazily around her waist and pulled her to him.

She felt her body soften and slacken at his touch, but with a little toss of her head she pulled away from him and pretended to be concentrating on the dance. Her pulses were racing, however, as her thoughts tumbled over themselves in confusion as she tried to work out what he was up to with this sudden about-face. After his recent coldness towards her this unheralded attention was disconcerting. She pursed her lips and kept her eyes turned determinedly straight ahead. He would find it wasn't that easy to get round her whenever the whim took him!

The dancer had the attention of all the crowd standing round the beaten earth of the square. She carried a fan and

was making much play with it, widening her eyes flirta-
tiously and deliberately holding the glance of different men
in the crowd as she twisted and turned with seductive art-
istry.

Eventually she would make her choice by tapping one of
the men in the audience on the shoulder and together they
would begin a teasing game of enticement and rebuff.

Frankie gave Tristan a surreptitious look from beneath
her eyelashes, but turned back quickly to the spectacle
when he caught her glance. What was happening out there
was an ironic mirroring of what was now happening between the two of them. The irony of it was not lost on
Tristan either. She felt the pressure of his arm around her
waist increase.

Frankie knew how the dance would progress because she
had watched the girl rehearsing it earlier that day. Now,
though, it was different. There was a sense that the practice was over and her glances were all for real. Frankie
stiffened when she saw her approach, and, reaching out,
tap the tall Englishman on the shoulder.

She half expected Tristan to decline with an embarrassed shrug like any other tourist, until she remembered,
when he stepped exuberantly on to the floor, that he was
no tourist and, in the words used so disparagingly those
weeks before had 'gone native'.

He certainly put up a good show—obviously familiar
with the strange rhythms of the music and able to follow
the intricate steps of the woman with a sensuous delight
that was obvious from the smile on his face.

The love game eventually came to an end in the traditional way—with neither side touching. But to Frankie's
chagrin, Tristan, instead of rejoining her, followed the
woman off the dance floor on to the verandah that ran
along one side of the open-air space where the dancing was
taking place.

He was gone an agonising fifteen minutes. Every minute painfully counted itself off in Frankie's tortured imagination. She felt sick as she tried to concentrate on the subsequent dancing. Then Tristan appeared as suddenly, if more unobtrusively, than he had left, appearing, she observed, rather more dishevelled than before.

'You enjoyed that, did you?' She couldn't keep the note of accusation out of her voice. She turned her head away abruptly.

'She's an old friend of mine and swore she would drag me out there one of these days,' he told her, attempting to put his arm round her waist again.

'Good for her!'

'Hey, Frankie! Are you jealous?' He laughed at her, trying to drag her up against him without success. 'No need to worry,' he grinned, 'In Bali things always end the same way—with restraint!'

'How unfortunate for you!' She could tell he was turned on. It made her temples pound furiously. The dancer's deliberate, and to be fair, beautiful enacted seduction of him, had turned him on! But Balinese women were said to be strict—now he could scarcely stop himself from letting his hand roam over her body—in public too—as if he regarded her as a convenient substitute. He obviously had no respect for her whatsoever. She forget his earlier attempt to breach the rift between them, and roundly blamed herself for giving him an excuse to regard her in an unfavourable light.

She turned on him fiercely. 'Leave me alone! I hate you. You make me feel sick,' she whispered passionately.

An odd look flickered over the handsome levels of his face and a boyish lock of black hair flicked forward on to his brow as he bent to catch her words. She saw a puzzled frown appear. 'Take your hands off me!' she hissed, just in case he hadn't got the message.

Anger sparked dangerously in his eyes, making her shrink away from him. He slid after her and before she knew what was happening he was calmly folding her to his side so that she had no choice but to allow him to ease her discreetly through the crowd towards the open door of the school.

Everyone was standing with their eyes glued to the dancers, so it wasn't surprising that Tristan soon managed to find an empty room off the square into which he bundled Frankie without a word.

Props were scattered everywhere. Exotic masks representing demons and kings glowered or smiled benignly down at them both.

He pinned her roughly against the wooden wall with his body. She twisted and turned in a fury to escape, but he had her well and truly trapped. She felt her body slacken as the heat of his desire was transmitted to it with the speed of light.

'No!' she choked, twisting her head as she felt his lips come down to seek out the soft yielding of her own. But she might as well have saved her protestations. His lips took hers in one smooth breath-stopping movement that made the universe spin in a kaleidoscope of colour as confusing as the gaudy whirl of the dancers' bejewelled robes.

When he released her she was panting for breath. 'He needs to be curbed, my dear,' she unexpectedly remembered Lady Manning telling her. Somehow it gave her the strength to gather her two fists and give him a good solid punch in the chest. Physically he was too strong for her, but at least his smile wavered.

'Do you really mean it, Frankie?'

'Yes,' she choked. 'Yes, I do mean it—Lord Manning!'

He let his hands drop slowly from where he held her. 'Yes?' His face was full of questions.

She knew it was for the last time. *'Yes,'* she repeated in a voice barely above a whisper.

Tristan stepped back, and she walked heavily towards the door.

The masks looked somehow tawdry at close range, lit only by the unshaded electric light bulb hanging from a wrinkled cord in the ceiling. His immaculate white cotton trousers were creased too, she noticed.

Rejected so emphatically, he gazed after her without moving. Frankie went out, aware that he was not following her. The dance was still in progress, but she saw nothing of it, merely observing a meaningless frenzy of people going through the motions of an ancient story. Sita, the wife of King Rama, is kidnapped. The ape king and his monkey army rescue her after a spectacular battle, and she is carried home in triumph to the king.

Frankie's eyes glistened.

'I'm rather tired, my dear,' a voice broke in at her elbow. 'Now they seem to have finished and have started their endless eating and drinking again, would you mind helping me back home? You can come straight back in the car afterwards, of course.'

Lady Manning took the hand that Frankie automatically proffered.

FRANKIE DIDN'T return that night. She went straight to bed. She lay for a long time, tossing and turning between the warm sheets, the air-conditioning loud enough to keep her from sleep, until the added sound of someone entering the compound and stealthily coming up the steps into the house gave her the release she needed. She fell asleep almost as soon as the footsteps over the creaking wooden boards trailed away to a distant bedroom.

IT WAS mid-morning when she awoke. Coming down to
find Lady Manning already out on the verandah, she was
unsurprised to learn that Tristan had once again left for the
islands. Frankie held in her hand the typewritten letter on
green paper that had come for her the previous day. Its
contents at any other time would have lifted her spirits into
a seventh heaven and she would have flown about the
house in a transport of joy, spilling out her future plans
and hopes and fears with anybody who would listen—but
when she had first read the letter she had been too miserable to absorb its contents properly. Now she saw it as her
salvation.

She showed the letter hesitantly to Lady Manning.

'Zig Zag Dance Company?' exclaimed the older woman.
'They're offering you a position as a member of the Company?'

Frankie nodded. Her fingers were figuratively crossed
as she then broached her request.

Lady Manning gave her a searching glance. 'It's wonderful news, Frankie. Really wonderful. You mentioned to
me before that they're a very prestigious new company. It's
quite a feather in your cap to have been chosen to work
with them!'

She gave Frankie a puzzled look. 'But you don't seem
particularly happy about it—?'

Frankie bit her lip and tried to avoid Lady Manning's
searching glance. 'I find the climate rather exhausting,' she
invented, wiping one hand languidly over her own brow.

Lady Manning sighed. 'Frankie, if you feel you must
leave us, then you must.' She paused. 'I notice the date
they want you to join them isn't until the end of next
month...?'

Frankie shrugged. 'I feel I ought to go back as soon as
possible,' she floundered.

Lady Manning's piercing glance seemed to reveal her innermost thoughts without any need for her own words of explanation. 'Very well, my dear.' Her voice was gentle. 'Are there—any messages?'

Frankie shook her head vigorously. 'No. Nothing,' she replied emphatically. 'Thank you...'

CHAPTER NINE

THE SILENCE in the empty house seemed to weigh down on it like a funeral pall.

Davey had gone off to Greece for the summer with some of his sixth form friends before they all scattered to their respective universities in the autumn.

Rani was experimentally holidaying in Yugoslavia with her family, pleased that there had been a reconciliation of sorts with her father but as determined as ever not to be forced into the sort of academic career she did not want. She had got a place in a department of performing arts to read for a B.A. and was cautiously optimistic that her father would at least agree to finance her for the full four years.

Frankie had been back in England for three weeks and had had a card after ten days or so from Lady Manning on her return to England. It invited her to dinner and an evening of holiday reminiscences. She had declined, arguing pressure of work: it wasn't a total untruth. Although the dance centre was closed throughout August, she had work to prepare for her debut with Zig Zag.

Even Matty, she moaned to herself as she roamed the empty house, had deserted her—having gone to stay with an old friend from his dancing days who now lived with some elegance, if little money, in the Dordogne. Matty had generously given her the key to the studios before he left.

'You may as well keep an eye on the place for me, pretty one...and no doubt after your somewhat curiously curtailed vacation, you'll be in need of some proper practice. And remember, Frankie, eat plenty of protein!'

She had been relieved that he hadn't put to her the question which was obviously uppermost in his mind once he had dealt with the, to him, more important instructions to lock up properly and ingest protein. She knew she could have confided in him without any qualms—it was just that there seemed little point in it. Chewing over the past seemed a fruitless activity and it would have revived painful memories which were best put rigorously to the back of her mind. And what could she have said to him anyway? she ruminated, fretfully—that she had been stupid enough to give one night of pleasure to a philandering aristocrat who patently saw her as just another conquest, and that she was now suffering for her stupidity?

'More fool you,' he would probably reply. 'You're old enough to know better.'

It was almost Victorian, she thought bitterly—the master descending below stairs to take his pleasure among the serving wenches. The trouble was, this serving wench was hopelessly in love with the cad. Stifling the acrimony that rose up to choke her, she checked through her rehearsal gear for the hundredth time.

With a generous parting cheque from Lady Manning and the prospect of at last earning a proper salary, she treated herself to a few days in London where she picked out the current trends in dancewear and splurged out on some clothes that had the sole function of boosting her flagging confidence. She didn't want to play the role of country mouse, and when she wasn't crying inwardly over Tristan, she was worrying over whether she would be able to match the cosmopolitan sophistication of the other members of the company.

Her confidence was at such a low ebb, she had to force herself to get on with all the things that had to be done before she left. But she could scarcely drag herself around. It was as if there was a great leaden weight on her shoulders. Even a simple thing such as opening a drawer and catching sight of the saffron sarong neatly folded away among her ordinary clothes brought a hot flood of searing pain flashing up and down her body. With it came the painful vision of Tristan, that slight, ironic turn of the head as he smiled down at her the night of the *legong* dance. Would she ever dare wear the sarong again? Was it possible that she would ever be able to cope with the memories it would bring back?

Their lovemaking had been like the eruption of a volcano, and now all that remained of the spectacular fireworks show was dead ash.

LADY MANNING had no further need of her services, but she rang Frankie the day before she left to join the company to wish her good luck.

'The future of the Hall is still in the balance, I'm afraid,' she told Frankie. 'Tristan is still most reluctant to take over,' she gave a sigh of regret. 'Of course, I can quite sympathise with his point of view, having witnessed for myself the alternative open to him, but I shall be brokenhearted to see the place go out of the family after all.'

Frankie tried to keep her voice steady as she made polite enquiries about the possibility of the younger brother taking over.

'He's farming in Africa,' Lady Manning returned, 'but perhaps there is a possibility there. He and his family are returning shortly to spend August in England.'

It was on the tip of Frankie's tongue to ask after Tristan, but she couldn't trust herself to mention his name without breaking down. As it was, the question was answered for her by Lady Manning herself.

'Tristan appears to have found something to keep him a little longer in Indonesia than expected. I don't suppose we'll see him this summer after all,' she told her. With final good wishes and a request that Frankie keep her informed of her future progress, Lady Manning replaced the phone.

Frankie stood for a long time with the receiver in her hand after the final click—the click that cut her off, irrevocably, finally, from anything to do with Tristan de Vere Manning.

'The end! *Finis! Finito!*' she exclaimed, then she gave a long sigh that seemed to drain her body of all its energy.

OVER THE next few days she managed to scrape up enough self-discipline to work all-out on her dance technique—it had the side effect of momentarily eradicating the burning memories that haunted her. The net result was that by the time she caught the train to London, she was, physically at least, back in top form.

Tristan seemed ever-present no matter how hard she worked, but by chance she stumbled on a way of exorcising the pain—instead of repressing the memory and her feelings for him, she deliberately used them in order to choreograph a short dance solo. She decided that as soon as she had time she would immerse herself in recordings of the hypnotic gamelan sound that had accompanied their brief affair and if possible try to find an opening for performing her own work with the company. Anything was better than giving in spinelessly to the anguish and lack of self-worth that seemed to be closing in around her.

THE DANCE company was centred on a large old Nonconformist chapel in a seedy part of North London. Still puzzled as to how they had come to offer her a job without auditioning her, Frankie wondered if she would be expected to be merely one of the indistinguishable members of the corps, not really a full dancing member, fulfilling the function of a kind of apprentice who would be expected to make a careful observation of the senior members of the company, studying their technique and so on, as was the case with some of the large subsidised companies. Her salary, on the other hand, seemed sufficient proof of their faith in her professional abilities.

She was pondering these things as she stuffed her A-Z back into her grip, turned the next corner, and with a sense of relief, found herself bang opposite the building she had been looking for.

A friendly woman with red hair and the multi-layered working gear of the dancer met her in the entrance. 'Hi, I guess you're Frankie,' she stuck out a slim hand. 'I'm Patti. Come on, I'll show you round.' She swivelled and plunged off into the cavernous building loud with the sound of several different rehearsals going on simultaneously.

Observing the dancers at work in the different studios they passed through Frankie was relieved to note that she wasn't going to show herself up after all. She felt immediately at home.

Patti led her finally into a cluttered office at the top of the building. 'Meet the gaffer!' she grinned with a nod towards the man sitting behind an enormous desk.

Frankie had a small but pleasant shock, which answered many of her speculations, for a balding man beamed genially at her and she gasped—it was the one she had mistaken for an accountant early in the summer—when Matty, the old trickster, had specially asked her to do the *Pierrot* piece—the time, she shuddered, when she had been suffering from that ridiculous and now almost totally forgotten adolescent infatuation for Tristan de Vere

Manning. Her thoughts swerved wildly away from the raw wound she still bore.

Parker Morandi shook her by the hand with an ebullient smile. 'I have a hunch about you. Don't prove me wrong. I can't afford to lose face in front of the animals in this zoo I run,' he told her without preamble.

'I'll do my best not to let you down, then!' she replied at once with a brief flare of her old spirit.

He twinkled back. 'Patti here will take care of any problems, accommodations, lost tights, boyfriends, pay cheques, anything!'

The phone shrilled. He was obviously a busy man.

'New York on the line,' his secretary announced, even as he was shepherding them to the door.

FROM THAT moment Frankie scarcely had time to breathe, let alone think. She was plunged at once into a punishing schedule of rehearsals and a more thorough-going practice routine than anything she had ever experienced. Every night she returned to the rambling flat she shared with three other girls in the company more tired than she had ever thought possible. But she could feel her agility and technique improving daily. And she was happy.

In the long hours when she was dancing, she was truly happy. It was only in the odd, unexpected, unplanned moments, when she wasn't actually rushing to and from rehearsals, or cooking hurried communal meals, or sharing a rare drink in the pub with everyone else, that pain like a knife seared through her.

Instead of the memory of those hated brown eyes, the clean-cut humorous face that could so quickly become an enigmatic blank, the glistening tanned torso illuminated by just one oil lamp in the pagoda by the lake, fading, as it should have done, with the passage of time, it would spring up into her consciousness as clear and undimmed as if it had all happened only yesterday.

Even the prospect of her first public performance refused to dim the memory.

WHEN, AT last, after two months of gruelling work, the time came for Frankie to make her first appearance before a live audience, she stood in the wings, her mind numb with fear, a great growing knot of anxiety turning her stomach to lead.

For the first time she could hear the living response of the audience out there as the curtain went up, could hear its stillness, its sudden roar, its sigh of approval—and in the middle of all this, abruptly and so sharply that it made her gasp, the familiar face seemed to swim before her eyes. It haunted and taunted her at the very rim of her conscious thoughts. She was immobilised by it and, with an attack of stage fright too, if she could have lifted her feet out of the blocks of concrete in which they seemed to be encased, she would have flown out of the theatre and down the street—and caught the next train home.

Luckily, stage fright kept her paralysed until she heard her cue from the orchestra. And suddenly the transformation took place. Tristan miraculously released her and she was flying out across the brilliant stage into the loving embrace of the audience.

AFTERWARDS SHE was incoherent with happiness.

They *liked* me! she kept saying to herself over and over again. They *liked* me! She felt humble and grateful and immensely powerful all at once. It was an intoxication that made her at once an addict.

The next two months sped by in a haze, for after a short season in the South of England, the company was flown to New York where they danced to packed houses.

Frankie's performances received good notices and her status in the company took wing. Parker was delighted with her but took all the credit for himself. Frankie didn't begrudge him it. She was used to the same thing from Matty.

When they returned to Europe, they did a few performances in Paris and returned to England just before Christmas.

Matty himself came to the first of their two London performances. Frankie met him afterwards, throwing herself rapturously into his arms.

'I don't have to ask how you're enjoying yourself,' he remarked, beaming paternally into her face. He introduced his friend, a dance critic from one of the dance magazines, and Frankie was gratified to notice that her performance had impressed the critic.

Before leaving, Matty squeezed her arm. 'Any other help I can give...' he nodded meaningfully over his shoulder, 'anything, Frankie—just give me a call.' He held her face between his two hands. 'You have a haunted look,' he told her. 'Luckily it suits you!'

She kissed him on the cheek. 'No help needed, Matty.' She knew what it was he was too tactful to mention outright. 'I can cope.' When he had gone and she was alone her eyes misted briefly. Dancing was where she put all her heart and soul now—not with people.

The next night Rani and some friends from college were in the audience and afterwards the party backstage went on until the small hours. Most of the company were going their separate ways the next day—some to spend the few days of Christmas with their families, some to have a well-earned rest, and one or two, like Frankie, to stay in London with the intention of working in the extra time available during the break between rehearsals.

To a casual observer Frankie appeared to be thoroughly enjoying herself. She and Rani chatted briefly about what they had both been doing since the summer, but Frankie was relieved that her friend made no mention of Tristan.

'Where are you spending Christmas?' asked Rani when they met up again by the makeshift bar erected on stage.

'I'm staying in town,' Frankie told her. 'I thought I'd do some work.'

'Work? You're a glutton for punishment!' joked Rani, her brown eyes wide with more than mere sympathy. Frankie turned abruptly.

'It's Parker,' she said, averting her glance. 'He saw me working on a piece of my own and asked me to polish it up.' She gave a darting glance. 'He said, "Let me see it after the break. Think of it in terms of a duet." So that's what I'm going to do.' It was all quite true. She had been overjoyed and hugged herself with excitement. To have caught Parker's eye among so many good dancers was one thing—to be invited to show him one of her own pieces was something else again. It made her feel that Fate wasn't entirely against her.

She later broached the question of turning the piece into a duet with Mark Santos. He was the dancer with whose work she was most at home. There was more in his favour. He knew and liked the gamelan piece, having watched her working on it one morning. He had too, she noted with masochistic satisfaction, just the right sort of athletic dark good-looks of the unwitting progenitor of the work. To add to all these advantages, he was involved in a heavy emotional entanglement with one of the older male dancers.

Consciously, perhaps, Frankie had avoided those men in the company who might have harboured any romantic expectations of her, indifferent to the fact that some of them, at any rate, now thought of her as naturally rather frigid. She was happy to find that Mark was willing and able to work with her over the break. His friend lived permanently in town in an elegant flat overlooking Chelsea Reach and Mark had been looking for a suitable excuse to hang around so as not to miss out on the Christmas festivities that he knew his friend would be hosting.

She didn't tell Rani all of this—it might have provoked some questions about the piece, and to have to mention the name of Tristan de Vere Manning was the very last thing Frankie wanted.

It was three o'clock in the morning by the time everybody piled out of the theatre. Frankie waved Rani off in a taxi to the hotel where her parents were staying, then Mark took her into his arms and gave her the comfortable, undemanding embrace of a brother.

'Early start tomorrow then, love,' he stated.

A car parked just down the road from the stage door switched its headlamps on, then off, and began to drive slowly past where they were standing on the pavement.

'Come on,' Mark pulled her into the crook of his arm, 'I'll walk you back to your flat—it's too late to be out alone.'

They ambled contentedly along, arms linked companionably, chewing over the events of the last few hectic weeks.

As she let herself into the flat Frankie saw the same car that had passed them outside the theatre do a U-turn and come back on the far side of the road. It gathered speed as it drew level and was soon roaring off out of sight and into the night.

Frankie stifled a shudder.

It was a similar model to the one *he* had driven—when she had behaved so badly that night in the rain. There must be hundreds of cars like that in London.

NEXT MORNING she arrived at the rehearsal rooms just as Mark came steaming up on his bike. He looked fit, she noted with satisfaction, despite the weeks of living out of suitcases. Together they were certainly going to show Parker a thing or two.

It was an exhausting though fruitful morning. Mark had a wild, surreal imagination, and wasn't afraid to push himself to the limits of his physical capabilities. Frankie felt fired by his imagination and together they began to discover the outlines of an exciting *pas de deux*.

'Let's put the tape on now and go through what we've got so far, then we can see how it's beginning to shape up,' he suggested after a short rest.

'Right!' Frankie sprang to her feet.

Soon the music was echoing loudly around the building, loud enough to cut out any disturbance to their concentration. It had been a coolly lyrical piece when it had merely been Frankie's solo, but now, with Mark's sinewy masculine grace and knife-sharp command of timing, it had developed into an ardent *pas de deux* expressing the fervently emotional elements underlying the hypnotic rhythms of the music.

Their steps emphasised the plasticity of their bodies with twiningly tender arabesques and lifts and falls. Mark was strong and lifted her petite body with ease above his head as he executed an intricate sequence of runs and strides.

When he finally lowered her to the ground she looked up, laughing into his face as they both came to a simultaneous gap in their run of ideas.

'It's going to be great, love!' Mark grinned, hugging her delightedly.

Frankie gave a sudden gasp and froze in his arms. Over his shoulder she thought she caught a glimpse of a painfully familiar face. It had been framed briefly in a panel of glass in the door, but as she raised her head to look properly, it had vanished abruptly.

Hot and cold by turns, she snatched herself out of Mark's arms, one hand flying to her mouth as her eyes widened. With a brief word of apology she ran to the door and scanned the corridor. It was empty.

Was she mad? Was she now beginning to hallucinate? Even as she threw herself headlong towards the street, she tried to tell herself that it was her imagination—playing tricks because of all the memories the gamelan had conjured up.

There was no possible way he could be here in London in the rehearsal room—staring at her with that strange, haunted look on his face as if... She must be working too hard, she told herself, the strain of all the recent months of touring was beginning to tell.

But as she pushed open the heavy wooden doors that gave on to the street, however, she was just in time to see the familiar lithe figure reach the M.G. parked by the kerb.

He was real enough! He was no hallucination!

The first time she tried to speak his name no sound would come.

'Tristan!' she shrieked, in a sudden panic that he would drive away without seeing her reaching out to him.

The cry made him pause with his hand on the car door and when he looked back at her his face was as black as thunder. She swallowed, aware now of a feeling worse than any stage fright that turned her body to a block of marble.

For a long time neither of them said anything. Frankie found herself willing him to speak, to say anything, anything at all to break the pall of silence that weighed over them.

At last, with an effort, he straightened. She saw again the old mocking smile that tugged agonisingly at her heartstrings as he loped slowly back across the pavement towards her.

He gave her a slow, measuring, up and down look from beneath hooded lids. 'You're looking very...fit,' he told her slowly.

'I have to be.' Her hands fluttered nervously over her hair, teasing it back from her face, smoothing down her wrinkled practice clothes.

'Yes.'

There was another heavy silence.

When he gazed down at her with that lazy grin that somehow managed to obscure whatever he was really feeling, she floundered even more. He looked so relaxed, so in control of himself. He made one or two casual remarks about happening to find himself in London, and, being at a loose end, deciding to look her up. The words he chose hurt her. They seemed to sum up so aptly his feeling, or rather lack of it, towards her.

She forced herself to stay calm and allowed her eyes to hold his unwaveringly, giving nothing away.

It was as if the intervening months had faded away and it was dawn on that first morning when she had woken to the full impact of her love for him. It had never been mere lust. There was more to it than that, had always been more to it than that, at least for her. But what now?

She waited for him to stop talking. Her face felt stiff with unshed tears and there was an awkward pause when his words came to an end. With an effort she made herself speak.

'I saw your car last night,' she told him gravely.

He half turned with a trapped motion of his shoulders. 'Yes,' he admitted, 'I thought I might as well spend an evening at the theatre and your lot happened to be on.'

'I'm glad you were there.'

'You're quite a dancer, Frankie. I'm sorry if I ever belittled your talent.'

Frankie reached out and touched him impulsively on the arm. 'I wish I'd known you were there,' she whispered. There was such a note of regret in her voice that his glance held her own in a sudden access of feeling.

'The summer seems a long time ago now,' he suggested tentatively. 'It seems like another world.'

She was holding her breath and it hurt. Tristan put a hand on her shoulder. There was a pause in which neither of them seemed able to speak, then his face tightened into a hard mask and he rasped, 'You'd better not keep your partner waiting, though, had you?'

She felt his fingers bite deep into her shoulder and then to her utter astonishment he swung abruptly on his heel and was striding rapidly back towards the car without another word.

He was already sitting in the driver's seat when she came to life. 'Tristan! Wait!' she called. Running lightly over to the car, she hung on to the door. 'Is that all?' she breathed, vainly searching for the appropriate words without success. 'I—I—I mean, how long are you down here for? How long in England? Where are you staying?' The meaningless questions fell from her lips.

Tristan started the engine and gave a glance into the rearview mirror. 'I'm off back North today,' he told her. 'Look me up if you ever venture north of Watford again!'

Then, to her ultimate dismay, the car began to slide off into the stream of traffic, and in a moment it was obscured by a double-decker bus.

'Oh God, oh no! No!' Frankie felt the tears rush silently down her cheeks. 'No! No!' she cried aloud, fists clenching and unclenching helplessly by her sides. With a cry she turned and ran blindly back into the studio.

Mark was already coming down the corridor to find out what had happened to her when she burst in through the doors. In a moment she had sobbed out the whole story, and when he saw what a state she was in he stroked her hair and vainly tried to calm her. 'Poor lamb, poor lamb,' he soothed over and over until the sobbing ceased.

'There now,' he murmured, wiping the last of her tears away with a tissue, 'I'm going to take you across the road for a good stiff drink. It'd be inhuman to try to get you to work on this particular piece after going through all that.'

He pushed her towards the changing room. 'I'll give you five minutes to put on a public face. All right?'

'Believe me,' he told her later over a drink, 'I know what swine men can be!' But there was little he could do to temper her heart's pain apart from offer his shoulder to cry on.

FOR THE next few days Frankie jumped everytime the 'phone rang, and when she wasn't working she haunted the window that looked out into the street, just in case a dark green sports car should happen to draw up outside the house. Slowly it became obvious that what Tristan had implied when he had told her he had just happened to stop by to see her was in fact true—his appearance at the rehearsal studios had been as casual as he had said it was and there had been no deeper motive.

She knew she would have to make another supreme effort and put their brief meeting firmly into its place in the past with all her other memories of him. It had, after all, been for him just a quick affair, with no meaning at all.

She threw herself back into her work with even greater dedication now. For the next few days there was nothing but work, work and more work.

It had its results. Parker was duly impressed by the new *pas de deux* when it was finished and he promised to put it into their new London season at Easter. Frankie was gratified. At least there was something positive to show for all the months of heartache.

BEFORE THE new spring season started she returned North with the intention of supervising the sale of the house, and she and Davey got horribly drunk together and said a lot of maudlin things about the break-up of the family.

He was enjoying himself and she knew he would never want to come back to live here.

Nor would she, she told him. 'I'm now firmly settled in my London life, Davey, though precious little time is actually spent in town.' She gave a half-hearted smile. 'The company is becoming one of the big successes in the dancing world.'

'I know. I read all your reviews,' he clapped her on the shoulder with a smile that expressed his brotherly pride in her.

While she was home she decided she would have to make time to see Matty. The Centre was looking prosperous and he had taken a lease on a listed building next door in order to extend his studio space. His friend, late of the Dordogne, was thinking of coming into partnership with him and they invited Frankie to dinner, regaling her with stories of their own days as dancers in the same company.

They all drank a lot and laughed a lot, but when Toby went out of the room for a moment, Matty leaned across to take Frankie's two hands in his.

'We haven't got long for anything private, so spill the beans, honey. What's up?'

Frankie's instinct was to hedge, but her attempt only brought a grim frown to Matty's face.

'Baby, I know you well enough to see that something isn't quite right. I said last time I saw you—if there's anything I can do...'

'No one can do anything, Matty, not even you.' She shrugged dispiritedly. There was no point in pretending with Matty; he seemed to see everything. 'I've just got a painfully long memory, that's all. It's bound to fade.'

He looked stern. 'That aristocratic swine's at the bottom of this, is he? Well, just make sure you don't work yourself into the ground, that's all!'

Toby came in and Frankie felt ashamed to find hot tears stinging her cheeks.

'Man trouble!' explained Matty with a dismissive wave of the hand.

'Oh, that! How we suffer!' Toby sank down beside her and gave her a sympathetic pat on the shoulder.

'Why doesn't Matty just tell me to eat more protein or something?' Frankie muttered between great gulping sobs. 'I can't bear sympathy—it's the sympathy that makes me cry!'

The two men put on mock bullying tones and ordered her to snap out of it, but underneath the banter, Frankie could see that Matty was truly concerned.

IT TOOK a good two days to clear the house, and when Davey finally left to go back to university, she got a dealer in second-hand furniture to come and cart away the things neither of them wanted.

Stripped of carpets and furniture with only a few packing cases heaped against the walls, the poor old place looked desolate.

Frankie's bag was already packed and she was just having a final check round when the 'phone shrilled from the room downstairs.

She leaped two at a time down the now uncarpeted stairs, thinking that it must be the estate agent, but when she picked it up she froze.

A familiar voice at the other end asked, 'Is that Frankie?'

'Yes, Lady Manning,' she replied faintly.

'Thank heavens for that! I've been away and only just arrived back here the day before yesterday. I heard you were selling up, but I hoped I might see you before you left.'

'I'm sorry. I'm just off now, actually,' Frankie told her, not untruthfully. She had almost finished her work on the house.

'That's a great shame, my dear. Perhaps if I sent a car out for you you'd be able to come over for half an hour right away?'

There was a pause while Frankie's heart began to pound with the sudden flood of memories that came surging back. It would be fitting, came the thought, if, in the final day of winding up her life here, she could lay the ghost of her memories once and for all.

'What do you say, Frankie?' Lady Manning was asking hopefully.

Unable to resist visiting the place once more, Frankie cautiously agreed. She gripped the 'phone, feeling suddenly breathless at her own folly. Hadn't she already plumbed her capacity for pain? How could she contemplate yet more?

'Expect a car within the hour. Then,' Lady Manning added proudly, 'I think I shall stroll down the drive to meet you!'

Frankie replaced the phone in a turmoil.

She didn't even know if *he* was there, or back in Bali again with whatever 'pressing reason' had kept him there all last summer. She was crazy to hope! All the self-discipline that had made her able to carry on with her work was nothing against the raging flood of memories that threatened to engulf her. She had already seen how indif-

ferent he was to her at their last meeting. Was the humiliation of having the experience repeated really worth it—
just for one last glimpse of him?

She stalked nervously about the echoing rooms trying in
vain to get herself under control. What a fool she had been
to say 'yes' to Lady Manning. She should have stuck to her
decision to have nothing more to do with the source of this
raging pain.

IN WELL under half an hour the sound of a car pulling up
outside sent her flying to an upstairs window.

She gripped the edge of the sill in a sudden faint. Her
worst nightmare was yet to come. Even as she watched,
Tristan himself was uncoiling himself from the little two-
seater.

White-faced, Frankie forced herself to walk back
downstairs. Agonisingly conscious that every step took her
closer to an encounter that could only turn the knife deeper
into her heart, she approached the front door. There she
paused, with her head resting on the door jamb for a moment. It was all that was left to protect her from the cruel
indifference of his glance . . .

Taking a grip upon herself, she turned the lock and
pulled the door wide. She saw him striding rapidly up the
path towards her. Before she could even open her mouth
to speak, he had gained the entrance, and without a word,
his arms came round her, crumpling her against him in a
feverish spasm of emotion.

They swayed together for a moment without speaking.
Frankie felt her hands come up of their own accord to bury
themselves in his thick, dark hair. Then his lips burned a
course down the side of her face and came to a stop over
her astonished mouth. She felt the slow waves of a deli-
cious warmth melt away the pain of long days and nights
of wanting him.

Eventually he lifted his head to gaze broodingly into her face. 'Hell, Frankie, you've driven me to the edge of despair!' he murmured smokily. His grip tightened. 'I haven't slept a night through since I saw you in the arms of that dancer bloke,' he went on huskily.

'Mark? You mean Mark?' She found herself laughing and crying at once. 'He can't be the reason you suddenly drove off like a maniac that day in London, surely?' she whispered.

'A case of old-fashioned jealousy,' he confessed. 'I never guessed it could feel as bad as that!'

'I thought you just didn't care.' Tears at past pain filled her eyes.

'You beautiful little fool—I'm crazy about you. Didn't you guess?' He held her at arm's length for a moment. 'But tell me honestly, Frankie, I must know if there really is anything between you both?'

'Never has been and never will be—except work!' she told him simply.

He folded her tiny body into his arms once again. 'I confess I came along that day fully intending to force an apology from you for running away from me in Bali,' he gave a grimace, 'but the tables were very neatly turned, and it was me who did the running in the end!'

'I hated you when you disappeared with that Balinese dancer, then came back all turned on, apparently expecting me to be suddenly available after you'd ignored me for days on end straight after—' she faltered, 'after that night by the lake...it just seemed to confirm that you only wanted me for...' Her voice became inaudible and he had to bend his head so that his lips brushed her ear. 'I just had to get away from you.'

'I feel so bad about it all now.' His arms tightened again. 'I was in a state of total confusion. I felt I had to ignore you. It was either that—or marry you!'

Her eyes widened and he went on, 'When it came to standing next to you at the New Moon Festival I realised that I just couldn't resist you. That I was being an utter fool even to contemplate resistance!' He laughed huskily and dragged her hard against him. 'It was standing next to you that turned me on—and I'd tried to fight it! How I tried!'

'But it was deliberate?' Frankie dropped her glance, thoughts raced in confusion.

'I didn't mean to hurt you,' Tristan explained quietly. 'I tried to tell myself that it was just a game for us both, that you were sufficiently experienced to know what you were doing and sensible enough not to let yourself get hurt. I made myself fly to Bali instead of coming straight back to Pelabutan Ratu because while I was in Djakarta it suddenly hit me that I wanted to marry you.' He pressed her closer as if afraid of losing her. 'The idea seemed crazy, but I couldn't get rid of it. I didn't want to have to be bothered with a wife, dragging her around the rain forests, listening to her complaints about the heat and the mosquitoes. Marriage seemed to be a trap for fools.' He paused. 'I didn't want it. I hated the idea. Yet it didn't seem right to go on making love to you . . .'

His face took on a more serious expression. 'My mind was in a turmoil. I think I probably guessed how much that night meant to you too—one part of me wanted it to mean as much to you as it did to me—yet I also thought that if we continued like that it would weaken my resistance to you—and before I knew it, I'd be proposing and spoiling all my plans!'

His lips caressed her forehead. 'Of course, that's exactly what has happened—and without all those months of lovemaking too. I could kick myself!' He gave her a devilish grin that was like a slow pulse along the whole length of her body. Then he kissed her. It started as a light touching of lips, but then it deepened and spread in a molten fire flow that swept them into the glowing coils of a long-pent passion.

MUCH LATER Frankie, starry-eyed, turned to Tristan. 'What you were saying earlier sounded horribly like a proposal, Lord Manning!'

He moulded her naked body to his own. 'Oh, Frankie,' he murmured, 'I know it can work. But have I the right to affect your career?' He looked serious. 'My younger brother came over in the summer with his family. He took to the idea of resettling here—things are becoming a little dicey in Africa. He's selling up there now and has agreed to take over the farm. Mother of course is delighted. And so am I. It means that I no longer have the threat of having to become a farmer hanging over my head. I can have a base in England anywhere now...' He paused. 'I thought maybe a place in London would be a good idea. What do you say?'

'Sounds wonderful,' she murmured, not quite believing that this was really happening.

His eyes were alight. 'I shall have to spend part of each year out East—but I thought of maybe taking a choreographer along with me to help notate some of the more complicated dances for students of the art over here. And, of course,' he added as she began to smile, 'a base in London would be very convenient, with all those theatres to go to—I've heard there's a pretty good dance company around these days!'

He kissed her deeply on the mouth. 'Are you with me so far, sweetheart?'

'Oh, Tristan,' she breathed, tilting back her head so that she could look full into his beloved face. 'I'm with you now and always.'

IT TOOK Tristan longer than Lady Manning had expected to pick up Frankie from her house in the town and bring her out in time for luncheon.

She had been strolling up and down for some time before her son's old M.G. came roaring and spitting round the corner of the lane on to the gravel drive.

One look at both their faces told her that it would be quite in order to peck Francesca on the cheek with motherly affection. She had always had a hankering for a daughter—one who would take up the dancing career she herself had had to forgo.

Tristan put his arms round Frankie's waist. His mother could get up the steps unaided now. Frankie, however, was a different matter.

It was the sarong she wore that made things difficult. It had a habit of unwinding itself in one long sinuous movement, as he had recently discovered.

He put a hand firmly round her waist. 'Just in case it slips again!' he murmured in her ear.

She bit him discreetly on the ear. 'Ever thought about a job as dresser in a theatre?' she teased. Her head tilted back so that her long, waist-length hair snaked over her shoulders. 'Though "undresser" would be more your line!'

He pulled her back for a minute before going in through the doors and it was only the sound of the dinner gong that brought them back to the matter of lunch.

'Come on, my lady, we have something to celebrate. Then it's back into town to take old Matty out for a celebration drink. He's probably been sitting beside the phone all morning—ever since he stuck his head out to ring me.'

'So that's how . . . !' Frankie smiled. Darling old Matty. How could she ever thank him?

Together they moved on into the house.

'I wonder if Matty would like to give me away...' she began, thinking of the wedding.

'It's all right,' quipped Tristan. 'I told him I'd pay up.' He kissed her once on the nose. 'I know you're going to be worth every penny—whatever the asking price!'

THE AUTHOR

Sandra Clark was born in Yorkshire. After leaving university she had several jobs, including running an art gallery, a guest house and a boutique. In addition to romance writing she has written several plays for theater and television. To relax she turns to sailing, reading and interior decorating, and she helps out at a children's nursery whenever she can. The author now lives in York with her two teenage children.

The Last Barrier

Edwina Shore

She'd had time to get over things. So everyone said. Physically Paula had recovered, but the guilty feeling of being responsible for the accident that killed her fiancé and his small son still overwhelmed her.

She agreed to spend time at a cottage on the Scottish estate of her publisher's friend, old Sir Iain Cameron—to pull herself together and to redo the book illustrations she'd been shocked to find were unacceptable.

But she wouldn't have come if she'd known about young Jamie and his disturbing uncle Hugo, for inevitably they broke through the barrier she'd erected between herself and life . . . and love.

CHAPTER ONE

PAULA SAT on the bench against the rough stone wall of the cottage. The blank page of the sketch-pad on her lap gleamed white in the late afternoon sunlight—but unthreateningly. And that was the difference five weeks on the island had made: a blank page was just a blank page and not the end of the world. Tomorrow she might fill it; then again, she might not. Lazily contented, Paula leaned back and watched the child.

Jamie lay on the ground a few feet away, engrossed in stacking stones of varying sizes into some mysterious shape that presumably had its counterpart in his imagination. He was a small dark wisp of a boy; a Celtic child with his pale skin and dark blue eyes under the crop of black curls. Paula found she could look at him without any image of Stephen rearing in her mind and that was something she wouldn't have believed possible when she first arrived on the island and discovered him staying with his grandfather at the main house.

Then, every small boy, any shape or size, was still a painful reminder of Stephen, and Paula had been furious that her publisher hadn't told her about Jamie when he organised her stay on the island. If she had known about the child she wouldn't have come, and that was probably why Roger hadn't told her. Mild subterfuge perhaps, but for someone so invariably predictable during all the years Paula had known him, Roger had suddenly taken to acting startlingly out of character.

He had astounded her at their lunch six weeks ago when she handed over her illustrations for the new children's book his company was about to publish. Her first attempt since the car crash, Paula's heart and soul had gone into them and she had sat back, expecting...what? Approval...? Delighted congratulations...? Roger's reaction shocked her speechless.

The kind, concerned friend who had gently bullied her into taking the commission in the first place turned into a stranger who lashed her ruthlessly about reproducing stuff she had done years ago, about using Stephen as the model for the small body in the book.

'Stephen's dead,' Roger had stated cruelly, 'and sticking him into every book from now to Kingdom Come won't bring him back to life. He's wrong for this book, Paula, and if you can't see that, you'd better think about another line of work, because the Paula Halstead who was on her way to becoming one of the top illustrators in the business doesn't exist anymore.'

Paula hadn't been able to believe her ears. 'It's a year since the accident, Paula—time enough to pull yourself together and get over things,' Roger told her with that same calculated cruelty, and Paula had never hated anyone as she did Roger Harris at that moment. What did Roger know about 'getting over things'? She had caused the accident which had taken the life of her fiancé and his four-year-old son, and that wasn't something a year—or any number of years—could wipe out. Mark's death she might have coped with, but a child's...? Was it any wonder it was Stephen's little face she had drawn on every page willy-nilly?

'You need to get away for a while and I know just the place,' Roger said, and Paula had heard that before—a lot. Ever since she had recovered from the accident—physically at any rate—everyone was always trying to pack her off somewhere. Glazed-eyed, Paula had listened to count-less versions of 'just the place'; Italy was her mother's panacea for anything from a cold to a nervous break-down, but there had been Spanish beaches, Swiss moun-tains, she had rejected them all.

And Roger's version?

A remote Scottish island. Peace, quiet, no distractions; no memories of Mark and Stephen was what he meant of course. And the way Roger put it, she would practically be doing his old friend Sir Iain Cameron a favour by staying in the cottage on Sir Iain's estate for a couple of months. The retired heart specialist had recently lost a son and daughter-in-law in an air disaster in America and would be grateful for her company.

The selling points were mere formality. Having just shocked the daylights out of her, Roger could have packed her off anywhere he chose, and it was just as well his friend only lived off the coast of Scotland and not Africa, Paula thought with a wry smile as she put the sketch-pad on the bench and felt her hair. It was almost dry. She ran her fin-gers through the curls to ruffle the last moisture out of them and thought idly about getting her hair cut, but it seemed too much trouble.

Mark had liked her hair very short—a curly red-gold cap close to her head. He said the style brought out the gold flecks in her green eyes, but the artist in her saw it was wrong and disliked it. At five feet eight, she was too tall for such a small cap of hair but had given in and worn it that way to please him. There had been other things she had given in about. A shutter clicked down in her mind. She did not want to think about Mark. Paula sighed audibly and Jamie lifted his head.

'Will Uncle Hugo come today?' he asked—as he asked almost every day and probably not just of her; his grand-father, Anna the housekeeper and even Neil, the odd-job man, must have come in for their share of the heartbreaking question.

Paula smiled down at the upturned face and gave a small shrug. 'You'll have to ask your grandfather.' Her standard answer.

'I did ask him,' Jamie muttered stonily. 'He said Uncle Hugo didn't tell him.'

'Then it will be a lovely surprise when he does come, won't it?' Paula said lightly, resenting the uncle who could so casually leave a small boy waiting without a word.

Jamie gave her a long searching look. The penetrating gaze of the dark velvety eyes made Paula uncomfortable. Her comment had been patronising and the boy deserved better than that—if only the truth.

'I'm sorry Jamie, I just don't know when your uncle will come. But I'm sure it must be very soon now,' she added in spite of herself because she couldn't bear the blank, distancing look that came into the child's eyes.

Jamie dropped his eyes from her face. A deliberate sweep of the small hand scattered the carefully-balanced construction into an untidy heap of stones. He got to his feet and without a word started down the path to the water.

Paula watched him go with despairing helplessness. There was no point in calling him back because she couldn't give the answer he wanted any more than his grandfather; only Hugo Cameron could do that and he apparently chose not to.

She had held back from questioning Sir Iain about his son's absence, but concern for Jamie, and, Paula had to admit, an element of curiosity, had made her broach the subject with the housekeeper.

'It's not that he doesn't want the lad,' Anna hastily assured her. 'Jamie is his own brother's son after all, but it's barely three months since the tragedy and there is still so much Mr Hugo has to attend to, putting things into trust for Jamie and the good Lord only knows what else. It's a mercy Mr Hugo is such a fine businessman, else it would take forever, what with all the extra work his brother's death has created for him. Mind you, he did have the boy with him in London for the first month but it wasn't easy for a man in his position so he thought it would be best for everybody if the lad stayed with Sir Iain awhile. When Mr Hugo gets back from America he'll be making more permanent arrangements.'

To suit his own convenience and never mind about Jamie. Paula managed to restrain herself from voicing her conclusions aloud, but the picture built up in her mind; she thought Hugo Cameron a monstrously selfish man and took Anna's indulgent explanations with a very large pinch of salt. To hear the old housekeeper talk, 'Mr Hugo' ran financial empires single-handed and in his spare time walked on water.

Paula got up abruptly and wandered down the path. Jamie had not gone far and she saw him immediately. She rounded the small slope that blocked the view of the sea from her cottage. He was sitting on a rock a short way up the beach, waiting for her. His face brightened as she reached him. 'Are you coming to the house for dinner this evening?' he asked, by way of telling her that his little fit of depression was over.

'Yes, your grandfather has asked me,' Paula replied with a smile.

'Oh good. I shall come and call for you. I like coming to call for you,' he added shyly.

'I like it too.'

Escorting her to the house on the evenings she dined there made him feel grown-up and important, but it made Paula sad and at the same time unaccountably angry that such a small thing should be such a highlight in his life. She turned away so he wouldn't see the expression on her face. 'Come on, Jamie, let's play follow-my-leader.'

They took it in turns to lead the way, jumping from rock to rock in the green shallows, the leader selecting the most difficult rocks. The one who slipped off into the water the least times won, and it was a moot point as to which of them derived the more enjoyment from the simple game. 'Larking about' Mark would have called it—and disapproved.

Paula jumped off the last rock of the outcrop and Jamie followed, laughing at her heels. 'We'll call it a draw. Home now, Jamie, it's getting too chilly to stay any longer and Anna will have to clean you up before dinner. Your jeans are soaked.'

'So are yours,' he retorted cheekily. 'Race you back to the house.' He grinned—more gaps than teeth, and started sprinting lightly across the sand in the direction of the path to the main house. Paula gave him a head start then set off after him.

At the top of the slope where the ground levelled out and the solid two-storey stone house came into view, there was a rough stretch of path before it became smoother again closer to the house. Jamie was intent on picking his way over the uneven stony surface which was why Paula saw the car before he did, and stopped in her tracks.

She had never seen anything like it. Forced to guess, she would have said it was one of those fantastic Italian jobs, but low and sleek, all curves and glass, the navy sports-car looked as exotically alien as a spaceship. Who in their right mind would bring a car like that on to an island which boasted a main street about the width of a London alley? 'Uncle Hugo is here!' Paula heard Jamie suddenly shriek. 'Uncle Hugo,' who else? And if that was Uncle Hugo's style then she disliked it as much as she already disliked the man.

Jamie stood transfixed until she reached him. 'Uncle Hugo is here,' he repeated, and seemed so stunned he could barely get the strangled whisper out. He grabbed her hand. 'Hurry Paula, Uncle Hugo is here,' he squeaked again and together they ran past the car to the house.

The front door was ajar. Jamie flung himself against it like a miniature whirlwind. 'Easy, Jamie,' Paula laughed, trying to catch her breath as he literally dragged her into the spacious hall, a room in itself with the large open fire-place facing the front door.

The man crossing the hall turned at the commotion they made, then stopped and they all just stood there and stared at each other.

Her vicious mental picture of 'Uncle Hugo' had not in-cluded any physical details, but Paula would have recog-nised the man in front of her a mile off. It was like seeing the Sir Iain of thirty years ago—or Jamie thirty years on, a tall powerfully-built man, with the bones of his face more pronounced, the nose and jaw stronger but with that same remarkable colouring. Only surely without that hardness in the handsome face?

It was a long, awkward moment; Hugo Cameron at one end of the hall, she and Jamie at the other, the child grip-ping her hand with excruciating fierceness. Hugo Cam-eron made the first move—a sudden gesture, abruptly raising his hands as if he was opening his arms to the child. He dropped them again as Jamie stayed rooted to the spot. The boy might have been fretting for his uncle, but face to face with him at last was acting as if he was terrified of the man.

'Do you plan on staying there all day?' There was an edge to the smooth voice that carried no trace of his fa-ther's brogue.

Paula unprised the vice-like little fingers and gave Jamie a gentle push. Set into motion, he strode towards the man, almost bravely, and held out his hand. 'Hello, Uncle Hugo,' he said formally, in a low unsteady voice, with his head lowered and eyes fixed somewhere around his uncle's feet.

Paula winced. Any other child would have hurled himself at the man like an excited puppy. Not Jamie. Hugo Cameron's nephew feared rejection too much and had waited too long to risk it.

They shook hands with a solemnity that might have amused her if it hadn't been so heart-rendingly pathetic. Jamie finally took his eyes off his uncle's shoes and Hugo suddenly smiled down at him. From across the hall the eyes looked as black as the eyebrows and the wayward lock of hair above them, but closer, Paula knew they would be the same startling dark blue as the child's. As Hugo smiled they lit up, relaxing the hardness of his face and giving it an unexpected warmth. He put his hand to the boy's head and ran his fingers through the springy black curls that resembled his own. 'Hello, young man,' he said gently.

She hadn't realised she had been holding her breath. Paula felt herself relax. There was affection in the man's gesture and in his voice. She felt vaguely reassured and could only hope that Jamie felt the same way.

Hugo raised his eyes to her over Jamie's head. The warmth which had lit up their dark depths when he smiled at the child was so very definitely absent Paula wondered if she had imagined it. They ranged over her unhurriedly, with casual but unmistakable expertise. It was a blatantly sexual appraisal and Hugo Cameron made no attempt to disguise that from her.

As his eyes returned to her face, Paula stiffened with hostility, heat streaking her cheeks as she tried to push back the rising consciousness of her untidy mass of wind-blown curls, the shapeless sweater and damp jeans above the inelegant Wellingtons. She stared back stonily, irritatingly aware she presented a picture of overgrown ragamuffin while in his superbly cut navy slacks and cameltoned pullover, Hugo Cameron could have stepped out of the pages of a fashion magazine—too smooth and suave by half; Paula wished he'd step right back into them and disappear from sight.

Jamie moved to his uncle's side and gave her a blissful beam. 'This is my Uncle Hugo.' He effected his childish introduction with the air of an amateur magician pulling a rabbit out of a hat—with desperate panache and a grateful relief that it had been in there at all.

Hugo's mouth gave a quirk at the boy's proud announcement. 'And who's your friend, Jamie?' he queried drily.

Paula was livid at being addressed through the child.

'Paula. She's pretty, isn't she?' Jamie looked up anxiously at his uncle for confirmation of his statement.

'Yes. Very pretty.' The cool voice agreed smoothly while the eyes took in her growing discomfort with something that looked very much like satisfaction.

Paula hated being called pretty. She was not pretty; unusual-looking, yes. The upward slant of the almond-shaped eyes were paralleled by the long line of the eyebrows; the nose was straight but her mouth she had always considered too wide and the bottom lip too full. Her colouring was the most striking feature and the bones were in the right place, as her sculptor mother would say. The overall effect was interesting but it needed more than a casual glance, no matter how expert, to pick that up. The child's assessment was innocent enough; the man's comment strictly patronising and meant to embarrass.

Paula unfroze her face into marginally less antagonistic lines for Jamie's sake. 'I'm sure Jamie is very happy to see you—at last, Mr Cameron.' She squeezed the words out through her teeth and turned with a sweep to the door.

'Just a moment…Paula.' Her name was included as an afterthought and with a deliberate familiarity that made her bristle.

Paula reversed her turn. 'Yes, Mr Cameron?' she bit out frostily and was pleased to note from the momentary scowl that she'd hit the right tone of voice—the one that needled him.

Hugo's mouth tightened into a thin straight line of displeasure. 'The boy needs a bath,' he said with clipped coldness.

Completely taken aback, all Paula could do was agree. 'Yes, he does.' Jamie usually needed a bath and a change of clothes after one of their more exuberant sessions on the beach and Anna usually gave him one.

'Then I suggest you take him upstairs and give him one,' Hugo snapped, pushing Jamie towards her. Paula was too astonished to react. 'You look as if you could do with one yourself,' Hugo observed drily, his mouth giving a satisfied twist as the impertinence hit home. Flaring like a beacon, Paula opened her mouth and shut it again.

'See to the child.' Hugo gave a curt nod of dismissal and walked away leaving Paula speechless.

On the point of a seizure, she watched him disappear through the doorway into the living-room and then it was all she could do to stop herself lunging after him, and demanding to know just who the hell he thought he was to be speaking to her like that—or more to the point, who did he think she was?

The answer was fairly obvious when the consuming fury died down to a low seething burn: he had taken her for a maid, or Jamie's nanny. Well, there were worse things to be taken for and that wasn't what made Paula so furious—it was the sheer arrogance and familiarity accompanying the assumption that took her breath away.

Jamie looked up, eyes clouded with puzzlement and hurt, the scene he had just witnessed way beyond his comprehension. Paula put a not-very-steady hand on his rigid little shoulder. 'Perhaps we had better do what your uncle wants, Jamie,' she said in a voice so controlled she amazed herself.

It was a quick bath and quick change into clean clothes—all achieved without a word. Jamie might not have understood what had gone on downstairs—Paula wasn't sure she understood herself—but the child was hurt and she could sense that part of his silent reproach was directed at her, as if she too had somehow failed him.

And in a way he was right. She had unwittingly created the unhappy situation just by being there. Hugo Cameron had been much too sharp to miss her antagonism and had gone out of his way to needle her and while she hadn't done much more than glare her dislike, the result was the same as if they had engaged in an all-out slanging match. And poor Jamie had suffered for it.

Paula ran a comb through his damp hair. 'There now, you'd better go and show yourself to your uncle again.'

Jamie gave her an expressionless stare. 'I hate him,' he said, very quietly and without any emotion.

Paula said nothing. She understood how he felt and when downstairs outside the door to the living-room he clung to her hand and pleaded 'Please come in with me, Paula,' she couldn't find it in herself to refuse.

Head thrown back, eyes closed, Hugo was stretched out in an armchair by the fireplace where the peat burnt warmly; mid-May brought no guarantee of warmth to the island, and Anna laid the fire daily. The long, powerful frame swamped Sir Iain's favourite chair but his son seemed totally at ease in it and surprisingly, very much part of the warm, mellow room. Paula felt an unreasonable stirring of resentment to see him blend in so easily—as if

he belonged. She thought he was asleep until Hugo flicked
his eyes open, and moving his head slightly met her eyes.

'Your nephew has been given a bath—as ordered,' she
said tightly, and tried out a waxy smile on him. If he
thought she was Jamie's nanny, she would act the part for
him.

'A decided improvement,' Hugo smiled—at the child,
then swept a quick look over her. Paula glared him a dare
to comment on her own unaltered appearance but he
passed up the challenge and turned his head towards the
far end of the room—to the woman standing in the deeply-
recessed bay of the large front window. Paula wondered
how she could have possibly missed noticing her.

'This is my nephew, Louise...James's son.' Hugo motioned Jamie towards the woman. 'Go and say how-do-
you-do to Miss Hunt, Jamie.'

Jamie dutifully crossed the room to the elegant brunette in the russet suede slacks with a matching jacket
draped loosely over a white silk shirt.

'It's lovely to meet you, Jamie,' she murmured in a low
husky voice, and ignoring Jamie's extended hand, reached
out to ruffle his hair.

Dropping his hand, Jamie stepped back abruptly—quite
rudely, out of her reach, and Miss Hunt's smile was momentarily superceded by a flash of dislike. Then shrugging elegantly, she dropped her own hand and turned her
eyes on Paula—or rather, Paula surmised, returned them;
the woman must have been watching her all the time.

Paula met the bland stare with a slight smile and might
have saved her muscles the bother; it went completely un-
acknowledged. The beautifully made-up eyes looked right
through her before Louise Hunt lifted her ever-so-slightly
too-prominent chin and looked away. The airy little snub
left Paula white with outrage. She did not have to stand for
this sort of treatment from anybody. 'If you'll excuse me,'

she said with a civility that almost choked her and turned to the door.

'Wait!' Hugo Cameron shot the word at her back. Paula froze. The urge to ignore him and flounce out of the room was overpowering and for a split second she thought she would. But she turned around slowly, deliberately keeping her hand on the door knob. She didn't speak because she wasn't sure she could be accountable for any words that came out of her mouth. Arching a shapely eyebrow with all the haughtiness she could produce, Paula gave what Roger always called her fish-eyed stare. It was usually effective—it riled people no end, and Hugo Cameron was no exception. His eyes narrowed dangerously.

After the pause that went on for too long, he said icily, 'I'll want a word with you later—I'll let you know when it's convenient.'

Don't hold your breath, Paula would have loved to have spat at him but didn't quite have the nerve, and there was something about him that made her feel quite glad she was not Jamie's nanny after all. She made a non-committal movement of her head that was open to any interpretation he chose to put on it, then with a glance and a quick smile at the miserable-looking Jamie trapped by the window near Miss Hunt, Paula walked out.

With remarkable restraint she closed the door very quietly behind her—only because she sensed the unbelievably arrogant man in the living-room was expecting her to slam it and she was not going to give him even that small satisfaction if she could help it.

Just around the corner of the corridor off the hall, Anna was saying something in incomprehensible but very loud Gaelic. To Paula's consternation, Sir Iain's voice murmured a reply a step closer. Another moment and they'd be upon her and Sir Iain would insist on taking her back into the living-room to introduce her formally to his son.

No thank you. She'd had about as much of his disagreeable son as she could stand for one day. Paula shot to the front door.

A couple of hurried steps down the path she stopped, suddenly remembering she was expected to dine at the house that evening. Sit at table with Hugo Cameron? She'd rather starve to death. Paula hesitated. Make her excuses to Sir Iain now or wait until later when she had calmed down a little?

As she dithered, the front door opened and slammed shut again. Paula spun around to see Jamie flying down the steps towards her, his face telling all. No longer his uncle's 'young man' he was simply a very unhappy and hurt small boy, and unthinkingly, Paula dropped to her knees and let him run into her arms.

She held him close until his emotional spasm passed then released him. 'Would you like me to take you back inside now?''

Jamie gave an agitated shake of his head. 'No. Uncle Hugo doesn't like me.'

It would have been easy to dismiss his accusation with the pat adult 'nonsense.' She had only his uncle's smile to go by, and the way he had run his fingers through Jamie's hair, but Paula sensed that despite his brusqueness Hugo did like the boy. 'I think he does like you, Jamie. You'll just have to give him more time to get used to you again,' she said honestly. 'I'd like you to go back now. Go and have a talk with your grandfather, tell him how you feel.'

Jamie considered that carefully, then to Paula's relief nodded. 'And will you please tell him that I won't be able to come to dinner this evening,' Paula added hurriedly.

He looked at her, moist eyes speaking volumes. She was betraying him, deserting him. 'Another evening, Jamie, not tonight,' Paula said briskly. 'Please tell your grandfather that.' She bent down suddenly and kissed him quickly on the cheek. 'Go on, now.'

Jamie's resolute obedience was painful to watch. Paula followed him up the path with her eyes and waited until he had closed the door behind him before she turned—and found herself looking into Hugo Cameron's eyes through the living-room window. She started guiltily, a malicious heat flooding her cheeks, then jerked her eyes away and sped down the path, furious with herself for the idiotic reaction.

CHAPTER TWO

SHE WAS in the act of glancing at her watch when the tap on the door sounded. Eight o'clock on the dot. Jamie? Had he come for her after she had distinctly told him she wouldn't be dining at the house? Paula sighed in frustration; he probably hadn't even passed on her message to his grandfather.

She put down the book she had been attempting to read without much success. She could not concentrate and had Hugo Cameron to thank for that; he had made a very thorough job of ruffling her feathers and they refused to lie down. The most frustrating thing was that she kept thinking up all the snide, cutting retorts which had eluded her when she had been face to face with the rude man. Next time she'd be ready—if there had to be a next time.

Paula pattered to the door, determined to be very firm with the child. She was in slippers and her thick grey woollen dressing-gown after the bath that Hugo Cameron thought she had needed so badly, but not yet ready for bed. There were still hours to fill in before she could go to bed with any assurance of sleep; sleep was not something that came easily since the accident and Paula didn't want a night of tossing and turning which was the usual result if she went to bed too early.

'I hope I'm not disturbing you.' Sir Iain's tall, spare frame filled the doorway.

Paula swallowed her surprise and gave a quick shake of the head, wishing she had not flung the door open with such bad-tempered force. 'I wasn't expecting a visitor. Would you like to come in?' she invited uneasily, wondering what he was doing on her doorstep, and was relieved when Sir Iain shook his head. 'I hope Jamie gave you my message?' Paula asked, a little sharply.

"Yes, the lad did that,' Sir Iain assured her. 'And that's what I'd like to talk to you about.'

'I'd prefer not to come this evening, Sir Iain,' Paula anticipated quickly.

Sir Iain gave her a long look. 'I gather my son was rude to you this afternoon, Paula, and I've come to apologise on his behalf,' he said without preamble, and with a solemn sincerity that made Paula blush with embarrassment—mainly for the old gentleman standing in front of her. How dare Hugo use his father as an errand boy. 'That's very kind of you, Sir Iain,' she murmured, 'but really not necessary.'

'I think it is,' he corrected her gently. 'You're here as my guest and I won't have you upset. Hugo wanted to come himself.' He caught the flash of disbelief across her face and smiled faintly. 'I assure you he did, but I wouldn't let him, because, my dear, I felt he might not have succeeded in persuading you to join us for dinner.'

Very true, but she doubted his father would have any more success. 'I'd rather not,' Paula repeated firmly. 'Not this evening. It's a family occasion and you don't want me there, not on Mr Cameron's first evening and...' She shrugged. And besides which, I can't stand your son, was what she actually had in mind.

'We do want you, or I wouldn't be asking.'

'We?' Paula repeated his plural, almost mockingly.

'Jamie, myself—and yes, Hugo.' Sir Iain's mouth gave a wry tilt—a softer version of his son's ready twist. 'I know he's not made a very good impression on you but he really would like the opportunity to make amends.'

And Paula could guess how—by laying on the charm with a trowel. Hugo Cameron would be very adept at that—men like him always were. It didn't require too much stretch of the imagination to visualise the dark blue eyes crinkling in a disarming smile—but not missing a trick; they'd be carefully gauging the effect on the victim at the same time. Well, the charming Mr Cameron would have to practise his art on someone else tonight. Miss Hunt?

'I'd rather not. Thank you for coming to apologise—on Mr Cameron's behalf.' Paula sounded more stiffly formal than she intended.

The old man frowned at her unexpected intransigence. 'It was an honest mistake, Paula. Hugo told me he mistook you for a local girl caring for Jamie, and I imagine he treated you accordingly.' He allowed himself a rueful smile. 'I'm afraid Hugo does have a tendency to order people about at the best of times and just recently he's been under a lot of stress so he was probably worse than usual. But he does regret it, and if you could overlook his mistake and join us, it would please me very much. And Hugo is not a bad chap, as you'll find when you get to know him better.'

Getting to know Hugo Cameron better was not high on her list of priorities. The last thing she wanted was to offend the kindly old man and if he thought her churlish, she was sorry. Paula dug her heels in.

'It's very kind of you to take this trouble, but...' She shrugged, momentarily at a loss how to make her point.

The bushy silver eyebrows rose to form an interrogatory peak above the prominent nose that was tending to beakiness in old age. Sir Iain studied her, blue eyes uncomfortably sharp. 'If there's anything else that's happened to make you upset?'

'No. No, of course not,' Paula returned hastily. There was nothing else—not unless she told him that she objected to his son eyeing her like a chunk of meat in a butcher's window, and, furious as she was, Paula wasn't about to do that. 'It's just that I have a slight headache and am not up to company.' She felt ashamed at having to trot out that tired old fib, and felt worse when it was accepted with a gracious display of tact.

'I'm sorry to hear that,' Sir Iain said simply, ambiguously perhaps, and after he'd left, Paula would have liked nothing better than to let Hugo Cameron have a piece of her mind for putting her into such a position. Just for a moment—a very fleeting one—she was almost inclined to take up the dinner invitation after all.

By the time she finally went to bed, Paula had calmed down and resisted the temptation to take a sleeping-pill. Scared to be without them, she had brought a large bottle with her but had not taken one since arriving on the island and was proud of herself for it. Why let one unsettling afternoon spoil her track record? More precisely, why let Hugo Cameron spoil it?

THE NIGHTMARE brought her awake with a violent lurch of panic. Wild-eyed, Paula reared off the pillow, mouthing a voiceless scream, then fell back and lay very still with her eyes clamped shut as the sound of squealing brakes and shattering glass died away in her ears. The silence that followed was so complete she felt marooned in it; the only person left in the world. Then, very slowly, her mind started to function again and Paula became conscious of the cotton pyjamas sticking sweatily to her skin. She took a deep, shuddering breath but felt too drained to move. The nightmare always had that effect on her.

The dream never varied; it was always the last fatal drive with Mark and Stephen. They had been to stay with her parents at the farm for the weekend and, as always, Mark hadn't wanted to go but Paula had insisted because it was her parents' wedding anniversary; her two sisters were going to be there with their husbands and children—a family occasion and Paula wanted to be part of it.

She wanted Mark but more particularly, Stephen, to be part of it too. After his parents' divorce and wrangling custody case, the little boy needed every bit of family warmth and security he could get, but it was more than that. In a curious way Paula needed him there. Both her sisters were younger than Paula and between them had three children already, whereas at twenty-four all Paula had was a very promising career. Having Stephen with her—and Mark too, of course—somehow made her feel more complete, as if a void she was only subconsciously aware of was filled. Perhaps if it hadn't been for Stephen she might have realised sooner that Mark wasn't the man for her.

Opposites attract. Trite, but it had been true. Paula had taken to the quiet, unassuming solicitor when she met him through Roger at a literary party. Mark was light-years away from her fun-loving friends and, for a short time at least, rather reminded Paula of her father.

They had become engaged within months of their meeting and only later did Paula come to understand that under the quiet, dependable front was a very insecure man. Mark had found her voluble, easy-going family overwhelming, and in some way threatening, especially her mother. The fact that Karen Halstead was a sculptor of repute might have even impressed the snob in Mark—if only she hadn't been quite so 'different.'

Paula had always felt her mother deliberately went out of her way to jolt Mark a little out of his conventionality. And she had jolted him all right, with her free-flowing mass of bright red hair, colourful garb, her hit-and-miss housekeeping and general scattiness. All the things that enchanted her husband and that her three daughters took in their stride Mark had found quite shocking. It was possible he had been afraid that Paula's own artistic background would turn her into someone as exotically unconventional as her mother, but whatever his reasons, he had set about changing her.

It had started with trivial things, like how she wore her hair, then her clothes, then progressed to the places they went and the people they saw: less and less of Paula's family and old friends from Art School and more of Mark's solicitor friends—most as conservative as himself, and with wives to match. It had been such a slow insidious process, Paula was barely aware it was happening or how much suppressed resentment she was harbouring.

On that drive back to London, Stephen had suddenly said—with that sometimes startling insight small children come out with—'Daddy doesn't like Karen, does he?'

Mark had muttered something inarticulate and the thought had seared through Paula's mind: 'No, he doesn't. And I don't like Mark.' The realisation had taken the wind out of her. A couple of miles on, she had blurted out, without any awareness that she was about to speak, 'I can't marry you, Mark. I'm sorry.' She had chosen her moment badly. The shock of her unexpected statement had swept Mark's customary caution aside and he had taken his eyes off the wet road for a few seconds too long. Weeks later, still in hospital, Paula had learnt what had happened and felt so guilty she wanted to die too.

Paula opened her eyes and stared blankly up at the ceiling. In a moment she would get up and take a bath. She moved her right leg gingerly. It felt stiff and heavy, and she sighed in exasperation. It had happened again; every time she had the nightmare the leg seized up. It lasted four or five hours, but was a nuisance. There was nothing wrong with the leg itself any more; the doctor had explained it was all in her mind and as soon as she stopped feeling guilty

over the accident the nightmares would cease and the leg
would never bother her again. It sounded simple enough.

Paula got up and made herself coffee in slow motion,
her mind as seized up as the leg. Everything took ages and
she felt exhausted by the time she sat down with her coffee at the small table that did duty as dining and work-
table. She heard the footsteps on the stony path as she took
her first sip. The cup still at her lips she listened, frowning
as they came closer; too impatient to be Sir Iain's; too
heavy and loud for Jamie's. Paula put the cup down and
waited. The peremptory rap at the door confirmed her
suspicions. Pretend she was out? The thought shot through
her mind. With the door unlocked? Too risky. Paula rose
slowly and went to answer it.

Barely glancing at her, Hugo Cameron strode in without invitation.

'And good morning to you too, Mr Cameron,' Paula
snapped cantankerously at his back.

He swung to her suddenly. The first look glanced off
her, then his eyes came back and focused on her face. 'Are
you all right, Paula?' The concern was sharp—and unwelcome. 'You look . . .'

'Tired, Mr Cameron?' Paula interrupted snappishly.
'Yes, I know. I didn't sleep very well.' She was piqued he
had noticed she looked like a wreck—and so quickly; a
man too obviously used to seeing women first thing in the
morning—and his women probably looked as glamorous
as they did the night before, Paula thought resentfully, remaining by the door. She was afraid to move in case he
noticed the limp as well, and her pride couldn't have coped
with that.

'"Mr Cameron"? Still on our high horse, are we?' he
mocked, but without any real edge—almost mechanically, as if he had other things on his mind than annoying
her.

'Look, if you've come to apologise about yesterday…'
Paula started

'I haven't,' said Hugo shortly. 'It was a harmless mix-up,
so if you're expecting me to grovel, you're in for a disappointment. Besides, you got your own back by reneging on
dinner.'

So much for Sir Iain's version of his son's remorse.
Hugo showed about as much remorse as a rock. Paula gave
a tart smile. 'My mistake, but since nine-thirty in the
morning is somewhat early for a social call, what exactly
have you come for… Mr Cameron?' The icy emphasis on
the address was too heavy-handed to miss.

Hugo scowled. 'The name's Hugo, why don't you use
it?' he suggested irritably. 'And I came to ask if there is
anything you planned to do today that can't be put off
until tomorrow?'

'What do you mean?' Paula frowned uneasily, her eyes
wary.

'Just what I say—have you anything lined up that can't
wait?'

Paula could recognise a loaded question when she heard
one. 'Why?' she demanded, ready to reject anything he
was about to spring on her, but vaguely curious as to what
it was going to be.

Hugo took a step towards her and Paula made a twitchy
movement backwards without actually taking a step. Her
hand went fluttering up to the top of her dressing-gown to
make sure that the fronts were still pulled together.

'Must you stand at the door like that?' Hugo muttered
testily. 'You needn't look so ready to flee—I'm not going
to pounce on you.'

Her reaction had been instinctive, but silly, and Paula
coloured in annoyance for her exhibition of alarmed
modesty. She wasn't going to be able to walk very far to-

day, let alone flee, but was not expecting him to pounce. She doubted the Hugo Camerons of the world ever needed to pounce.

'I want you to come to see the fort,' Hugo said, referring to one of the island's main tourist attractions. His eyes dropped from her face to her hand which seemed to have stuck to the lapels of her gown.

'Why?'

He looked up, not quite meeting her eyes. 'I thought you might be interested.' It was too nonchalant to be anything but a downright lie.

'I've seen it, but thank you for asking me,' Paula replied with precise politeness, and it did happen to be true. She had already seen the remains of the old fort, thought to have been built against Roman invaders. Sir Iain had arranged a trip for her during her first days on the island and while Paula had meant to go back for another look around, the days, weeks, had somehow fled and she hadn't found the time. However, she had no intention of making time for Hugo Cameron.

Hugo's face darkened. 'Then you can see it again,' he barked. 'I want you to come, and before you snap out another curt little "why?", the answer is the wretched boy won't go without you. You've got too much influence with him and I don't like it,' he finished in a bad-tempered mutter.

'What? You've no right to say that!' The fiery indignation welled up on the heels of her first surprise.

'Haven't I just?' Hugo countered with a return glare, then turned and walked moodily to the silk-screen curtain Paula had hung up to divide the one main room of the cottage into bedroom and living-areas. Hands in pockets, he stood staring at it with his back to her and Paula took the opportunity to edge crabwise to the chair and sit down before he turned around again.

Finished with the curtain, Hugo wandered to the tiny dresser. A pile of sketches lay on the top of it, most of them of Jamie, and Paula watched silently as he flipped through them, pausing every now and then when a particular one held his attention. He was invading her privacy but in too distracted a way for it to be deliberate. Paula checked her resentment.

'Why force the child to go if he doesn't want to?' Still seething with indignation at his accusation, she made a superhuman attempt to be reasonable.

Hugo spun around. 'Because it will do him good, that is why,' he shot at her irritably. Paula didn't believe him and her face showed it. Hugo made a vague gesture with his hand. There was a tinge of added colour in his face. 'Miss Hunt—Louise—arranged an outing, a sort of family picnic. And you can spare me that snide, knowing look. It's not for Louise. I want Jamie to come.'

'Even if it means dragging him along against his will—and me with him?' Reasonableness fled out of the window. Paula felt her temper rising.

'It won't kill either of you. Damn it, I break my neck getting here to see the kid and he acts as if he can't stand the sight of me.'

'And you're blaming me for that?' Paula hurled at him in mock astonishment. The anger was very real.

'Calm down, I'm not blaming you for anything,' Hugo muttered peevishly. They locked eyes, Paula ready to jump down his throat, when Hugo suddenly changed tack mid-scowl. His face cleared and he smiled—quite charmingly. 'Do join us, Paula; I'd like you to come.' His eyes ranged over her face, gauging her reaction to this new approach. 'And if you've had a bad night, the fresh air will do you the world of good.'

Her face stony, Paula looked back without a flicker. What did he think she was? A naive adolescent to be

bowled over by one charming smile? She wasn't about to
be disarmed that easily, but she was thinking that if she
refused to go, Jamie would feel she had let him down, and,
after yesterday she couldn't do that to him. Her leg would
probably be all right if she didn't walk around. Was it all
that much to ask of her? Only smile or no smile, Hugo
Cameron was not exactly asking.

He was watching her questioningly and his face would
have looked quite pleasant if it hadn't been for the impatience lurking in the eyes.

Paula produced an overdone smile. 'How can I refuse
when you put it so charmingly, Hugo,' she said in a deliberate little gush.

Hugo's scowl resurfaced. 'I'm glad you see it my way.
If you could be at the house in an hour, I'd appreciate it.'

Even at her slow-motion pace, Paula was showered and
dressed in under half an hour. She had decided on her dark
woollen slacks instead of the usual jeans because they
wouldn't show up her movement so much and if she was
careful, the limp might escape notice completely. It was not
very cold but she had put on a long jacket over her sweater
just for extra camouflage.

With a fresh cup of coffee, Paula sat down at the table
and used up the rest of the hour putting on make-up—
something she hadn't done for a very long time. She never
bothered with it on the island, and if she thought back, she
hadn't bothered much before coming to the island either.
When she finished, she felt she looked like a clown with
smudged lipstick rubbed into her cheeks to give her colour. Who was she trying to impress anyway.

Jamie was in the hall, hovering around the front door,
nervous and wary and not the picture of someone about to
enjoy an outing. When Paula walked into the living-room
she realised immediately why the child had opted for
hanging about the hall.

Hugo was standing edgily by the fireplace and glanced impatiently at his watch as she came in. Louise Hunt was in the armchair a little way back from the fire. You could have cut the tension with a knife. They've had a fight, Paula thought, trying not to look at either of them.

'You've met my personal assistant, Louise,' Hugo said abruptly, and Louise Hunt jerked the corners of her mouth upwards without disturbing the fixed look in her eyes.

Personal assistant—and the rest! Paula reproduced a reciprocal jerk of acknowledgement, noting with surprise that Louise didn't look as if she was planning on going anywhere, and certainly not on a picnic she had supposedly organised.

'Well, now that you're here, we can leave. Louise won't be joining us,' Hugo added tightly without offering any explanation.

And which of them had decided on that, Paula wondered with tart interest.

'I'm sure you'll manage without me,' Louise said, and the curious tinge of coyness was glaringly out of character for someone dressed with such cool sophistication in tweed and cashmere. There was no string of pearls around her neck to add to the effect but Louise showed a nice set of teeth in a pained smile. 'I have a lot of work to get through for Hugo before we head back to London tomorrow,' she said as Hugo marched out of the room, and made it sound as if her time was much too valuable to waste on picnics. The woman's suppressed huff conveyed the distinct impression that it had been Hugo who was responsible for the sudden change in plans. But London, tomorrow? Disturbed, Paula followed Hugo out of the room.

Anna was in the hall, handing over a large hamper to Hugo. Jamie presumably was already outside in the car. Paula glanced around the hall. 'What about your father?'

'What about him?' Hugo asked carelessly.

'Isn't he coming too?'

'Whatever gave you that idea?' Hugo gave a short laugh as he carried the hamper out of the front door, Anna following him with a bundle of rugs over her arm.

Paula trailed after them slowly, wincing a little as she tried not to limp, and furious that she had been inveigled into the excursion under false pretences—well, almost. Hugo hadn't said his father was coming in so many words, but he certainly had not made it clear that he wasn't. 'Family picnic,' Hugo said and Paula had jumped to the conclusion that everybody would be coming—and that meant Sir Iain as well as Louise Hunt. Under the circumstances the supercilious personal assistant would have been a welcome addition.

Paula settled back into the sleek navy suede comfort of the exotic car without a word and they started off in a strained silence. It was Hugo's expedition—let him jolly his troops, she thought sullenly, determined not to volunteer a word, and they were half way across the island before the silence was broken by Jamie piping up, 'I want to go to the toilet, please, Uncle Hugo.'

His uncle clicked his tongue in annoyance. 'Why didn't you go before we left?'

'I didn't want to go then,' the boy replied with irrefutable reason and Paula almost laughed.

Hugo pulled the car over to the side of the deserted road and stopped. 'Out you hop then.' He glanced irritably at Paula and suddenly grinned. 'If you've got to go you've got to go,' he quipped, and she returned a smile in spite of herself. But if Hugo thought she was ready to lay down arms and burst into chattiness, he had another think coming. Paula was not going to give an inch and while the temperature of the atmosphere might have gone up a degree or two, the silence continued until they reached the ruins of the fort.

The tourist attraction was not without a sprinkling of
early tourists. It was Saturday, Paula remembered, and
that meant the odd local family might have decided to
make a day of it too. There were several cars dotted about
and she noted figures trailing about the ruins and thanked
her lucky stars that it was not like the day she had come
with Sir Iain when they had been the only ones there.
Safety in numbers? The relief seemed a bit excessive. What
was she expecting Hugo to do? Try to murder her?

'What do you want to do, walk around first?' Hugo
asked when he had taken the picnic paraphernalia out of
the car and spread the rug a short distance from it.

'No. You and Jamie can do that. I'd rather just sit here.
I don't feel like walking around for the moment.' Half-
expecting to be marched around to admire the sights,
Paula was pleasantly surprised when Hugo didn't press.

She watched them wander off together, side by side, but
not too close. Uncle doing avuncular duty for a day before taking off to London again. For how long this time?
Louise Hunt had overlooked that bit, but the point was
that Hugo was going away at all, not for how long. And he
had the nerve to wonder why the child treated him with
such reserve—if not downright distrust.

After a while Paula pulled out the small sketch-pad she
always carried about with her in her bag and started
sketching the outline of the ruins of the ancient fort. She
was absorbed in it when Hugo returned, alone.

'Jamie met up with a kid from one of the other parties,
they seemed to be enjoying themselves.' Hugo stood looking down over her shoulder.

Paula hated people looking over her shoulder while she
sketched. She snapped the pad shut.

'Don't stop,' Hugo said, but she had already slipped the sketch-pad into her bag.

Hugo lowered himself down on to the rug, and stretching out full-length, propped himself up on an elbow. 'You haven't done much lately, have you? Illustration work, I mean,' he started, conversationally.

'No,' she replied tersely, expecting the sharp brevity of the reply to put paid to further personal questions.

'My father mentioned that you haven't been well,' Hugo went on in the same conversational tone.

That was one way of putting it. 'Yes,' Paula said discouragingly, wondering how much Sir Iain had let out of the bag, but crediting him with more tact—or compassion—than to pass on to his son what he had drawn out from her about her emotional meltdown following the accident.

'And how's your current project coming along?' Hugo asked, and sounded as if he really wanted to know.

'Fine. It's almost complete,' she answered, casually. 'All I have to do is get it to the finished artwork stage, and that shouldn't take long,' she added, deliberately forthcoming, to let him know she wouldn't be staying around for much longer—if that's what he was fishing about, and she couldn't think what else it could be.

'And after that? Have you something else already lined up?'

Her sixth sense sprang into alertness. 'No,' Paula admitted cagily, on guard because Hugo's questions were not random; they were leading up to something. 'Why are you asking me all these questions?' she demanded outright, swinging her head abruptly to look him fully in the face. She put a hand to her hair to flick it back from her face and then toyed absently with a loose strand.

Hugo was studying her hair in the way Roger often did—with the same quiet mesmerised expression.

'You have very beautiful hair,' he murmured, and Paula actually blushed, dropping her hand quickly so as not to draw any more attention to her hair.

'You haven't answered my question. You're leading up to something and I want to know what it is,' she said with a surge of belligerence to cover up her embarrassment at his unexpected compliment. She was not used to compliments any more, and when they came from Hugo Cameron there had to be an ulterior motive anyway.

'Are you always so distrustful of men—or just of me?' Hugo gave an ironic smile then raised himself to a half-sitting position and said, briskly, 'Yes, you're right. I have been leading up to something. I wanted to know how you were placed because I want to offer you a job—of sorts,' he qualified cryptically.

For a crazy moment it crossed her mind that he had a publishing company tucked away in his business stable and was about to offer her a commission.

'Looking after Jamie for a few months,' Hugo said and watched her face carefully as her expression changed to project utter astonishment.

Was he serious? Paula stared at him. Hugo looked back, perfectly serious, and Paula made a sound like a cross between a snort and a disbelieving laugh. She shook her head, sending the hair flying around her face. 'No. Oh, no. You can forget that. I'm not interested. Definitely not,' she finished off the string of negatives with an abrupt laugh. 'Thanks anyway.'

Faint surprise at her vehemence showed on Hugo's face. 'But I'm not talking about a long-term commitment,' he said, painstakingly, as if she had misunderstood him. 'It would only be for a couple of months, just until...' Paula was shaking her head again. 'But you're fond of the child and he needs you. Jamie's become very attached to you,'

Hugo persisted, his voice sharper. He studied her with a renewed intensity, his brow slightly furrowed.

Paula gave another shake of the head. 'No way.'

'And what about Jamie? Have you thought how he's going to feel if you just up and leave?'

Straight-out emotional blackmail—as low as you could get. Only Hugo Cameron had picked the wrong person. She was an expert on emotional blackmail. Hadn't Mark plied his own subtle version of it on her? 'Stephen needs this...Stephen needs that...'

'Don't try saddling your responsibilities on me! Why don't you ask yourself how Jamie is going to feel when you flit off again with Miss Whatsit tomorrow? How long is he going to have to fret for you this time?' Her voice was raised to just this side of a screech but Paula didn't care.

Taken aback, Hugo flushed. 'It's only for a couple of days,' he told her, defensively.

'Oh yes, give or take four or five weeks,' Paula hurled contemptuously, then backed away in alarm as Hugo moved towards her across the rug.

'That's it—out at last. You've been itching to throw that at me—the heartless uncle abandoning the poor child...that's how you've got me taped, isn't it?'

'If the cap fits,' Paula muttered under breath meaning Hugo to hear only not expecting his reaction. He lunged at her suddenly and gripped her shoulder hard. Paula yelped an 'ouch' and Hugo let go immediately but his eyes raged down on her alarmed face.

'Just what the hell do you think I've been doing while I've been away? Flitting, as you call it, from party to party? Chasing women? Is that what you think I've been doing while knowing the boy's here waiting for me, disturbed and upset? What do you take me for, for God's sake?' His face was contorted with jagged fury and so close Paula could have started counting the pores.

She shook her head, rattled. It sounded monstrous when said aloud, but yes, it was exactly what she thought.

Hugo pulled back, breathing hard. 'You don't like me and that's your prerogative, but you've no right to pass judgment on me, and you've no right turning the child against me.'

Paula rallied out of her fright. 'That's absurd,' she said shakily.

'Is it? I'm no fool. It's only too plain that you've influenced Jamie's attitude towards me—oh, I've no doubt you've been very subtle about it, just a word here, a word there about callous old Uncle Hugo—too busy having a good time to spare his little nephew a thought.'

'You're crazy! I would never say anything like that,' Paula protested heatedly.

'But you happen to think it's true.'

'I've never said anything against you to Jamie,' she mumbled, uncomfortably.

'How charitable of you,' Hugo mocked viciously. 'But you haven't needed to, have you? Your attitude is enough. You stared at me so furiously yesterday afternoon when you clapped eyes on me it's a wonder you didn't go cross-eyed with the effort—or turn me to stone. The boy can put two and two together, and you've made it add up to Uncle Hugo being a heartless meanie.'

Paula put a hand across her eyes, holding it there as if it would block out his contempt. She sat in silence, pricked by shame, but not convinced—not fully—that she was totally wrong about him. She took her hand away and met Hugo's eyes. 'You could have written, or telephoned, just once in a while. It would have made all the difference to him.'

Hugo's face went quite blank. 'I could have . . . what?' There was no anger in his eyes any more, instead, a gathering concern. 'What has Jamie been telling you?' he asked in a rather odd voice.

'It's a bit late to look so concerned now,' Paula returned dismissively. 'And given that we appear to think so little of each other, I wonder that you're offering me the job of looking after the child. I would have thought I'd be the last person you would choose under the circumstances.'

Hugo's mouth gave a bitter twist. 'The circumstances being what they are, I don't have much choice,' he said, almost helplessly. 'Jamie likes you, probably even loves you, and he's been through a lot. If having you around can make him happier while I sort everything out, then I'm prepared to put up with a supercilious young woman who thinks I'm the world's original cad, and makes no bones about it.' Hugo tried out a wry smile on her.

Paula looked away without response. In the distance she picked out Jamie heading towards them, a small solitary figure.

'Besides which,' Hugo continued in a curious change of voice, his eyes on her profile, 'I might find it interesting to see how quickly I can persuade her to change her opinion of me.' He lifted a hand to her averted face and ran a finger lightly down the smooth warm curve of her cheek.

Something snapped inside her at his touch, at his sardonically intimate voice—or both. Paula struck at the hand, slapping it away from her. 'Get your hands off me!' she hissed like a cat about to leap in mindless attack. 'I don't like being pawed any more than I like being ogled. Keep it for your girlfriends, I'm sure they love it—and while you're at it, why don't you ask one of them to play mummies and daddies with you!'

CHAPTER THREE

SURPRISE, OR rather shock, was the first thing Hugo's eyes registered; the anger came a second later with the sweep of ugly crimson over his face. Ashen with her own fury, Paula stared him out and Hugo turned his face away, muttering something in a harsh undertone as he shifted angrily to the corner of the rug. She caught the first words, which were 'You little...' and suspected that what she missed was probably 'bitch.'

Paula pulled herself together with an effort as Jamie approached. Unsure of his reception, the boy stopped several feet away and whatever he saw in their faces didn't do anything to reassure him. He sized them up nervously without coming any closer.

Paula smiled shakily. 'Come and sit down, Jamie,' she invited in a hopelessly unnatural voice and Jamie edged unwillingly to a corner of the rug and sat down—as far away from both adults as possible. Then there was nothing for it but to go through the charade of having a picnic. It didn't last very long but was awful while it did.

Hugo made persistent attempts to draw the boy out, questioning him about what he had been doing with his little friend, and in the process came over like a prosecutor in full stride. Almost visibly, Jamie shrank deeper into himself until his uncle couldn't get a word out of him, and while it made Paula want to yell at Hugo to leave the miserable child alone, her own efforts weren't much better when she tried to alleviate the situation by pressing Jamie to eat in a sort of bright nag.

Feeling wretched, Paula gave up, and since no one was bothering with the pretence of eating, started packing the things away. 'I think we ought to start back, don't you, Hugo?' She addressed him for the first time in Jamie's presence with sickening pleasantness.

'Yes, I suppose so,' Hugo agreed sourly without looking at her. He got to his feet and Jamie sprang up without urging.

'Well, let's be off then, shall we? Your grandfather will be wondering what's become of us,' Hugo said to Jamie, making a last-ditch stand to be hearty.

At one o'clock, when they'd barely been gone two hours? What did he take the child for? Paula stood up—too quickly, without remembering to favour her bad leg, and gave an involuntary yelp of surprised pain when she stumbled. Hugo shot out a hand and gripped her arm preventing the fall.

He glared down at her trousered legs—at both, since he had no way of telling which was causing the trouble. 'What's the matter with your leg?' he demanded, unsympathetically, digging his fingers into her arm with far more pressure than needed to support her.

'Nothing,' Paula lied shortly, then in view of the fact that she was going to limp pretty noticeably to the car under his watchful eye, added in a mutter, 'Just a pulled muscle.' She tried to move herself clear of his grip. 'It's all right, only a bit seized up, probably from sitting too long.'

'And when did this happen?' Hugo wasn't letting her go.

Avoiding his eyes, Paula shrugged. 'I don't remember; most likely walking over the rocks yesterday,' she lied.

'Yesterday?' Hugo picked up the word. 'Yesterday?' he repeated angrily. 'Then why the hell didn't you tell me this morning?' He let loose with a shout that made Jamie jump back in alarm.

'And would it have made any difference if I had?' Paula's voice rose in a retaliatory shout. 'You'd have dragged me along anyway.'

Hugo gave a raspy whistle under his breath and shook his head in disbelief. 'Boy, you really have got it down to a fine art, haven't you—making a man feel a heel.' Before Paula could retaliate, he turned sharply to Jamie who looked as if he was about to cry. 'Take the rug to the car Jamie, I'll bring the hamper in a moment. Come on, I'll help you to the car,' he said brusquely, and since his hand hadn't left her arm, it was pointless to protest. Paula allowed herself to be led carefully down the slope.

'I'm not exactly an invalid,' she snapped as Hugo eased her into the front seat like a fragile geriatric.

'Shut up,' Hugo returned evenly, but with a look in his eyes that made it clear he would have preferred to throw her bodily into the car—or possibly under it.

It was an illusion that the return trip was shorter since they went the same route, but it was definitely quicker with Hugo's foot planted hard on the accelerator for most of the way. Jamie scrambled out of the back seat the moment they pulled up in front of the house and bolted as fast as his little legs would carry him. Given half the chance, Paula would have done the same.

'You'd better let my father take a look at that leg,' Hugo said tersely, helping her out of the car as solicitously as he had put her into it—and with the same murderous look in his eyes. 'And before you trot out your objection,' he blocked off her protest as Paula opened her mouth, 'my father would like a word with you. There's something he wants to discuss. I didn't get the chance to mention it before.'

Louise Hunt lifted her eyes from the magazine on her lap. 'Goodness, back already?' she exclaimed, farcically wide-eyed with exaggerated surprise as Hugo led Paula into the living-room. Louise was sitting under the large window that gave on to the path and the drive, and Paula would have bet her last penny that the woman had been standing at it moments before.

The sherry-brown eyes did a quick summing-up of the tightly-controlled faces and were obviously pleased by what they saw; the picnic had not been a success. Louise kept the pleasure out of her voice.

'Has there been an accident?' she asked solicitously.

'No,' Hugo answered curtly as he shunted Paula across the room to the armchair by the fire. 'Where's my father?'

'In the study I presume—now that I'm out of it,' Louise said with a pointed tartness which Hugo chose to ignore. 'I finished the report you wanted,' Louise added a little less tartly.

'Good.' Hugo moved to the small round table that Sir Iain used as a drink-stand, and turned to Paula. 'What will you have? Or would you prefer tea?'

The only thing Paula really wanted was to get back to the cottage and away from the disagreeable pair as quickly as she could. 'Tea. Thank you,' she replied after a moment.

'Right.' Hugo replaced the whisky bottle on the tray without pouring himself a drink, or offering Louise one. 'I'll get Anna to make us some.'

With Hugo out of the room there was a long uncomfortable silence. Paula felt at a disadvantage with Louise out of eye's range. The woman's eyes seemed to be boring into her right ear. Paula shifted herself slightly so she could turn her head towards the window. Unabashed, Louise carried on with her silent scrutiny.

'It's a pity you weren't able to come with us. The place has rather an atmosphere about it and the ruin is very interesting,' Paula said for something to break the silence and heard herself sounding like a blurb on a third-rate tourist brochure.

Louise lifted the corners of her mouth a barely-perceptible fraction. 'I'm sure it's very interesting, but I'm not one to intrude on family outings. Hugo has had so little time with his nephew that it seemed a shame for a stranger to tag along.' She looked Paula straight in the eye.

Without a blink, Paula stared back, quite impressed that anyone could come out with such calculated rudeness. Like employer, like employee, she thought with grim satisfaction, but at least Hugo had some grounds for disliking her—or imagined he had. Louise Hunt had none... unless... Could the woman possibly see her as some sort of competition? A threat? The notion was too preposterous to be more than a passing thought. 'But I understand Mr Cameron will be returning in a couple of days to spend more time with Jamie,' Paula said carefully, and realised she was fishing.

Louise affected surprise with her eyebrows. 'Really?' The voice carried amused tolerance—an adult humouring a naïve child—and this time Paula flushed with annoyance.

'Hugo is a very busy man,' Louise said, painstakingly, again in that adult-to-dimwitted-child voice. 'We have a lot of things to attend to before we return to the States shortly, so it's very unlikely we'll be able to squeeze in another trip up here—much as we'd like to, of course.'

The 'we' was glaring—and deliberate, and Paula was too human not to feel an irritating flare of curiosity. It was stronger than her anger at being patronised. 'Do you always travel with Mr Cameron?' she asked, rising to the dangled bait because she couldn't help herself.

Louise's mouth curved in a genuinely pleased smile. 'Of course. I'm Hugo's personal assistant.'

'Of course,' Paula murmured drily, giving herself a mental kick, and wondered why she should feel so disturbed by something she had suspected all along. The pair could fly to the moon together for all she cared . . . only . . . Only it was plain there wasn't room for Jamie on any of their jaunts.

They had nothing to say to each other after that. Louise picked up the magazine again and started flicking through it. Paula sat staring into the fire and when Hugo returned, they had been silent for at least five minutes, so she was more than startled when Louise said, brightly, 'We'll have to continue our chat another time, Paula. I did so enjoy it.'

Hugo tossed both of them a curious look, as if he couldn't quite believe his ears either. 'My father would like a word with you now, if you don't mind, Paula.'

Paula froze him off with her eyes as he came towards her—ready to aid the invalid again—and Hugo went back to the door and held it open for her. She heard him say as the door closed behind her, 'I'd like to see that report now please, Louise.' Very businesslike. Exactly like a boss talking to an employee. Keeping up a front for her benefit, Paula surmised acidly, and couldn't imagine why they bothered.

Sir Iain rose from his desk as Paula hesitated in the doorway. 'Come in, lass, and sit down. Leg hurting today?' he asked softly as Paula eased herself into the chair. She nodded briefly. 'Pulled muscle, is it?' he smiled whimsically but his eyes were serious, and Paula dropped her gaze in faint embarrassment for her childish subterfuge. Sir Iain contemplated her from his position by the window. 'It's been a while since you've had that nightmare. I think you told me the last time was about a week before leaving London.' His magnificent eyebrows jerked upwards in concentration. 'That must make it about six weeks ago.'

'Yes,' Paula said, knowing exactly to the day—or night. It had been after Roger had lashed out at her for making a mess of the illustrations, and she had gone back home and howled herself sick. That night she had had the nightmare—for the last time she had thought.

'I thought it had gone for good,' Sir Iain murmured sympathetically.

'So did I.' And had been kidding herself. Paula shrugged, and Sir Iain turned to the window. Hands locked behind his back, he stared out over the flowers, which, despite the climate, managed to grow in quite astonishing profusion inside the walled garden.

'What did you want to see me about, Sir Iain?' Paula asked, finishing her study of the back of his head... Hugo's head; good bones must run in the family. As a sculptor, her mother would have loved to get her hands on them.

He turned back slowly. The blue eyes had lost the startling dark quality of his son's and grandson's, but they were still bright—and shrewd. 'Why didn't you tell Hugo the truth about your leg?' he asked, either ignoring her question, or so intent on his own train of thought that he had missed hearing it. Paula made an indeterminate movement of her head. 'Oh well, it doesn't matter,' Sir Iain murmured, then unexpectedly gave a soft throaty chuckle. 'Rubbed you up the wrong way, that son of mine, hasn't he?'

Paula smiled wanly at the colossal understatement. 'You wanted to see me.'

'Yes, I did. I wanted to ask if I could prevail upon you to look after Jamie.' He smiled. 'You see I...' he started, and that was as far as he got.

'No.' In an ungainly scramble, Paula was out of her seat, shaking her head agitatedly. Sir Iain's smile froze, then vanished. He stared at Paula as if she had taken leave of her senses, and she probably had. She was so incensed that Hugo had roped in his father to put the pressure on her to accept the job she couldn't see straight. 'No, you can't ask me to do that—it's unfair! You must know how I feel. I've explained. After Stephen...I...' She looked at him despairingly. 'Hugo had no right to ask you.'

Sir Iain recovered himself and came towards her. 'My dear, I'm sorry. I'm so sorry. I had no idea that you would feel so distressed. It was thoughtless of me. I would never have asked you to mind the lad if I'd known.' He patted her awkwardly on the shoulder. 'It's all right. I'll just postpone my trip down to London for a while, until Hugo gets back. I can go another time; it's not that important.'

Paula stared at the kindly, distressed old face, then sank down on to the chair and closed her eyes. After a moment, when she thought she had everything straightened out in her head, she snapped them open. 'Did you mean looking after Jamie...here? Just while you went away?' she asked, slowly.

'Yes, of course I did,' Sir Iain replied, slowly too, and they both looked at each other wordlessly while their crossed wires untangled themselves. 'I need to go to London for a week or so—to see my doctor, for one thing. No, just a check-up,' he assured her as Paula's eyes widened in concern. 'As you know, we've all been under some strain recently and it's good to keep a check on things. I wouldn't normally have considered leaving Jamie, but since you're here, I thought...' He finished off with a vague shrug and Paula wanted to sink through the floor.

'Heavens, I'm sorry. Of course I can look after Jamie. I'd love it, really I would. I don't know what you must think of me flying off the handle like that. I thought...

well, I...I misinterpreted things.' Paula blushed, stammered and in the end just stared helplessly. It wasn't much of an explanation and how anyone would consider entrusting a child to her care after that neurotic performance, she wasn't sure.

'I think I understand, my dear,' Sir Iain said tactfully, without making clear what it was he thought he understood from her garbled explanation. 'If you're sure,' he began doubtfully.

'I'd love to help out,' Paula assured him in a burst of repentant fervour.

Sir Iain smiled. 'In that case I can leave as planned. Hugo has suggested flying, instead of driving. He thinks the drive might be a bit too much for me, and I have to agree. He'll take the car back with him next time. We intended to leave tomorrow morning but if that doesn't suit you, we can put it off a day or two.'

'Tomorrow's fine, really it is.' Then something occurred to her and Paula frowned. 'Jamie...does he know about you leaving?'

Sir Iain nodded. 'Yes, I've already explained to him—and Hugo has too—or tried to. I know the lad takes Hugo's absences very badly; it's understandable after the loss of his parents, but it doesn't make things any easier for Hugo. Try as he might, it seems that nothing but Hugo's actual presence will do.'

A peculiar doubt sprang into Paula's mind. She said without emphasis, 'Hugo does keep in touch though, doesn't he, when he's away?'

'Yes, of course he does—all the time,' Sir Iain replied quickly. He looked at her worriedly—the same way Hugo had looked earlier. 'Has Jamie been saying that he doesn't?' he asked, his voice unintentionally sharp.

'No, he's never said that,' Paula said hurriedly and Sir Iain's face cleared, but he sighed heavily. 'Sometimes I've wondered whether Hugo's constant phone calls and letters haven't made it worse for the child; when you're six years old and been through what Jamie's been through, a disembodied voice on the other end of the telephone can't really allay all the terrors and anxieties, can it?' he smiled sadly, and made a helpless gesture with his hands. 'But what can you do?'

Nothing. But she could have asked—five weeks ago. One direct question to Sir Iain or Anna; or Jamie himself, that's all it would have taken to find out how things really stood. Instead she had—and with satisfaction at that—built up her own misguided picture of a callous, uncaring man. And just how much had her po-faced attitude towards 'Uncle Hugo' rubbed off on the child? She had never deliberately said anything against the man, but perhaps Hugo was right; perhaps she hadn't needed to state her disapproval for the child to pick it up and become more confused than he already was.

She should have searched Hugo out and apologised straight away. She had meant to, but he had still been closeted in the living-room with Louise and Paula hadn't been able to face him. And that made her feel worse—a coward, on top of a shrew.

She took a sleeping-pill that night, and took it early because she couldn't stand the prospect of hours of emotional turmoil trying to come to terms with herself, trying to rationalise her hysterical attacks, when she knew they didn't lend themselves to any rationalisation. Flying off the handle at Hugo had been bad enough; turning on Sir Iain like a demented fishwife was unpardonable, however she had misinterpreted his request to mind the child.

What price all her back-patting and self-congratulations now? Paula asked herself miserably, staring out through the window at the fading light as she lay in bed waiting for the pill to do its job. She might have her work under control but if the crazy outbursts were anything to go by, she was still a very long way from sorting out the mess inside her head, and she didn't know where to start.

At bottom, it seemed that the problem was still her tangled feelings of guilt about Stephen, and not wanting to get involved with another child was understandable. Her overreaction both with Hugo and Sir Iain had been a self-protective measure, but was that all there was to it? That still did not explain why she had been so outraged when Hugo had made his pass. A pass, that's all it had been, Paula reminded herself; other men had made passes before and she had never reacted with such wild-eyed outrage. But then, she had never felt so... threatened.

In the morning Paula felt thick-headed and listless—the usual side-effect of the sleeping-pill, but infinitely preferable to yet another re-run of the nightmare. She got herself moving with an effort, and having promised to be with Jamie when the party left for the airport, was at the house and holding the child's hand as the sedan drove away. Sir Iain was in the front seat with Neil; Hugo in the back with a very pleased-looking Louise Hunt.

Hugo's last words had been 'see you both in a few days.' He had his arm around Jamie's shoulder as he said them but had been looking directly into Paula's eyes.

'I'm sure Jamie will be looking forward to that,' Paula had replied, intending to sound casual, and had come across surly and disbelieving, and that was not the way she had meant to sound, but her embarrassment at not having yet apologised to him had got in the way. The angry flash in Hugo's eyes told her he simply thought she didn't believe him.

At the end of the day, Anna took the call from London, Paula was there when Jamie spoke to his grandfather and then to Hugo. Paula didn't ask him about the call and two minutes later Jamie was acting as if he hadn't spoken to his uncle at all. It was grandfather this and grandfather that. So that's how it had been, Paula thought with a renewed stab of guilt that she hadn't forced herself to apologise to Hugo before he had left.

Anna's day off fell on the fourth day after Hugo's departure. The old lady usually spent the day and night with her daughter in the island's main town and it was only after she was gone that Paula became aware of how much difference Anna's voluble presence had made. Without it, the house seemed unnaturally silent. She and Jamie stayed by the fire in the living-room all day. The wind was working itself up into a passable imitation of a gale, but even without it they probably would have remained in the house since both of them seemed to have ground to a sort of apathetic halt and neither wanted to do anything.

Paula felt on edge and as the evening drew on the edginess increased. She blamed it on the wind and told herself not to be stupid as she pottered about the large comfortable kitchen putting together the meal Anna had prepared for them before leaving. Jamie seemed edgy too. There had been no call from Hugo that day and neither of them referred to the fact. Jamie had withdrawn into himself and was silent while she got him ready for bed. When she tucked him in, he looked at her steadily, a too-old depth in his eyes. 'I'm a nuisance, aren't I?' he said expressionlessly.

Paula stared at him in horror. 'No, Jamie! Where in heaven's name did you get an idea like that?'

'Miss Hunt told me,' he replied with an adult casualness. 'I don't care. I hate everybody. I don't care if Uncle Hugo doesn't come back.'

In the murderous fury that shot through her, Paula would have cheerfully strangled the woman with her bare hands. 'Your uncle will be back, Jamie,' she said harshly. 'He told you he will and you must believe him.'

Jamie turned his face to the wall and Paula sat helpless and silent until the smooth rise and fall of his shoulders told her he was asleep. Back in the kitchen, she hurled the few dishes through some hot water in the sink with a savageness that would have given Anna a seizure, and came to a decision. When Hugo returned, she would tell him she would accept his job of looking after Jamie; she didn't have a choice any more; the child needed her, badly.

Later, in the bath, Paula was still thinking about it, and had swung from the first initial doubt to almost light-headed cheerfulness. A couple of months—just to tide Jamie over his patch of insecurity, and help Hugo out at the same time. After misjudging him as she had, she owed him at least that.

In spite of the heavy woollen dressing-gown, Paula shivered when she came out of the warm, steamy bath-room. The wind had not let up once, only now it sounded as if it had joined forces with a torrential downpour of rain and developed into one of those full-scale storms that hit the island without any warning. Securely tucked up in her cosy cottage, she loved listening to them; alone in a very large house with only a sleeping child, the storm gave her the creeps. The lights were on all over the house but they didn't allay the nervousness that had set in. Paula shivered again and hurried into Jamie's room to check on the child.

He was tossing restlessly, the bedclothes pushed half-way down the bed, and whimpered softly as she drew the covers over him. After a moment's hesitation, Paula climbed on to the bed and lay alongside the small restless body, placing an arm over it. The warmth of it seemed to quieten him; the breathing became more regular again and Jamie stopped tossing. Paula closed her own eyes.

Some time later she jerked awake, rearing into a sitting position. Utterly disorientated, it took her a few moments

to realise that the warm shape beside her was Jamie. Her
watch was in the guest-room and Paula had no idea how
long she had been asleep; it might have been minutes or
hours. The light was on in the room—they were still on all
over the house, yet she felt alarmed, certain that some
sound had woken her. As she strained her ears against the
wind and rain lashing at the window, very definite sounds
carried into the room—sounds of someone in the house,
coming up the stairs, Her heart stopped, then the next
second started racing madly.

Paula froze into rigidity, and, even half-senseless with
fright, was vaguely conscious that her tension had penetrated Jamie's sleep. He shifted uneasily against her while
she couldn't have moved to save her life. Eyes dilated like
a terrified child's, she waited and when the figure came
through the doorway the only reason she didn't scream was
she couldn't find her voice.

Her eyes told her the man was Hugo Cameron, but the
message was a long time reaching her brain. When she
came out of her freeze, Hugo was bending over her, calm-
ing her. 'It's okay Paula, it's okay. It's me—Hugo.' His
voice was soft, gruff—shocked. 'For God's sake don't
stare at me like that. I didn't mean to frighten you. The
lights were on. I thought you were awake, I called out.'

She let the trapped air out of her lungs in short shallow
gasps and turned on him—savagely. 'Of all the damn stupid things to do! What do you mean by sneaking up on me
like that?' she hissed through lips that wouldn't stop
quivering. Her shoulders still shook violently under his
arm.

Hugo tightened his hold. 'I didn't sneak.' He cut off his
hiss midway because Jamie was stirring. They both stared
down at him, waiting for him to be still again. Paula's own
shaking was subsiding. She made a sharp, angry movement with her shoulder. 'I'm all right now.'

Taking the hint, Hugo removed his arm and very carefully Paula eased herself away from Jamie's body and out of the bed. She rammed her feet into her slippers, then leant over and tucked the blanket more securely around Jamie's shoulders. As she straightened up she met Hugo's eyes, watching her with an unfamiliar intensity, and something disconcerting mingling with the concern in them. Instinctively, her hands reached for the lapels of her dressing-gown, yanking them together. Her nerves must still have been shot, because she blushed suddenly for no reason at all. 'It was an idiotic thing to do,' she snapped at him in an undertone to cover her momentary confusion.

Outside the door, Hugo tried putting his arm around her again, then, on second thoughts, took it off smartly. 'Come downstairs; you need a drink. I gave you a bad fright. I'm sorry,' he said with a small, contrite smile.

Terrified out of her wits, she couldn't deny she needed the drink. Paula nodded. 'I'll get dressed,' she said brusquely.

Hugo made an impatient gesture with his hand. 'There's no need for that. The fire's still going in the living-room.' He flicked an eye over the dressing-gown. 'You'll be warm enough as you are.'

It was not the cold Paula was thinking about. She felt uncomfortable and at a disadvantage in the dressing-gown—why, she couldn't have said; it would have been as easy to see through a lead door as its weighty thickness. She went downstairs with him as she was.

CHAPTER FOUR

SHE STOOD by the fire holding her hands down to it, feeling the warmth start at her fingertips and seep slowly through her. When Hugo handed her the whisky Paula took it without a word; the glass felt cold and she curved her hands around it, bringing it closer to the fire.

'Drink it,' Hugo ordered and must have realised how sharp that sounded, because he added, cajolingly, 'Drink it up, Paula, you need it. I'll make you a cup of tea later, if you like,' he offered as an afterthought, and sounded . . . kind.

Granted she had had a bad fright, but he didn't have to turn around and treat her like a recalcitrant invalid to be humoured and bullied into taking her medicine. Paula took a small sip.

'Good girl,' Hugo encouraged approvingly in a voice she had used herself with Jamie, and Paula made a mental note to avoid using it with the child in future. She moved away from him and sat down in the armchair at the other end of the fireplace and took another sip of the whisky, swirling the fiery liquid around her mouth before swallowing it. 'How did you get here?' she asked, suddenly curious. The clock on the mantelpiece showed nine-thirty but it was long past the last ferry or plane from the mainland.

'Flew in. The plane was delayed in Glasgow for ages because of the weather, otherwise I would have been here hours ago,' Hugo explained.

They were about eight miles from the town and the airport. Paula remembered noticing a heavy black mac tossed across the back of a chair in the hall. She frowned at Hugo's shoes. They looked dampish but his dark business suit was dry. 'But how did you get . . . here?'

Hugo gave an abrupt laugh. 'I didn't walk, if that's what you're thinking. I rang up Calum from the airport. The good chap came away from his fireplace and got out his old monstrosity of a cab. We do have a few facilities on the island, you know.' Hugo smiled, teasingly, and Paula was quite aware that he was going all out to relax her. And well might he after scaring her half to death.

They remained silent for a minute or two, listening to the sounds of the storm outside, and the room seemed mellower . . . cosier, just for having another person in it. She thought of Jamie sleeping peacefully upstairs and felt vaguely happy for him, visualising the child's relief when he woke and found that Uncle Hugo had kept his promise and come back after all. Paula lifted her eyes from the glass on her lap.

'I. . .we. . .didn't expect you back.' Back tonight, she had meant, and started quickly to clarify. 'What I meant was . . .'

'Is that so?' Hugo countered tightly without letting her finish. His features were already seized up into a scowl and the hazy façade of companionableness was gone in a flash.

Irrationally angry he had taken her up the wrong way, and conscience just a little pricked by the shadow of doubt that had stayed willy-nilly in her mind, Paula swung blindly into attack. 'And how long is Jamie going to have you around this time?' she sniped.

Hugo grimaced then gave a surly shrug. 'Two weeks— longer, if I can manage it,' he muttered, and she was a little surprised he had chosen to answer without a retaliatory snipe.

'And then?' She really wanted to know, but couldn't do anything about the acid in her voice.

'And then.' Hugo took an angry step towards her and Paula backed into her chair, faintly alarmed by the look on his face. 'And then, since you're so interested in my activities, I'm going back to the States to try and sort out the rest of the mess that my brother left behind him.' Two paces from her, Hugo stopped and turned to the fire. He put both hands on the high mantelpiece and stared down into the flames. With his head down, and body in slump, he did not look arrogant, angry or any of the other derogatory adjectives Paula associated with him. Hugo looked...worn out, and she felt a jab of guilt that she was sitting about needling him when he should have been in bed getting some rest.

'Look, I didn't mean to sound like that...I...' The 'I'm sorry' stayed stranded in her throat.

Hugo turned to her slowly and studied her contemplatively, as if he was trying to make up his mind about her, or about something. 'You may not know it,' he began without any anger, or indeed any emotion at all in his voice, 'but my brother, Jamie's father, was my business partner and there are legalities to iron out that will take months. He was in America looking after that side of the business, and he made a right royal mess of it.'

'You don't have to tell me, it's not my business,' Paula cut in hastily.

'The best that can be said of James's business dealings,' Hugo went on as if she had not spoken, 'was that he was...careless. I could use other words, and some people do, words like incompetent, and a great deal worse. There's talk of embezzlement.' His mouth gave a sour twist at the horror on her face. 'Shareholders over there are queuing around for blocks to sue the pants off me, and it will take me months to get some sort of order into the mess—even if I work twenty-four hours a day.' He looked at her bleakly, as if he was seeing a picture of those unpleasant months in front of him. 'It hasn't been easy on any of us...my father...'

'It's not my business,' Paula interrupted again, wanting him to stop. She felt more shaken by what she was seeing than hearing; Hugo with his guard down, unexpectedly vulnerable. Behind the bitter flippancy as he spoke of his brother, she could detect the hurt and grief in his voice.

'You seem to have made it your business,' Hugo accused wearily. 'You've jumped to your conclusions and made your judgments about me.'

Paula felt gutted by shame. 'I was wrong. I'm sorry,' she said in a small voice and caught him by surprise. The look he gave her was not quite of suspicion, but close. 'I did...jump to conclusions, about you and Jamie. I had no right. I'm sorry.' She offered the apology she should have made days ago.

After a very long silence Hugo gave a quick jerky nod. He didn't ask how she had come to realise her mistake, and didn't appear at all interested. He said gruffly, 'The boy's been through a rough patch.'

And so have you, Paula suddenly thought and felt a surge of compassion, and of helplessness. 'I'm sorry about your brother.' It sounded facile, but there was no other way of offering her compassion, and she couldn't be sure that Hugo would want it from her.

Hugo pressed his eyes shut, face contorted as if with pain. 'I loved him,' he burst out angrily, in spite of himself, Paula thought, then opening his eyes, looked at her with a sort of bewildered bleakness she had sometimes seen in Jamie's eyes. Seeing it in the man caught her off guard. Another moment and she would have given in to the instinct that made her want to reach out and fold him in her arms to comfort him.

Disconcerted by the momentary intensity of her feelings, Paula said quickly, 'There's something I wanted to tell you. I've thought over your offer and I've decided to accept.' She stopped. Hugo was looking blank and she hurried on, flushing a little. 'Looking after Jamie for you. I'm prepared to do it, just for a couple of months of course, but it should help you out.' She finished off her slightly disjointed speech with a self-conscious smile.

At the back of her mind Paula supposed she must have been expecting Hugo would be pleased—perhaps not rapturously, but she was not expecting that tight closed-up expression that made him look as if he didn't know what she was talking about—or didn't want to know. 'If the offer still stands, that is,' she put in with a tinge of huffiness because all at once she felt embarrassed.

'It doesn't,' he told her, quite abruptly with a shake of the head, and her first reaction was an odd sensation of disappointment.

'Why not?'

Hugo shrugged, uncomfortably. Paula stared puzzled.

'You've found someone else.' She plucked the only logical explanation out of the air.

'No, I haven't,' Hugo muttered.

'But if you haven't found anyone else, then why?' Paula heard herself protesting heatedly and shut up, overcome with confusion.

'Let's just say I've changed my mind as well.' Hugo cocked his head to one side and looked at her curiously. 'Don't tell me you're disappointed?' he asked with a hint of a wry smile.

Caught out, the red seared into her face. 'Don't be ridiculous. I didn't want the job in the first place.' That was not the way she was acting. She was behaving with all the hurt and resentment of having a prize job snatched away from her. 'I was only thinking of Jamie,' she explained pointedly. 'He's been feeling so terribly insecure and I thought...'

'That you would overcome your dislike of me for the child's sake?' Hugo prompted, a faint sarcastic edge in his voice.

'Something like that, yes,' Paula agreed shakily, wondering how on earth she had thought the man needed her help, how he had brought out that strange intense concern in her moments ago.

'Then you'll no doubt be relieved that I'm not taking you up on it. Thank you for the offer,' Hugo added with an ironic courtesy that made Paula feel she had just propositioned him and been turned down flat. It was a very galling feeling.

'What I've decided,' Hugo started again conversationally, without the ironic overtones, 'is that Jamie will stay on here with my father until I get back from the States, then I'll take him down to London with me.'

Where half a dozen Louise Hunts would fall over themselves racing to the aid of the guardian in distress, and none of them would give a damn about the child. Paula sprang to her feet. 'That's your business. You don't have to explain anything to me,' she said, hackles on end, and quite appalled she was behaving so irrationally. She looked about for somewhere to slam down her glass before it dropped out of her shaking hand.

Hugo moved to her side and plucked the glass from her fingers. He put it on the mantelpiece beside his own. 'Look here, Paula, I didn't mean to make you angry,' he began testily. 'It was very kind of you to reconsider my request, and I appreciate it,' he said stiffly. 'It's just not necessary any more, that's all. I... well...' he shrugged, 'there are reasons.'

The addition was curiously evasive, and about to try and push past him, Paula picked up the curious tone of voice and stopped. She stared at him, frowning. What reasons? What could have happened in the space of less than a week for Hugo to change his mind and not want her?

And it came to her... the slow trickle of realisation that some time during the last couple of days Sir Iain must have filled Hugo in about her. And why not? She had not consulted the retired doctor as a patient, she had simply confided in him as a friend and it hadn't occurred to her to bind him to secrecy. So naturally, he would have told Hugo about Mark and Stephen, the accident, and her terrible guilt; probably her nightmares too. No wonder Hugo had changed his mind. With that sort of emotionally messy background she'd hardly be anybody's choice for looking after a child. She should have realised Hugo would find out about her sooner or later.

'I quite understand,' Paula said tightly, all at once feeling as exposed and as vulnerable as Hugo had looked a short while ago when he had been talking about his brother. She swerved her eyes away from his baffled face and tried to move past him again.

Hugo caught her roughly by the arm. 'What is it, Paula? What in heaven's name have I said? I didn't mean to upset you.'

Paula bit hard into her bottom lip which had started to quiver. She shook her head miserably as Hugo stared at her, completely at a loss. Then unexpectedly, as if it was the only thing he could think of, he wrapped his arms around her and pulling her to him, held her so tightly Paula could not have moved even if she'd wanted to. Calmed into a vague numbness, she didn't react when Hugo put a hand under her chin and lifted her face. She closed her eyes and stayed motionless as his mouth brushed her lips lightly in a soft kiss that might have meant 'I'm sorry'—or nothing at all.

The kiss would have ended on the vaguely comforting, almost impassive note, if her lips hadn't parted suddenly in response—a pleading response that caught Hugo off-guard in the act of pulling his mouth away. Paula felt his momentary surprise before his lips resumed the kiss with increased pressure. Easing his hands caressingly into her hair, Hugo tilted her head back gently to give his mouth more leverage and Paula slackened yieldingly against him on a wave of warm, mindless desire.

The part of her brain that was standing back, coldly looking on, told her she was doing the kissing now, and that the intensity and urgency were hers; Hugo was not holding back but he was allowing her all the initiative.

And she took it, urged on by an instinctive hunger for his mouth, the pressure of his body. Hugo's hands slid down the curve of her back, holding her hard against himself while her own hands reached around his neck, twining into his hair and kneading agitatedly into his shoulders as Paula abandoned herself to satisfying the wild surge of longing that was carrying the kiss out of control.

Out of whose control? The lips moving down the arch of her throat knew exactly what they were doing. Paula pulled away in a breathless daze. With their arms still locked around each other she looked into Hugo's eyes and read the desire in them, and the need. Or was it her own eyes reflected back at her? There was a question too, in his dark blue depths: Hugo was virtually asking her where she wanted to go from here.

The image that flooded her mind told her where she wanted to go. The picture was so erotic—and graphic—it made Paula catch back a gasp of shock, and brought a wave of heat into her cheeks. She wasn't conscious she had moved closer against him but was aware she had started to tremble. Hugo tightened his arms around her. His eyes hadn't left her face. The question was still in them and every nerve in her body throbbed her answer for her in the silence that seemed to be extending into eons.

Then suddenly, Paula shook her head and took her hands away from Hugo's neck. Abruptly, he unclasped his arms from her back; the expression in his eyes changed to having no expression at all.

'No, of course not,' he said in a brusque undertone—more to himself than to her, and made no move to stop her as Paula fled the room.

Another kiss, that's all it would have taken to sweep her back into that exquisite mindlessness and the last of her reservations would have melted into thin air. A man of Hugo's experience must have known that, and yet he had let her walk away.

Hunched up on the bed in the guest-room, her hands wrapped around her knees, Paula told herself she should be feeling grateful instead of—resentful, there was no other word for it. There was no question she had wanted Hugo to make love to her—for all the wrong reasons. Love hadn't come into it; she did not love him; it was simply a momentary blend of sexual attraction and need of comforting and she had been ready to leap into bed with a man she barely knew—had wanted to, and hang the consequences.

Is that how one-night stands came about? She had often been curious about women who did that sort of thing, and now she had nearly done it herself—was even regretting that she hadn't.

But how did those women—'easy women,' she still thought of them as—feel the next morning? Did they wake up hating themselves? And how would she have felt, Paula wondered, when she had never before said 'yes' to a man in her life—even a man she thought she had loved—in the beginning at any rate.

Mark had tried to make love to her once, early in their relationship, and all this time later, the recollection of her reaction still made Paula cringe. She had turned to stone, appalled by the feel of his hand on her breast, and that was as far as they had got before she started bleating horrified 'nos'. It had been embarrassing and humiliating for both of them and after that first abortive attempt, Mark had never tried again.

And that in itself was curious. Had he been angry... frustrated, during their long, peculiarly platonic engagement, or had it never really mattered to him, with his main concern being to acquire a stepmother for Stephen?

Somewhere quite early along the line, Paula had sensed that that was the role in store for her, and had accepted it—without resentment, she thought. It seemed to tie in with her own need for a family, but perhaps deep down it had not been what she needed or wanted. Perhaps it had been the reason she had felt so cold towards Mark, unconsciously frozen up with resentment that he hadn't wanted her for herself.

And had she been sexually frustrated all that time without realising it...? That would go some way in explaining her unpredictable response to Hugo, and why her body had sent out its crazy urgent messages. Only her mind was another matter; she had come out a psychological mess after her relationship with Mark, not knowing who she was nor what she wanted any more; but jumping into bed with Hugo Cameron was unlikely to have solved that for her.

Paula drifted off into an uneasy sleep. She woke several times during the night feeling cold, but some time after the dismal grey streaks of dawn, fell into a heavy doze and it was late when she came out of it. She got up feeling she hadn't slept at all and flung herself into her dressing-gown as the soft tap sounded on the door. 'Yes?' Paula called, edgily, because it didn't sound like Jamie.

Hugo put his head around the door. His hair was still damp from a shower and his face had the pinkish smoothness that comes just after a shave.

'Hello, you're up,' he said lightly. 'I just wanted to let you know Jamie is in my bed, in case you looked in on him. I didn't want you to worry.'

'Oh,' Paula said, looking into his face rather fixedly so her eyes wouldn't stray down to the damp curling hair visible between the fronts of his heavy black towelling robe.

Hugo smiled, warily. 'He woke during the night and I took him into my room so he wouldn't disturb you,' he explained.

'Yes. I see. Thank you.' Paula produced the words in stiff jerks.

Hugo wanted to say more; she could see that. He stood in the doorway, hesitating, not coming nor going. In the end, he gave another tentative smile and said with jarring heartiness, 'Well, I'll see you down at breakfast when you're ready.'

She had been wondering how they would act towards each other in the morning; Hugo had given her the cue—act as if nothing had happened. 'Yes, fine. I'll be down soon,' Paula said, breezily.

Hugo was in the kitchen when she came downstairs. Unobserved, Paula stood in the doorway taking in the curiously domestic scene. Dressed in faded jeans and a well-worn sweater, Hugo looked completely at home in Anna's comfortable territory—as if making breakfast with a six-year-old dogging his heels was something he did every day of the week.

Appearances were deceptive; the strong whiff of burnt toast told the real story. Hugo suddenly swung from the frying-pan on the stove to the toaster on the workbench.

'Damn it, Jamie, I told you to watch that,' he chided, lifting out the charred bread and hurling it into the kitchen bin.

To Paula's surprise, Jamie laughed. 'Sorry, Uncle Hugo,' he chirped back cheerfully, not the least upset by his uncle's rebuke, and following on Hugo's heels like an excited puppy. There was no sign of the withdrawn little boy of the last couple of days. Paula couldn't help wondering what magic uncle had managed to work on nephew during the early hours of the morning when they were companionably tucked up in bed together.

She came into the room. 'Hello Jamie,' she smiled at the child.

'Uncle Hugo is making breakfast,' Jamie beamed and Hugo laughed, giving the boy's head an affectionate ruffle.

'Incredible optimist, this child. We could do with some help, couldn't we, Jamie?'

'Yes,' Jamie agreed, grinning.

Easier with the child around to take the edge off the strain between the adults. It had been like that with Stephen too, Paula remembered, that same artificial air of cosiness. The memory set off faint warning bells inside her head as they sat around the table.

'We're like a family, aren't we?' Munching on his toast, Jamie tossed in the ingenuous question without directing it at either of them.

After the slightest pause, Paula went on spreading marmalade on her toast with very intense concentration.

'Yes, we are, aren't we?' Hugo agreed, rather too airily after the long silence.

Paula looked up with no expression on her face, met Jamie's eyes, and forced out a thin smile. 'If you've finished your breakfast, Jamie, I'll start clearing away. I'm sure you and your uncle have a lot of things planned for today and you'll want to get started as soon as possible.'

'Oh, we're in no hurry,' Hugo said blandly, pouring himself another cup of tea. 'I'll be here long enough for us to do all the things we want.' He cast an eye towards the window. 'Looks like we'll be staying inside today, the weather is too dismal for anything else. We might try a spot of chess.'

'Uncle Hugo can teach you chess too, Paula,' Jamie offered, pathetically anxious to include her in their activities.

Paula's lips curved mechanically. 'That would have been nice,' she fibbed briskly, 'but I'm afraid I'll be too busy for that today. I need to pack because I'm leaving for London tomorrow.' She wasn't looking at Hugo as she said it, but was immediately aware that he had tensed. Jamie stared at her uncomprehendingly. It was not the way she would have chosen to break the news to the child, but until she announced it, the idea had not crossed her mind—her conscious mind that is; it must have been lurking in her subconscious from the moment she fled the living-room last night. Paula hurriedly, 'You can come down to the cottage later, Jamie, and we'll have a chat there.'

'No,' Jamie answered stonily and turned away from her with a jerk of his shoulder that looked a direct copy of one of his uncle's angry shrugs.

'I think you should go upstairs and make your bed, Jamie—I'll give you a call when I've got the chess set out.' Hugo came into the conversation at last.

Just for a moment, Jamie looked as if he was going to protest, then he rose from the table and marched huffishly out of the room.

Hugo stayed silent, watching Jamie disappear through the doorway, waiting to make sure the boy was out of earshot before he swung back to her. 'What the hell did you have to go and do that for?' he barked.

Paula reproduced Jamie's angry shrug. 'I'm leaving tomorrow,' she repeated.

'Over my dead body.'

'If that's the way you want it.' Paula squeezed out a pinched smile.

Hugo gave a raspy laugh. 'Oh, no, you're not leaving. You'll stay put. I'm not having Jamie upset just because you're miffed with me.'

Miffed? She was a little more than miffed—and it wasn't with Hugo. She was angry with herself for her own vulnerability to him, and downright scared if it came to that. 'I'm not miffed. I have things to attend to in London and need to get down there as soon as possible,' Paula said, reasonably.

Hugo contemplated her through his scowl for some moments. 'Look, about last night . . .' he began in a different tone of voice.

'Last night has got nothing to do with anything,' Paula cut him off, and rose to her feet.

Hugo gave a mocking smile. 'If you say so.' Then as Paula reached for Jamie's plate to take to the sink, Hugo leant across the table and caught her wrist, holding her hand down to the table. Paula winced slightly, stared down at him with hostile eyes, but made no attempt to pull her hand free.

'Last night happened,' Hugo said crisply, 'but it won't happen again. I'm not going to make any advances, so unless you want to make them to me—and mean them, I might add—we can forget the whole thing and you can stop acting as if I'd subjected you to a fate worse than death. You might remember that I didn't. We happen to have kissed. It was no big deal so let's leave it at that; there's no need to make a production out of it.'

Win some, lose some, that was his attitude, and it was a safe bet that Hugo Cameron won more than he lost, and that he didn't spend fruitless hours agonising about the whys and wherefores of every passionate encounter. Paula yanked at her hand. 'Let me go,' she snapped, stung by humiliation.

'Not before you tell me you're staying,' Hugo replied with infuriating calmness, his fingers not giving an inch.

'I can't. I've arranged to see my publisher.' The unpremeditated lie popped out to her rescue. Hugo released her wrist and Paula started rubbing at where his fingers had clamped the flesh.

'Really? I didn't know that,' Hugo said with sharp interest.

'Yes. It's been arranged for a while. I've promised to bring my illustrations. He wants to have a look at them.' Paula elaborated on the lie.

'But I thought you hadn't finished them yet.' Hugo's voice held a note of polite surprise.

'They're not quite finished,' Paula conceded, trying to remember how much she had told him at the picnic, 'but they're ready enough to be looked at.'

'Oh, I see. Your publisher is waiting on them now?'

This was all much easier than Paula expected. 'Yes, that's right. I'll be seeing him in a couple of days' time.'

'How many publishers are you working for?' Hugo asked lightly.

Paula looked at him perplexed, then gave a small laugh. 'Just the one—and that's enough.'

'Then who are you going to be seeing in London when Roger Harris is up here on the island?' Hugo sprang the question on her without any change in the blandness of his voice.

'What are you talking about?' Paula frowned, momentarily stumped.

Hugo bared his teeth snidely. 'Roger Harris had lunch with my father the other day and I gather they've arranged that he'll be coming up shortly. I understand your publisher has decided he needs to see you rather urgently. Do you think he's forgotten about your appointment with him in London?' Hugo asked with wide-eyed innocence, and Paula looked at him in dislike for letting her trip along with her lie for so long.

'That was a rotten thing to do.'

Hugo leaned back in his chair. 'Yes, wasn't it?' he agreed smugly. 'So what's your next excuse?'

CHAPTER FIVE

ANNA SAID, and it seemed like for the twentieth time in the last three days, 'The child's really come out of himself, Miss Paula; it's a joy to see him now; he feels he belongs again.' She put the coffee pot on the side-table within reach of the card-table set up near the fireplace, and turned to Paula with a quite remarkable display of teeth for someone who looked too old to have any. 'It's having you and Mr Hugo around that's doing it.' She nodded, sagely, a pleased wiry little gnome.

Busy stacking up the cards, Paula returned a perfunctory smile of acknowledgment with a lot of suppressed exasperation behind it. 'Yes, I suppose so,' she felt obliged to murmur, wishing the old lady would let up ramming her point home. Paula was only too aware of the change in Jamie—and the reason for it. She was pleased about the change; the reason worried her. They were playing at 'happy families' and it was not going to last forever. And what was going to happen to Jamie's sense of security when it was all over, when she left, when Hugo left again?

Then at the door, Anna said with all the subtlety of a sledgehammer, 'You can never tell what Fate has in store for the three of you, you get on so well.' She grinned into Paula's startled face.

Paula gave a sudden laugh. 'You're incorrigible, Anna,' she said, returning to the cards as Anna disappeared out of the door, but wasn't nearly as amused by the old lady's innuendo as she made out.

True; she and Hugo had got on surprisingly well, all things considered. The embarrassing episode in the living-room on the night of his return might never have happened—except that Paula couldn't get it out of her mind, and every now and then when she turned suddenly and found Hugo watching her, she knew from something in his expression that he hadn't forgotten it either.

They never referred to it, but there was an undercurrent of tension between them nevertheless. Hugo had never so much as touched her again. He had gone out of his way to be friendly, pleasant and amusing, and downright devious too, never insisting she take part in the activities he had planned with Jamie, just turning up at the cottage with Jamie in tow, all ready for the walk or drive, or the trip into town. The child took it for granted she was coming too, and when it came to the crunch, Paula couldn't refuse.

In the same way, she had been manoeuvred into joining them for the evening meal, and often a game of cards before Hugo took the child to bed. But very soon after, Hugo would walk her back to the cottage; they took great care never to be alone together for too long—but Anna would have missed that bit, just as she missed the tension in their attitude towards each other. The old lady saw only what she wanted to see, and on the surface, at least, they must have presented a very cosy picture. Appearances being what they were, was it any wonder Anna was whizzing through the air jumping to her outlandish conclusions?

And was the exasperating old lady all that far off the mark? The uneasy thought brought Paula's hand to a sudden standstill in the middle of clearing the card table. Could Hugo be playing his own little game with her, putting her through some sort of probationary exercise to test her suitability for looking after Jamie? Now that she thought about it, why else would he have pressured her

into staying. She was 'no big deal' in the romance stakes—
he had practically told her so, and he hadn't made another advance, just as he promised. But he did appear to
want her around, and Jamie was the obvious reason. She
was surprised that it hadn't occurred to her before.

Paula poured herself a cup of coffee then settled into the
armchair and waited impatiently for Hugo to return
downstairs. 'Listen,' she plunged in, the moment he entered the room, 'if you've changed your mind again and
want me to look after Jamie, I'm not interested.'

The unexpected tackle pulled Hugo up short. 'I haven't,'
he said, and gave her an odd look as he went over to get
himself coffee. He stayed by the coffee-table, eyeing her
curiously across the small distance between them.
''Whatever put that into your head?''

Without resorting to Anna's heavy-handed insinuations, Paula didn't have much of a reason. 'Nothing. I just
thought.' She shrugged and felt a twit.

'Well, whatever you thought, you can set your worried
little mind at rest. I told you I'd be making other arrangements.' Hugo smiled sardonically at her discomfort, then
suddenly frowned. 'I think it will work out all right. When
Jamie starts back at school in September, I'll get someone
in full-time.'

'One of your lady-friends, I suppose,' Paula astonished
herself with the caustic question.

Hugo's brows shot up above the rim of the cup. He
lowered the cup, his mouth curving wryly. 'Lady-friends?
How quaint.' The curve broadened into a sly grin. 'You're
not fishing about my girlfriends by any chance?'

Paula flared a furious red. 'Don't flatter yourself. I was
only concerned about Jamie.'

'I don't get much chance to flatter myself with you
around to keep my ego in check, do I?' Hugo laughed

teasingly. 'But aren't you the slightest bit curious about my . . . lady-friends . . . ?'

'Not the slightest,' Paula lied with a snap as a picture of the very elegant Louise Hunt beamed itself in front of her mind's eye.

'How very unfeminine of you.' Hugo's eyes glistened with amusement. 'However, as it happens, I don't have much time for lady-friends these days, not for one, let alone the hordes I suspect you so generously attribute to me.'

'What about Louise Hunt?' Paula could have bitten off her tongue.

'What about her?' Hugo countered guilelessly, deliberately sidestepping her question.

'She travels with you.' Paula was appalling herself with her curiosity—and amusing Hugo into the bargain.

'So she does,' he agreed blandly, without giving anything away.

And what did she want to know anyway? She could make a pretty good guess at what sort of travelling companion the arrogant brunette was. And it was not her business. Paula was rather surprised Hugo hadn't put her in her place and told her as much.

'You'll probably want to know about Dorothy too,' Hugo offered drily. 'She lives in my apartment.'

That took the wind out of her, and lynx-eyed, Hugo didn't miss her jolt. 'That's made you sit up.' He grinned appreciatively, then said super-casually, 'If it's any interest to you, Dorothy has been with me for about twelve years. She's my housekeeper,' he added.

'It's of no interest to me whatsoever,' Paula shot back indignantly, infuriated that Hugo was playing on her curiosity and knowing she deserved every bit of his amusement.

Hugo raised a sceptical eyebrow. 'I thought not,' he murmured drily, then studied her in silence for a moment or two. 'And when are you going to tell me about yourself?'

Paula gave a start. 'You wouldn't be interested, and there's nothing to tell,' she said shortly. And besides which, you know too much already, she thought, looking away from him. She stood up and took her coffee-cup to the table. 'I'd better get back to the cottage. I need to get on with my work.'

'Is that all you're interested in?' Hugo asked quietly but with an edge in his voice.

'It's important to me,' Paula answered quickly. Too important perhaps, but she had nothing else, and if she messed up the commission this time ... Paula tried not to think about it.

Hugo put his cup down. 'Couldn't you let it go, just for one evening?'

'Why?' she asked abruptly. 'Jamie's in bed.'

Hugo looked puzzled. 'What's that got to do with anything?'

Paula laughed a little harshly. 'It means,' she said pointedly, 'that I've put in my quota of "happy-family" time for one day and you don't need me around any more.'

Hugo's face twisted as if she had hit him. 'I had no idea you felt that way,' he said through thin lips.

Paula flushed. 'I'm sorry, that was rude. I ... I honestly don't mind ... helping you out with Jamie.'

Hugo stared at her. 'Is that what you've been doing?' he asked tonelessly.

'Well, yes. Isn't it?' she countered, dubiously. Did he think she had let him pressure her into staying on for any other reason? Somewhere at the back of her mind a tiny doubt stirred. How much pressure had Hugo really put on her? The answer, uncomfortably, was very little. He had simply told her Roger was coming to the island soon, and taken away her excuse for going back to London—hardly thumbscrew pressure, and she could have left regardless—if she had really wanted to.

Paula met Hugo's eyes uneasily, and had the embarrassing sensation he'd been following her train of thought. She turned away from him. 'I must get back,' she said for the second time, giving Hugo the opportunity to offer to walk her back as he usually did—an act of courtesy, because it was still always light and there was no real reason for him to do it.

'Must you? I was rather hoping you'd come out with me this evening,' Hugo said diffidently.

'Out?' Paula repeated, and then added, 'You mean just you and me—you and I?'

'I can never get the hang of that little point of grammar either.' Hugo smiled, but with an air of covering up nervousness. 'Just to one of the pubs. There's a bit of a gathering on tonight and I thought perhaps you might enjoy it. You've been working so hard on your drawings and I...we've been taking up a lot of your time. You could do with a break. We both could...from Jamie...the house,' Hugo trailed off, shrugging.

Hugo did not need to elaborate; Paula understood what he meant; what she had not realised was he'd been feeling like that too, almost swallowed up by the child's needs and always under that strain of acting as if nothing had happened between them. It hadn't occurred to her Hugo might be finding it was wearing on his nerves as she did.

Paula studied him silently for a moment, noting with surprise the lines of tension around the dark eyes and the faint grey shadow under them. How had she missed seeing that before? Hugo looked as if he needed a break—probably from her, as much as from Jamie.

He would probably go to the pub without her, and probably have a better time of it too, if she wasn't there to cramp his style. Suddenly, Paula wanted to go with him. 'I'd like to come. Thank you,' she said with a spontaneous smile and saw Hugo's eyes register relief—or so it seemed.

The main room of the pub was bursting at the seams with a few locals and lots of visitors, some unsuccessfully trying to pass themselves off as locals in their too-new heavy homeknits and tweeds. The place was thick with smoke and noisy talk and laughter. Somewhere from the back came the sound of music—home-made music, not the stereo variety, and above the din of voices talking, other voices were singing in the background. Paula laughed delightedly. Yes, this was what she needed.

Hugo smiled down at her. 'All right?' he asked and she nodded, hanging on to his arm as he edged her through the crush of bodies towards where the music was coming from.

If anything, the back room of the small pub was even more crowded, but with the proportions reversed. A few visitors, and lots of locals—islanders like Anna, with that same ready friendliness and the same blatant, almost childlike curiosity in their faces when Hugo introduced her around. He seemed to know everybody and everybody was delighted to see him.

The thing that struck Paula first was how few young people there were, and how often, when Hugo asked after somebody's son or daughter, he was told that whoever it was was working on the mainland. It was necessity, not the city lights, Paula realised, that took the youth away from the island, and that tourism could not support everybody. The old folk stayed on—or came back, like Sir Iain, when they retired. It made her momentarily sad.

'Ah, you've brought along your lassie,' said a positively ancient man who must have been responsible for some of the music because he had an accordion on his lap. Beside him, a marginally-less ancient one had a mouth organ in one hand, a glass in the other and was bringing each to his mouth in turn.

Paula waited for Hugo to explain that she was not 'his lassie'; Hugo chose not to, but contrarily, as if to confirm everybody's misconception about her role, placed an arm around her shoulder, drawing her closer to himself. It must have been the atmosphere, because it felt natural to have the arm around her as Hugo led her from group to group. Paula's self-consciousness lasted about half a minute and then she didn't give it a moment's thought.

When the singing started again, Hugo astonished her by casually joining in, and fitting into the cheerful unpretentious group in a way that Paula found strangely disconcerting. After a little while she moved away and found herself a chair by the wall from where she could watch and listen—watch mainly, since her eyes stayed fixed on Hugo, drawn by something she couldn't understand.

How many Hugo Camerons were there? Every time Paula turned, there seemed to be a different character facing her, and each a surprise. The real surprise, the part that perplexed her, was that he was prepared to show all the sides of himself so openly. She had seen the arrogant man; was aware of the hard-working businessman; seen the concerned, caring man worried about a small boy; and had glimpsed someone unexpectedly vulnerable that night in the living-room when he had spoken about his brother.

And now, yet another Hugo; relaxed, warm and eminently likeable. It was not just facile charm; he was getting warmth back from his friends in return and you couldn't get that by being charming—or patronising. Like Mark.

Involuntarily, the image rose to her mind. How reserved and up-tight Mark would have been among these

islanders whom he would have considered socially in-
ferior. Mark had been a great snob, and the unpalatable
part was that some of his attitudes had rubbed off on her;
not the snobbishness, she hoped, but that ever-present reserve—always being on guard against showing her real
feelings. Paula looked away from the cheerful scene and
stared down at her lap, not liking herself very much.

'Embarrassed I'll shatter the glassware?'

Paula glanced up to find Hugo in front of her, smiling
teasingly. He sat down beside her. 'Do you like this?' He
gestured at everybody and nobody in particular.

'Yes,' Paula said simply.

'Then we must come again.'

She wanted to say, 'yes, let's.' Something stopped her;
a shyness. 'I didn't know you were so musical,' she said
instead, injecting a softly teasing note into her voice.

A faint smile flickered over Hugo's face. 'There's a lot
we don't know about each other, isn't there?' he said,
seriously, his voice softly intimate.

That's just what she had realised moments before—and
had found so unsettling. Paula tried to laugh off Hugo's
seriousness but couldn't think of anything light and
amusing enough to counter it. She swung her face away
from his gaze, pretending sudden interest in an Anna
lookalike who was setting food out on a nearby table. Then
Hugo picked up her hand from her lap and drew her to her
feet. 'Come on, my girl.' His voice was light and teasing
again; the momentarily threatening intimacy gone. 'You're
going to have to sing for your supper like everybody else.'

'I can't,' Paula squealed in mock horror.

'Yes, you can.'

Not since before she met Mark had Paula sung songs in
a pub—not quite sung, because she didn't know the words
to the lilting island melodies. Hugo did that, but she

hummed along, laughingly earning her supper, and enjoying herself a lot.

It was the sort of night that would be a blur the next morning. Later, after the supper, when the chairs and tables had been moved aside, Paula caught herself skipping through an unfamiliar reel under Hugo's approving eyes and told herself it was just as well she wasn't going to remember much about 'making an exhibition of herself,' she could almost hear Mark saying.

And later still, came the schmaltzy, schmaltzy waltzes. The tenor of the evening changed. Paula watched the oddly-assorted couples on the improvised dance-floor and felt moved. There was something indescribably poignant and romantic about middle-aged and elderly couples gazing into each other's eyes as they danced slowly to the hauntingly sweet music.

'May I?' Hugo asked with a formality that at first Paula took to be ironic and then realised wasn't.

'I...I'm not dressed for it.' In a fluster of shyness she said the first thing that came into her head.

Hugo flicked his eyes over her skirt and winter cotton shirt, then at the practically identical sensible outfits of the other women. 'If that's the case, then neither is any other woman in the room.' He put an arm around her waist and led her on to the floor.

Paula was conscious of the knowing, approving smiles bestowed on them, and could imagine the innocent gossip running rife tomorrow—about Hugo Cameron and 'his lassie' wrapped in each other's arms on the pint-sized dance-floor in the back room of an old pub. What these nice, friendly people wouldn't know, however, was that by then she and Hugo would have reverted to their careful, impersonal friendliness, with their concern for Jamie providing the only and very tenuous bond, just like Stephen had between herself and Mark.

Only Paula did not want it to be like that again...not anymore. She was shocked by the intensity of the resentment she fleetingly felt towards Jamie—and then confused. What was she thinking? That she could be interested in Hugo Cameron if it wasn't for Jamie? That Hugo could possibly be interested in her?

Paula pulled up her thoughts sharply. The evening must have gone to her head. She had known Hugo Cameron for barely two weeks and any interest he had displayed in her was strictly of the standard male variety. And yes, despite his denials, he was still possibly interested in having her be nanny to Jamie for a while. One genuinely pleasant evening together did not change anything, and if she couldn't see that, she was getting soft.

They were very close, their bodies touching and they were dancing so slowly they were swaying to the music rather than dancing. Deliberately, Paula eased herself away from him, and after a moment, felt Hugo's hand withdraw the pressure from her back. Without a word they resumed a 'polite' dancing position, keeping careful distance between them until the music ended. Hugo did not suggest another dance.

In the car, Paula felt on edge and kept up a nervous stream of light remarks to cover it, about the various people they had met that evening, the island in general; and Hugo's remarks were in the same vein—and tone, and came just as readily as hers. If Paula didn't know better, she'd have said Hugo was nervous too.

There was not one gap in the conversation all the way home, but the constant stream of it had the effect of heightening the tension that had sprung up again between them since their last dance, not lessening it. Without even waiting for tomorrow they were back to where they had started from before the evening began—ill at ease with each other under the carefully friendly exterior. And it was best that way, Paula thought with irony, flushing suddenly as she remembered the idiotic thoughts that had drifted in and out of her mind when she had been in Hugo's arms during the first of the dreamy waltzes, before she realised she was being seduced by the music, the warmth of the evening, and by a glimpse of a side of Hugo she found likeable. She needed the drive home to put the evening back into perspective and get a grip on herself.

Then at the cottage door, it all went wrong; Paula turned to him—to invite him in, she supposed for coffee, but she wasn't at all clear about anything because as she looked into Hugo's face, her mind went haywire and everything catapulted out of perspective again.

You can actually ask a man to kiss you without putting it into words; Paula knew her eyes were doing the asking, and in the cold, quite stark light of the moon, Hugo's eyes told her he understood. An anticipatory little shiver shot through her.

'You're cold,' Hugo said, abruptly swinging the door open. He put a hand to her back and gently pushed her inside before Paula took in what was happening—that he'd knocked back her offer. Hugo followed her in, switching on the light as he came in through the door after her.

The harshness of the electric light brought Paula back to her senses. She hid her mortification behind a brilliant smile. 'I've had a lovely evening. Thank you,' she said effusively. They were standing too close, and without the haunting music and the protection of people around them the proximity of Hugo's body was threatening. Paula swung towards the kitchenette. 'Would you like some coffee?' she asked, a proper little hostess all at once and bright as a button in her nervousness.

Hugo reached out and caught her arm before she had reached the safety of the other side of the counter, and in almost a single movement, pulled her back to him and cupped her face roughly with his hands. Paula's lips parted in the hazy second it took for his mouth to reach them.

It was a short, deep, almost angry kiss and her mouth answered on a flare of response before Hugo pulled his mouth away with shattering suddenness, leaving her breathless and confused. Dropping his hands from her face, Hugo stared down at her confusion, then shook his head in a jerky movement and made a sound of frustration. For a split second Paula thought he would kiss her again, and was piercingly aware that she wanted him to.

'I won't stay... for coffee,' Hugo added with abrupt irony, and Paula felt heat sweep up her face.

And just what else did Hugo think she had been offering? 'As you like,' she returned in a scratchy attempt at off-handedness, mortified she had laid herself open to his assumption that she had been offering anything more than a polite cup of coffee, and a little frightened because far back in her mind something was telling her his assumption was perilously close to the truth.

Hugo turned to the door, then turned back again. 'By the way, I forgot to mention—your publisher is arriving on the ten-thirty plane tomorrow.'

Still floundering in her confusion, Paula was slow to take in his words. 'Roger Harris?' she asked, vaguely, as if she had difficulty coming up with her publisher's name. 'Tomorrow?' Then everything vanished—mortification included, before the rush of the old familiar panic. Roger; the illustrations; they weren't ready; she wasn't ready. 'But why didn't you tell me before?' Paula demanded accusingly.

From the door, Hugo looked at her with sharpened interest. 'It skipped my mind. I'm sorry,' he said. 'I didn't realise it was so important to you.'

'Of course it is. I wouldn't have gone out with you tonight if I'd known,' Paula returned in a wail. It was the way Hugo looked at her, his face tightening after the first flinch, that made her realise how unpleasant, if not downright churlish, that sounded. She hadn't meant it that way. She might be angry and confused, but she couldn't regret the evening—and didn't. She had only meant that she would have felt compelled to stay home and work on her drawings. 'I didn't meant that...I...' she started again.

'That's all right, you needn't explain. I understood you the first time,' Hugo said tightly.

Paula shook her head in frustration. 'That's just the trouble—you don't understand!' How could he understand how important Roger's assessment was going to be? That her career was virtually on the line? 'Does Anna know?' she asked apropos of nothing, as the domestic arrangements sprang into her mind.

Hugo gave a brief nod. 'Yes. I asked her to prepare one of the guest-rooms.' His eyes drifted slowly across the room towards the silk-screen curtain and stayed there. 'However, if you prefer to put up your boyfriend down here at the cottage, I'm sure Anna won't mind.'

Paula's eyes had followed the direction of his gaze and yet it took a long moment for the innuendo to sink in. Behind the curtain there was one single, very narrow bed. There could be no mistaking Hugo's meaning. Strangely, Paula did not feel angry. She brought her eyes back to Hugo's pinched face and met his eyes, intrigued as to what was going on behind their deep blue façade. Jealousy? Was that what prompted his astonishingly crude innuendo? If it was then it was of the dog-in-the-manger type. Hugo had made it pretty plain he was not particularly interested in her. The male ego was a curious thing, Paula thought, continuing her impassive scrutiny until Hugo dropped his eyes.

'Sorry. I didn't mean that. Forget it,' Hugo muttered, colouring unevenly.

Paula eyed his discomfort with a stab of satisfaction. Not on your life, she thought. She was not going to forget it. And if that was the track Hugo's mind was running along, then she'd make sure that she really gave him something to think about when Roger arrived.

'You'd better ask Neil to drive you to the airport if you want to meet the plane. I'll be busy,' Hugo said curtly.

'Fine,' Paula answered airily—to his back, because Hugo was already out of the door.

She watched him stride with long angry steps up the path. A little way up, he stopped and turned around uncertainly. Paula quickly closed the door. She didn't want him to come back—to apologise or anything else, and in a way was perversely glad the evening had ended on such a sour note. An angry, jealous Hugo Cameron was much less threatening than the warm, likeable man she had been with most of the evening. That one was too attractive by half and she was too vulnerable to him.

Paula glanced at her watch. It was well past midnight but she got out her illustrations, and this time was most grateful for the seizure of panic that managed to push Hugo Cameron temporarily from her mind.

CHAPTER SIX

As THE passengers started to drift out of the plane Paula recognised Sir Iain first and was surprised. Hugo had not mentioned his father's return and she wasn't expecting to see him. Roger was at his heels, grinning cheerfully, large pale eyes blinking with pleasure behind the thick glasses when he spotted her, and, nervous as she was, Paula was glad to see him.

Eyeing her in a way that would have sent her rigid with hostility had it been anyone with better eyesight, Roger kept shaking his head in disbelief. 'I can't believe it.' He turned to Sir Iain. 'I can't believe it's the same woman.'

'Island air,' Sir Iain explained cryptically, imitating his old housekeeper with a wry smile.

Paula chuckled under her breath. Anna's standard explanation for anything she thought wholesome was 'island air'—her euphemism for the gale-force blasts of wind that almost knocked Paula off her feet.

Roger couldn't take his eyes off her. 'You look positively marvellous—just like you used to look before...' Roger teetered on the brink of the yawning *faux pas*. 'You know...' He drew back from it with a mumble, faint pink sneaking into the thin, pallid cheeks.

Yes, Paula knew; before the accident, he meant...and before that even—before Mark drained her personality out of her.

'How have you been getting on with Hugo?' Sir Iain asked chattily on their way to the car, possibly in the misguided belief that he was rescuing the conversation from its sudden dip into the doldrums.

Paula swallowed a mouthful of air and let it out again in a tinny laugh. 'Oh, fine. Jamie is enjoying his uncle's company no end, they're always busy at something. He's been so happy since his uncle's return.' Paula heard herself prattling in a peculiarly high-pitched voice that sounded too jolly for words. 'You'll notice the change. And he can play chess now and...' She caught Sir Iain's slightly astonished look and broke off. 'It's nice to have you back, Sir Iain. Did you enjoy your stay in London?' Paula changed the subject hastily and they all talked safely of London during the drive back to the house.

As they pulled up beside Hugo's sleek sports-car at the side of the house, Roger let out a long, low whistle of admiration. 'I say,' he whispered, thrilled, and it was only because Paula could see where his eyes were focused that she realised what the object of his admiration was. Roger in raptures over a car? She'd have credited him with more sense.

Hugo was noticeable by his absence. Anna duly informed them he had taken Jamie sailing for the day and would not be back until later. He was 'very sorry to miss Mr Harris.' She passed on the message in good faith, and Paula for one did not believe it for a moment; but snub or no snub, was quite relieved by his absence. There was an ordeal ahead of her, and after last night's episode she could do without Hugo around to observe her every move—and Roger's.

Lunch was like filling in time before a dentist's appointment. The waiting was always the worst part with that awful sense of inevitability, but Paula would rather have had her teeth yanked out one by one than go through the heart-stopping assessment of her work again.

That was why Roger had come; she knew that. Whatever story he might have tactfully fabricated to get himself an invitation to the island, he had come for one reason and one only: to check on her work. Roger was a businessman, and while most people would have found it difficult to reconcile the nervous, slightly fumbling individual with a very profitable publishing company, Paula knew better. He had given her a second chance after she'd messed up the commission on the first attempt; that had been as a friend. But he had also invested in her work as a businessman, and now had come to check how his investment was coming along. She didn't resent it; she was just terrified.

Roger seemed as nervous as she was when they went down to the cottage after lunch. He picked up the large folder off the table where Paula had left it in readiness for him and took it outside into the brighter light. Paula followed him and watched with detached calm as he settled himself on the bench and placed the folder carefully alongside. Unable to take her eyes off him, she stood by as Roger flicked through the collection—off-handedly, without poring over them as he had done the first time. He was finished in a matter of minutes, but just sat there staring down at the closed folder. Wondering how to break it to her this time?

There was a bitter taste in her mouth. Paula walked away from him and turned her back. And she had actually thought she had made a good job of them. Her eyelids prickled uncomfortably and she wondered, quite unemotionally, if she was about to cry.

'These will have people stampeding to buy the book. I'll have to rework the print-run, we'll need to do a bigger run first off. Now let me see . . .'

Paula spun around and stared blankly as Roger's brow crinkled into furrows of concentration under the wind-blown wisps of fair hair. It seemed a very long time before a reluctant hope began to filter through the numbness, like sensation coming back after pins and needles. 'Roger!' she almost screamed. 'Roger, stop rambling and tell me this instant. Are they good?'

Roger came out of his mental maze of figures and peered at her, surprised. 'Of course they're good. They're the best you've ever done.' He frowned, puzzled. 'Couldn't you tell? I thought you were just keeping it back to make me nervous.'

Make him nervous! Paula slumped limply to the ground beside the bench. She wasn't sure whether the muffled sound in her throat was going to come out a laugh or a cry. 'I don't think I'm ever going to forgive you for this, Roger Harris.'

Roger was truly appalled. 'But honestly, Paula, I didn't mean you to think they weren't good. I thought you knew, really I did.' He was so contrite he looked comic. Paula laughed.

'When can you have the finished artwork ready?' Roger's mind switched back unthinkingly.

'Whenever you like, Roger darling,' Paula laughed again and felt she could do everything overnight on the wild euphoric wave of relief.

Bright-eyed and flushed with pleasure, Roger sprang up and held out a hand. Paula took it and let him draw her to her feet, and they stood facing each other, smiling like two idiots until she took a step towards him and Roger's arms closed around her.

He held her so lightly she could barely feel his arms at first, then very slowly, the hold tightened. Paula put her face against his chest and let out a long, shuddering sigh. Relief and a strange tiredness left her momentarily drained and she could have stayed in the snug cocoon of his arms forever. She stirred reluctantly and lifted her face up from the comforting expanse of new-smelling tweed. 'Thank you...for believing in me,' she smiled fondly into his eyes.

'I'm sorry...about the way I shocked you last time,' Roger mumbled. 'It was very cruel of me. I...'

'It's all right,' Paula intercepted quickly. She didn't want all that brought up again. 'I needed the jolt.'

Roger's eyes wavered over her face and zeroed in closer in slow motion. For a moment Paula was nonplussed by the unfamiliar intensity of his expression, and then, startled, she suddenly realised he was going to kiss her.

Like his embrace, Roger's lips were very uncertain at first, barely brushing her mouth, but when she didn't pull away they seemed to gain confidence and the tentative fluttering turned into a sweet lingering kiss. Unthinkingly, Paula curved her arms around his neck and returned the kiss, but without any of the urgency that Hugo's mouth had drawn from her. Roger's mouth was undemanding. It was an affectionate kiss between two friends. Unthreatening; Paula felt in full control, but when she disengaged herself from his arms Roger seemed embarrassed. He reached jerkily for the folder on the bench.

'I'll take these back to the house with me and study them properly if that's all right with you.' The briskness rang false. 'What are you going to do?'

Paula shrugged lightly. 'I don't know. Laugh...sing, cry a little. It hasn't penetrated yet—that the drawings are okay. It'll take time to sink in.' She omitted telling him that her first unaccountable reaction was wanting to rush away and tell Hugo—before she remembered she was angry with him, and that Hugo probably wouldn't be interested anyway.

With the folder tucked under his arm Roger seemed anxious to get away, yet unwilling to go.

'Oh go on, Roger, go and have a good look at them, you're simply dying to. I'll be happy to be alone for a

while. I'll see you at the house for dinner this evening.'
Paula was all of a sudden anxious for him to go too.

'Ah yes, dinner. That reminds me, what about lunch
tomorrow in town? I'll ask Sir Iain for the car,' Roger
suggested, hopefully.

'A celebration? Yes, I'd like that.' Impulsively, Paula
planted a kiss on his cheek and gave him a playful shove in
the direction of the path. 'Go on now.'

She stood watching him carefully pick his way along the
smoother patches of the rough path, looking like a long
thin child battling the stiff breeze. When he was out of
sight, Paula laughed, a little wildly, savouring the sharp
pang of exhilaration, and swept back into the cottage.
Laugh; sing; cry a little, she had told Roger. She threw
herself on the bed, happy, but too exhausted for anything, and stared at the ceiling, trying to remember how
she had felt those other times just after being told her work
was great.

It all seemed so long ago, but she could just picture herself rushing to Mark's office to break the news. He hadn't
liked her bursting into his office of course, but he must
have been pleased for her she supposed, because he had
taken her out to dinner. She had drunk a lot, Paula recol-
lected, and they had started bickering. There must have
been other occasions with Mark but they can't have been
very memorable because her mind was quite blank about
them.

The best time had been after her first commission when
the impromptu party her friends had put on had gone on
until dawn and ended with breakfast in a park. She had
been on top of the world—like now, Paula murmured to
herself as she fell asleep.

It was very, very quiet when she awakened. Paula lay
listening to the stillness. The wind had died down and even
straining her ears she could not hear the usual murmur of

waves beyond the cottage. Her mind was exquisitely blank. Then the moment passed and recollection flooded back. Roger had liked her illustrations. She could draw again; the spell was broken. Paula stretched luxuriously like a cat, then leapt off the bed.

It was not late and she had plenty of time to take a bath and get ready for dinner without rushing around. She pottered into the tiny kitchen and put the kettle on, then into the even tinier closet of a bathroom to run her bath, all the time her mind toying with the alternatives in her meagre wardrobe.

Paula had two dresses and wore them alternately to dinner at the house when she discovered that Sir Iain maintained a courtly formality and dressed for dinner. Both of them were Mark's preferred style and were almost the same dress, just different colours. Classic wool jersey; high round neck with long sleeves, a fitted bodice over a softly gathered skirt. One was grey, the other navy, and she hated both of them. But she did have something else.

Struck by the sudden thought, Paula raced behind the curtain into the bedroom area and pulled out the suitcase from under the bed. She did bring it, she was sure of it. She rummaged impatiently until her fingers felt the protective plastic wrapping at the bottom of the case.

Very carefully, she drew it out; silk; turquoise....madly Italian—and very Karen Halstead. Her mother had brought the dress home from her last trip to Italy and had tried to badger Paula into wearing it. Around the farm feeding the calves? Paula had protested sourly. There had been nowhere to wear it because she had not gone out since the accident, and besides, she hadn't worn anything so exotic since she'd met Mark. They had been 'too obvious' for Mark's taste.

Karen Halstead had watched Paula pack for this trip, checking her tongue as all the jeans, slacks and sensible skirts went into the case along with the thick warm sweaters, but when it came to the dinner dresses, it had been too much for her and she had taken out the turquoise silk and pleaded in frustration. In the end it had been less trouble to pack it than embark on an all-out argument with her mother. However, the last thing Paula had in mind was actually wearing it.

She gave the dress a light press and laid it on the bed, marvelling at the subtle understatement of the soft, lean lines that were designed to skim the body with just the right amount of sensuousness. Subtle it might be but by contrast the extravagant vee of the neckline was undeniably sexy and Paula found that a little frightening. She wasn't sure that she had the confidence for it any more—if she ever really had in the first place.

After the bath she studied the two sensible alternatives again, then slipped into the turquoise silk and knew exactly how Cinderella must have felt.

The only mirror in the cottage was not full-length and all she could see was vibrant colour around the shoulders and the long slender sleeves, but not much of it in front where the vee dipped down with precarious abandon. The style was not designed to accommodate a bra and there seemed to be an awful lot of creamy expanse left exposed. Paula stared objectively at the valley between the soft curves of breast. Mark would have been shocked. And all at once she was pleased, because she didn't care what Mark would have thought—and would never care again. She felt great, but then had a short sharp moment of doubt when she saw Jamie's face.

The child had come, punctual as always to escort her to the house. When Paula opened the door to him he stood transfixed, staring as if he could not believe his eyes.

'Don't you like it, Jamie?' Paula asked, nervously.

'You look beautiful, Paula,' he said at last in a voice full of awe and as much disbelief, and she was reassured and strangely happy.

Paula gave him a quick kiss as she took his hand. 'Thank you, Jamie.' Her trill of relieved laughter held a rather piercing note of recklessness which the child heard but obviously could not decipher. He looked puzzled.

'And what did you and your uncle do today? Did you go sailing?' Paula sang gaily, and was conscious she came over like a patronising adult.

Jamie nodded, wide-eyed gaze on her flushed face. 'You look different, Paula,' he said doubtfully, still unable to come to grips with the spectacular change in her appearance and manner. And that made two of them.

They walked along in silence for a while, then as they reached the drive, Jamie gave her a sidelong look from under his lashes—an arch sort of look, peculiarly adult, and it sat strangely on the childish features. 'It's for Uncle Hugo, isn't it?' He sprang his observation on her with an almost unpleasant coyness.

And hit the nail on the head.

Paula caught her breath. Angry with the child for his perception; angrier with herself for her transparency, and the fact that while it had lain just beneath the surface of her consciousness, it had taken Jamie's question to make her realise what was really behind her transformation. 'Whatever do you mean, Jamie?' she said stiffly and wondered whether she should race back to the cottage and change.

The boy picked up the hardness in her voice. He flushed guiltily without knowing what it was he had said wrong. 'Nothing, Paula, I didn't mean anything. We had a lovely day out in the boat,' he put in hastily.

Jamie was still prattling carefully about boats, without further mention of 'Uncle Hugo,' when they entered the house, and having performed his escort duty, he bolted for it in the direction of the kitchen.

There was a murmur of male voices coming from the living-room. Paula took a deep breath and flung the door open with a defiant flourish. In the silence that followed, the only thing audible was the crackling of the fire.

It was a very long time since Paula had set men on their ears when she walked into a room and she wasn't used to it any more. Horribly self-conscious, Paula took a step into the room, a brilliant smile focused on Sir Iain as the safest target.

'You look charming, my dear.' Sir Iain recovered admirably from his surprise and came forward to greet her.

Roger mumbled something indistinct. Hugo, leaning casually against the fireplace with one hand resting on the mantelpiece, pointedly said nothing but she saw his quick jolt and the odd hard look he gave Roger, and was instantly hostile. Fine, she thought, if that's the way you think it is, but you're not going to spoil my evening—nor Roger's. They had something to celebrate and Paula was determined that celebrate they would.

She didn't need any encouragement when Sir Iain handed her a drink. Downing it in two gulps she was ready for another. All the time the gallant old gentleman kept up a diligent flow of conversation, what about, Paula could not have said, nor had she any idea what was coming out of her own mouth in between the gay little bursts of laughter. By the time Anna came in to announce dinner, Paula had a vague idea the drink in her hand was the fourth.

Anna sucked in her breath in a stage gasp, and after a goggle-eyed start, eyed Paula up and down in the best tradition of a knowing look. From Paula, the gimlet eyes swivelled to Hugo, and then finally to Roger. It was possible the old lady thought her ancient features inscrutable, but even after four drinks in rapid succession, Paula had no trouble reading the awful innuendo in Anna's face. Clearly, the housekeeper thought Paula was rigged up to play *femme fatale,* and if Paula could see it, it must have been positively glaring to everyone else in the room.

'Dinner's ready,' Anna said after she'd done as much staring as her eyes could take in, and nerves shot, Paula gave a silly, high-pitched laugh as if the old lady had made a very funny joke.

If pre-dinner drinks were bad, dinner was worse. Unnervingly aware of Hugo's eyes on her, Paula deliberately concentrated the full beam of her slightly out-of-focus attention on Roger who seemed to go to pieces under the spotlight. He kept running his fingers through this hair, polishing his glasses and blinking inanely around the table. Paula could have shaken him in exasperation; all the more because she had the distinct impression Hugo was silently enjoying her publisher's retreat into helpless awkwardness.

Every time she chanced to glance at him, Hugo's gaze was on her. When he wasn't frozen up in a scowl he was openly—mockingly—admiring; eyes drifting insolently downwards until Paula found herself draping a hand over her bosom like an embarrassed schoolgirl. She knew she was drinking too much; laughing and talking too much. She was just sober enough to know she was quite drunk, and the saner part of her mind hoped desperately she wasn't making too much of an exhibition of herself; the reckless new self that had materialised when she had put on the dress didn't care.

As they were returning to the living-room for coffee, Paula darted upstairs to the bathroom and on her way back encountered Anna at the bottom of the stairs. It was

almost as if the old lady had been waiting for her. Paula
flashed her a spectacular if remote smile. 'It was a super
dinner, Anna; you really excelled yourself tonight,' she
gushed airily and was determined to keep the smile in place
in the face of Anna's po-faced disapproval.

'Feeling pretty pleased with yourself, are you?' Anna
inquired tartly.

Drunk, she meant of course. Paula laughed to hide her
embarrassment. The housekeeper was blocking her path
and she couldn't get past. Annoyed, Paula could guess
what was coming—a lecture on the evils of the demon
drink. Anna was a teetotaller, and pretty voluble on the
subject once she got started. Paula eyed her in challenge:
just try it, she thought belligerently. In her precarious high-
voltage mood she was not about to take a sermon—deserved or otherwise—with good grace.

Anna eyed her back. 'I just hope you know what you're
doing, my girl.'

Paula frowned. That didn't sound like a preamble to the
sermon. 'And what is that supposed to mean?' she returned sharply, but puzzled.

'You know very well what I mean, and it might be all
right back where you come from to lead a man on. Yes,
that's what I said, lead a man on,' she repeated as Paula's
face registered her astonishment. 'It means giving him expectations—false expectations.' Anna's voice gave the
words big black underlining. 'It's not nice and it's not kind
when your mind is on someone else.'

Paula was stunned. Hugo had expectations? And she
was supposed to be interested in Roger? She stared at the
old lady in amazement then burst out laughing. If Anna
had excelled herself tonight it wasn't just with the dinner.
'You're imagining things, Anna.' Paula shook her head,
still laughing softly.

Her face like an angry prune, Anna glared back. 'I've got eyes in my head and there's nothing wrong with them yet, the Lord be praised. The man is in love with you; I know him well enough to read the signs, and if you can't see that then it's not my eyes that need worrying about.'

Paula felt the amusement leave her in waves, washing right out of her. For a moment her heart made strange heavy thumps out of rhythm and crazy thoughts whizzed through her mind. Then she shook her head slowly. Hugo Cameron was not in love with her. He was jealous because he wasn't getting attention and Roger was, and that was simply male ego. Anna had put two and two together and had come up with her standard five. Paula realised she was very angry with the housekeeper for that one brief moment when she had wanted to believe her. 'You've got it all wrong Anna—as usual.' Paula's voice was cold, and shook a little. 'Mr Cameron is no more interested in me than I in him.'

'No?' Anna looked at her strangely, head cocked to one side like an old bird eyeing a curious object. 'But it's not Mr. Cameron I was talking about, and I know very well what's going on in that direction,' she said, eyes glinting.

Paula flushed. Then Anna said, with a kindish smile, 'It's a two-edged game you've been playing then, lass, without realising it, it seems, and I hope you'll let Mr Harris down lightly.' She turned and padded away down the corridor to the kitchen.

The disbelief came first, then the shock, in that order. Paula stared at the receding scrawny back. Roger? Yes, she had been playing up to him—shamelessly, but that had been to annoy Hugo, not to make Roger think... He couldn't possibly be thinking...? Paula was appalled. Then she laughed, uneasily. Anna was wrong. It wouldn't be the first time the old lady had jumped to outlandish conclusions, but she had to be sure. Worried, Paula made her way back to the living-room, wishing her head was clearer so she could observe Roger's reactions properly.

She didn't go into the room but stood in the doorway. The three men were standing in different parts of the room, very much as they had been when she had made her first stagy entrance. There was an air of uneasiness between them and Paula wondered vaguely whether it had been present earlier when she had been too self-conscious to notice anything. They all looked at her in something like relief. Ignoring Hugo at the fireplace, Paula smiled at Sir Iain who had started towards her. 'It's been a lovely evening Sir Iain,' she lied brightly. 'Thank you. If you don't mind I won't stay for coffee. I'm rather tired and would like to get back to the cottage now.' She looked at Roger, still under the portrait of some fierce-looking Cameron in a kilt. 'Will you walk me back please, Roger?' she asked, casually, she hoped. She was suddenly nervous of him but had to get some time alone with him to reassure herself that Anna had been wrong, otherwise she would never sleep.

Hugo was at her side, with a hand at her elbow while Roger was still looking about for somewhere to put down his glass of port. 'I'll see you back,' Hugo muttered without looking at her and bundled her into the hall before Paula could object.

'I asked Roger to take me back,' Paula snapped as they left the house. The cold was biting after the warmth of the house and she gave a sudden shiver, wishing she'd thought to bring a jacket with her. Hugo peeled off his jacket. 'No, don't. I'm all right.' She tried to forestall him, churlishly. He ignored her protest and put the jacket around her shoulders, then wrapped his arm around for good measure. Paula let both of them stay there; she needed the warmth from the one and the support from the other because her feet were unused to high heels at the best of times, and this was far from being one of them when the drink seemed to have moved from her head to her feet, and she practically required propping up just to stand. 'I said I asked Roger,' she started again in a belligerent mutter.

'I'm not deaf. I heard you,' Hugo interrupted testily. 'And if you weren't so drunk you'd remember that we haven't got a seeing-eye dog on the estate to bring him back to the house again. What did you have in mind, walking each other up and down the path all night?' he asked sourly.

She hadn't thought of Roger's poor eyesight. Paula had a sudden vision of herself and Roger, the half-blind leading the half-drunk, and vice versa. It was funny, momentarily, and she sniggered in spite of herself, then was annoyed that Hugo had to make his point so cuttingly. 'It was very kind of you to be so considerate of Roger,' she said snakily.

'Not at all,' he contradicted with sarcastic politeness. 'Your precious Roger can break his neck for all I care, only it'd be damn inconvenient having him do it here.'

There wasn't much to say to something so nasty, but furious at his callousness, Paula gave a sideways twist in an attempt to get herself out from under his arm. She stumbled.

'What are you trying to do now, break your neck?' Hugo's fingers sank savagely through the jacket into the soft flesh of her upper arm.

'You'd like that wouldn't you?' she taunted, sounding appallingly childish—or plain drunk. 'Or would that be inconvenient too?'

'Don't be absurd.' Hugo pushed her in through the cottage door and went straight into the little kitchen.

'Just what do you think you're doing?' Paula demanded, standing at the counter that separated the cooking-area from the living-room.

'Making you coffee,' Hugo replied, his back to her as he filled the kettle. 'You could do with a gallon—or two.'

'Am I supposed to construe from that that you think I'm raving drunk?' Paula asked tartly.

Hugo threw a glance over his shoulder. 'Thinking doesn't come into it. Why don't you sit down before you fall down,' he suggested curtly.

Paula hesitated then moved to the table. She tossed his jacket over the back of a chair and sat down. Her feet were killing her; she eased them out of the pinching grip of the shoes and would have liked to have done something similar for the tightness around her head. Looking up, she caught Hugo studying her from the kitchenette.

CHAPTER SEVEN

'SHEDDING THE glad rags already?' Hugo inquired mockingly. 'Pity, I rather like you like that.' His eyes fixed on the flesh between the vee of the front. Paula's hand twitched but she resisted the urge to bring it up over her breast as she had been doing half the night.

'You should doll yourself up more often,' Hugo observed with a mirthless smile. 'It's quite a change from the ubiquitous jeans and sensible skirts which is all I ever seem to see you in—not forgetting that bunny-rug of a dressing-gown of course.'

Paula contemplated him with dislike. 'You just can't help yourself, can you? Sneer, sneer, sneer. You have to spoil everything,' she said with a weary contempt. 'You do it deliberately. You did it deliberately tonight—turned the evening into a fiasco with your sneering and that air of superior amusement. Don't think I didn't notice.'

The flush darkening his face told her the contempt had found its mark. 'Frankly, I'm amazed you noticed anything,' Hugo returned angrily.

'I'm not that drunk. I may have had a few too many but there's no need to imply I'm ready for Alcoholics Anonymous. Damn it, I was happy this evening—really happy. Roger was happy too, and you had to go and spoil everything for us.' Paula raged at him like a thwarted child. At the back of her mind she knew she was being unreasonable to lay the blame for the wretched evening at Hugo's feet. It had been her fault as much as his. But if he hadn't insinuated there was something between herself and Roger in the first place, it wouldn't have occurred to her to act as if there was.

'The drink's gone to your imagination. I did not spoil anything,' Hugo said huffishly. 'And what was I supposed to be doing anyway—flinging bouquets and congratulations all around the place?'

So Roger had mentioned the illustrations after all, Paula thought, surprised; he must have done for Hugo to know about them. Hugo hadn't said a word; that was to be expected, but Paula was a little hurt that Sir Iain had not commented. 'It wouldn't have killed you to be a little bit pleasant. Today meant a lot to me—and to Roger. We had a lot to celebrate.'

Some of the colour went out of Hugo's face. 'Did you now?' The voice suddenly turned ugly.

Paula eyed him sullenly. Hugo could have no idea of what she had been through; no idea of the self-doubt—nor of the mind-blowing relief which he just put down to drunkenness. He didn't know how supportive Roger had been, nor how much she owed him. 'Yes, we did,' she muttered angrily.

Hugo said in the same ugly, very controlled voice, 'Then you should have made an announcement at dinner and let us all join in the happy occasion.'

Stand up beating her chest and announce her illustrations were the greatest? For all the inhibition-loosening drink, Paula had been too shy to refer to them. She had expected Roger to say something though, propose a toast, or whatever, to their success. She was disappointed that he hadn't. 'It was up to Roger,' Paula said, her voice faintly reproachful.

'Hmm. Not much of a one for initiative, is he?' Hugo jeered. 'But then he probably exhausted his supply of it this afternoon.'

'What are you talking about?' Paula's voice sharpened with suspicion while her fuzzy brain tried to work out the obscure insult to Roger.

Hugo showed his teeth. 'I'm talking about your heart-warming little scene outside the cottage this afternoon, very touching. Was that before or after he popped the question?'

Paula nearly fell off the chair.

'Don't worry,' Hugo assured her smoothly, his eyes hard. 'I didn't stay around to observe. I don't get my kicks that way. I was coming down to apologise for being so churlish last night. You happened to be in a clinch with your publisher—fiancé, I assume he is now, and while I know you don't credit me with any sensitivity, I left without intruding on the tender moment.'

Paula wasn't listening. She stared, wide-eyed and then became conscious that her mouth was open. She snapped it shut. So that's what Hugo had been getting at; he thought she and Roger had become engaged that afternoon, and that's why she had dressed herself up and carried on a treat. Hugo's face was tight, the bones of his jaw standing out in sharp, hard lines.

The kettle started its ear-splitting whistle and Hugo swung around to it. Paula stared at his back, noticing, almost mechanically, how rigid the shoulders were under the white shirt. Hugo was seized up—literally, with jealousy. She must have made a better job of her performance than she realised. Suddenly Paula wanted to laugh, but the next moment it wasn't funny at all. If that was Hugo's interpretation of her behaviour—on top of Anna's insinuations—then what about Roger? What was he thinking? Paula didn't want to know. She felt dreadful.

Hugo brought the cup of coffee to the table and slammed it down in front of her with just enough restraint not to break the cup. Paula looked down at the cup. 'I'd like you to go now, please,' she said miserably.

Hugo either didn't hear her or simply ignored her. 'And is this engagement going to drag on for fourteen months too?' he asked softly, and Paula was shocked again—angry-shocked this time. She jerked her head up. Hugo's eyes took stock of her shock with blatant satisfaction. 'I gather long engagements are rather in your line,' he said, chattily.

He knew about Mark; she had already worked that out, but until this moment, hadn't realised just how much. 'Your father had no right to...'

'My father has nothing to do with anything. Leave him out of this,' Hugo cut her off sharply.

'He's told you about Mark.'

'Not much—I had to find most of it out for myself.'

'How?' Paula demanded, when she really meant 'why.'

'By asking around,' Hugo replied casually. 'I've a lot of contacts, it wasn't difficult,' he smiled, self-deprecatingly, as if he didn't want to boast.

She knocked over the cup as she sprang to her feet and didn't even notice. Some of the hot coffee splashed on to the dress; Paula did not notice that either. 'How dare you go snooping and prying into my private business.' She was shaking with rage, wanting to lash out—wanting mostly just to hit him.

Hugo stood his ground, but tensed up as if on guard against a palm possibly flying at his face. 'I wanted to know about you, more than my father was prepared to tell me,' he said evenly. 'And I had no other way of finding out because you've been so determined not to let me through that nine-foot barrier you've built around yourself.' His mouth twisted. 'I slipped up about Harris, though, didn't I? How long has that little affair been going on?'

'You had no right,' Paula spluttered, choking with fury.

'That's neither here nor there,' Hugo dismissed his invasion of her privacy with infuriating nonchalance. 'But since you bring it up, I consider I have every right to an explanation.'

'Explanation? For what?'

'How about for leading me on, for a start, letting me think you were interested,' Hugo suggested nastily.

Old Anna's accusation almost word for word, only it was Roger she was supposed to have been leading on. And now Hugo? Paula grated out an involuntary laugh at the absurd irony of it and threw back the same answer she had thrown at Anna. 'You're imagining things.'

'Am I? Then what was that night all about—when I got back from London? And what about last night? If that wasn't an invitation, I don't know what is, so don't try to tell me I'm imagining things and that you're not interested. You practically exploded in my arms, Paula, but if I'd tried to take you up on it, you would have backed off just like the other night when your frigid little self took over.' Hugo was so angry there was a tremor running through his body, but he taunted her with deliberate coolness, probably guessing that it would infuriate her more than hot anger.

'Typical!' Paula screeched. 'The standard male jibe! You couldn't get me into bed, so now I'm supposed to be frigid.'

'Couldn't?' Hugo pulled back and studied her sarcastically. 'Couldn't?' He shook his head, his lips twisting with malice. 'You know perfectly well I could have—and that you wanted me to; but you wanted me to seduce you into it so that you wouldn't have to take responsibility for your own feelings. You wanted me, Paula—still want me but can't admit it. I doubt you've admitted your real feelings in your life—to yourself, let alone anyone else. They frighten you silly, don't they? Which is why you need to get

yourself engaged to prigs like Mark Naughton and helpless fumblers like Harris. You can handle them. They're
unthreatening because they don't ask for much and will
always be satisfied with the little you choose to give of
yourself.'

Every word hit a nerve but the anger saved her. 'That's
because they're not egomaniacs who think they're God's
gift to women,' she hissed back. 'Roger Harris is worth
dozens of you. And if you'd done your snooping a bit
better you'd know he's been my friend and publisher for
years. He's a good man. A kind, considerate, decent man.'
Paula crowded in every adjective and would have put in
more only she ran out of them.

Hugo laughed in her face. 'I don't doubt he's all those
wonderful things, but if you've been playing the same
game with him as you have with me, then he must also be
a very frustrated man.'

Another moment and she would launch herself at him
in frenzied mindless attack. 'Don't judge every man by
your own low-down standards. If you were more like him
you wouldn't be assuming that just because a woman
happens to kiss you she wants to fall into bed with you!'

'Doesn't she?' Hugo smiled unpleasantly. 'That wasn't
the message I got,' he said with soft menace and a fixed
glittering look in his eyes that set warning bells clanging in
her head—too late.

Paula shook her head wildly and raised a hand to ward
him off, pushing against his chest. Hugo made a sound of
angry derision as he snapped his fingers over her wrist and
swung it down unceremoniously, wrenching it behind her
and in the same moment plunged his other hand into the
curls at the back of her neck using the vicious grip to force
her head back. The pain momentarily blocked out the
panic. Paula mouthed a soundless cry before his mouth
blocked that out too.

There were no preliminaries. Hugo was not out to cajole with teasing or tenderness. He was hurting her and didn't care. With her free hand Paula made frantic attempts to push him away then gave up and stopped the ineffectual struggling altogether. But passivity was not what Hugo wanted. His mouth rammed violently, demanding response, and was not going to stop until it got what it wanted and she was just as determined not to give in to it.

Hugo released her wrist and eased himself away from her a little. Paula felt his hand insinuating itself into the silk front of the dress and with a gentleness that was at variance with the fiercely probing mouth, close over her bare breast. For a moment it lay still over the soft roundness, then the expert fingers began to do tormentingly exciting things to the hardening nipple. Paula's reaction was sudden and shattering. She arched uncontrollably under his hand and with a blinding explosion of urgency abandoned herself to sheer mindless sensation.

That was what Hugo had wanted. He gave a low, satisfied growl deep in his throat as her body took over, answering his demands with demands of its own, and when nothing mattered except easing the unbearable hunger, Hugo pulled back, eyes glowing darkly with his victory, and with something in their depths that looked quite crazy. 'Now tell me you don't want me,' he breathed at her.

Paula could not tell him anything because she had to fight to get enough air back into her lungs just to breathe. She shook her head dumbly. Hugo's lips curved tauntingly as he cupped his hands around her face and tilted it back. The lips were very gentle this time, and menacingly tender as his body moved against her with a controlled sensuousness, intent on rousing away her last shred of self-possession.

With a vague, cloudy awareness, Paula knew what he was doing to her: manipulating her body, using every trick in the book from violent passion to unbearable gentleness. And her body was revelling in every touch, crying out for more. It was no use denying it: she wanted Hugo Cameron as she had never wanted any man before.

Drawing back suddenly Hugo studied her flushed face through half-closed lids, examining it pore by pore. 'And do you think Roger Harris is going to make you feel this way?' he jeered softly.

She hit him then—across the face, with an unthinking, stinging swipe.

It took Hugo a fraction of a second to react and then he grabbed both her arms and twisted them savagely behind her back. 'You little she-devil,' he hissed as the ugly stain of colour surged into his cheek where her palm had landed. Then unexpectedly Hugo made a harsh grating sound that was a laugh of sorts, but his eyes stayed savage. 'I'm flattered, since that's more reaction than poor Harris is ever going to get out of you.' His face was very close. Paula could feel his hot breath brushing her cheek as she tried to avert her face. 'This is the real you, Paula, the one you've been trying to hide from yourself for so long, the passionate, demanding one that you're so scared of.' Hugo released her abruptly.

The chair was behind her. Paula could feel the edge of it at the back of her knees. She lowered herself on to it before her shaky legs gave out. Hugo took a step closer and she lifted a hand protectively in front of her, looking at him dumbfounded.

Hugo bent down to her, his face contorted with emotion that wasn't anger any more, and Paula dropped her eyes, fixing them unseeingly on his feet. Unable to move, she listened with a cold motionless tension as his words rained down on her head in an urgent impassioned torrent. 'You can't marry Roger Harris, Paula. He's wrong for you, you must see that. Yes, you'd be able to call all the shots—the guy worships the ground you walk on, anyone can see that. Only you don't want a man like that, Paula, any more than you wanted Mark Naughton. You want…'

Paula flipped her head up like a puppet. 'A man like you?' she jeered, her voice small and scratchy but vibrating with the anger that was coming back to life. Hugo shrugged with an easy arrogance that sent a bolt of trembling fury through her. 'I wouldn't marry you, Hugo Cameron, if you were the last man on earth.' Not very original but she was surprised she could come out with anything at all. The words bounced off him without rippling a line of his expression.

'Then it's just as well for me that I haven't asked you, isn't it?' Hugo smiled derisively as he looked down at her but his eyes wanted to kill her. Some of her scorn had penetrated his pride. Paula registered the look and stored it away mentally. Later, she might derive some kind of compensatory satisfaction that she had managed to prick his ego just that tiny bit.

She stared up, hating him. 'If you've quite finished psychoanalysing me, I suggest you get out.' She rose to her feet with a painful show of dignity, pushed past him and strode to the door. Paula flung it wide open, keeping her hand on the knob. 'I want you out. Now.' The scene was straight out of a melodrama but with some of the effect of her stance diminished by her stockinged feet and the large brown stain down the front of the dress.

Hugo picked up his jacket and came across the room unhurriedly. Every muscle in Paula's face felt like granite in the effort to prevent herself from dissolving into a heap in front of him.

'Congratulations—on your latest engagement.' Hugo got in the last soft parting shot before she could slam the door on him.

Eyes clamped shut, Paula leant against the closed door waiting for the impact of the shock to pass before she could trust herself to make it to the bed. Her mind was numb and she felt as if Hugo had peeled away layer upon layer of skin to expose something very vulnerable within her.

He was wrong about Roger; she could have told him there wasn't any engagement, nor would there be. It might have stopped him but Paula doubted it. Roger had not really been the issue tonight, only the springboard from which Hugo had launched his attack, as if he had only been waiting for an opportunity to break through the barrier he accused her of having built around herself.

And he was right there; something had happened to her during her relationship with Mark, a closing-in process, while after Mark she had become more closed in than ever. But how had Hugo known, guessed what lay behind the barrier? How could he possibly have suspected she was afraid of opening up to her feelings, needs? Frigid, he had called her and meant to hurt. Was she? Her shattering responses to him made Paula question that. The word wasn't frigid, it was distrust; she was riddled with it—distrust of herself, her own motives, and where before it had been of Mark's motives, now it was Hugo's.

What did Hugo want from her? Really want? As he pointed out so crudely, he could have bedded her without any trouble—and hadn't, so he couldn't be simply after a bedmate for his stay on the island. A nanny for Jamie? He denied that, but then Mark would have denied that he'd wanted her just as a stepmother for Stephen. What people—men, said and what they really wanted were two totally different things.

Paula opened her eyes and took in the messy table with the coffee-cup still precariously perched on its side right at the edge of the table. She looked down blankly at the ruined dress, then very slowly, as if it was an effort just to put one foot in front of the other, made her way to the bedroom area. Ripping off the soft silk, Paula hurled it into the corner where it fell in a bedraggled little heap.

Without bothering to undress further, she climbed into bed and hugged herself tightly around the shoulders, knees drawn up into her stomach as if she had the most terrible pain there. She rocked herself to and fro, moaning softly. The pain wasn't in her stomach and it wasn't anything that could be put to rights by an aspirin. 'I'm going to leave,' was her last conscious thought.

In the morning Paula woke with the vague feeling that she had to get away from something, and then she remembered: the something was Hugo and she was going to leave. Not today; she had no energy for that, but tomorrow she would get herself on to the first plane off the island.

Paula stretched out her right leg and jiggled it under the blanket. It felt fine and she had no recollection of a nightmare. Small mercies. Her head seemed all right, too—no hangover, just a terrible burnt-out feeling inside her brain that had nothing to do with the drink she had consumed. It made it very hard to think straight and she supposed she ought to be grateful for that.

She was bathed and dressed and toying with the idea of a long, hard walk along the beach when Roger turned up. She had already reasoned out that last night had nothing to do with him; that he'd probably have a mild stroke if he knew he was supposed to be engaged to her, but with all the innuendoes that had been hurled about by Hugo and Anna, Paula was instantly nervous at the sight of him.

'Have you forgotten our lunch?' Roger peered worriedly into her face.

Oh God. Lunch—alone with Roger. 'No. No, of course not,' Paula lied through her teeth with a bright smile. Her

mind raced over the range of excuses to get out of the date
and couldn't come up with any. 'I've been looking forward to it,' she lied again out of sheer guilt.

'Good. That's good,' said Roger, grinning in relief. He
looked her up and down. 'If you're ready we can make a
start now, can't we? It's going on for twelve-thirty.'

Paula was wearing the 'ubiquitous jeans' with a warm
pullover, no make-up and was aware she must look as if
she'd just got up off her death-bed. 'Yes, I'm ready,' she
replied carelessly, then experienced a twinge of guilt because it was so obvious she had not gone to any trouble for
their celebratory lunch.

There was no sign of Sir Iain's elderly sedan when they
reached the house; only Hugo's shining extravaganza was
poking its long sleek nose out of the garage by the side of
the house.

Roger walked right up to the garage and stuck his head
in, came out and looked around uncertainly. 'It's not here.
I can't understand it. I asked Sir Iain yesterday about using the car today.'

A mean little hope flared up. 'Neil may have taken it
somewhere. We might have to leave it for today.' Paula
caught sight of Hugo strolling out of the front door of the
house. 'Let's go back to the cottage,' she begged, momentarily reduced to panic at the prospect of an encounter. Her
face froze as Hugo sauntered towards them, hands in
pockets and looking none the worse for the late night.

He nodded curtly and Paula stared through him. 'You
look as if you've lost something.' Hugo addressed Roger
with a dryness just this side of a sneer.

Roger flushed. 'No…that is, do you know where the car
has gone? Your father's car.'

'Yes,' Hugo said shortly. 'Neil's taken Anna into town
for the shopping—and Jamie as well. Why? Was he to have
waited for you?'

Roger frowned. 'Into town? But I thought the car would be free today. Sir Iain didn't say anything about a shopping expedition. I should have checked I suppose,' he trailed off, embarrassed.

'It doesn't matter,' Paula said hastily, placing a hand on his arm wanting to lead him away as quickly as possible. Hugo was studying Roger with a snide amusement that made her hackles rise. He had been insulting enough about Roger last night and she was not going to let Roger stand around now and be sneered at.

'Were you planning on going somewhere?' Hugo asked Roger with some interest.

Roger gave a distracted grin. 'We had planned lunch in town.' His eyes had wandered longingly towards the expanse of glistening dark blue metal sticking out from the side of the house. Hugo followed his gaze and his shoulders gave a noticeable jerk of surprise.

Paula nearly yelped with shock. She stared at Roger, horrified. He couldn't possibly be thinking...? 'It's all right, Roger, let's just leave it. We can go another day.'

There was a long silence and nobody moved. They all studied the exotic vehicle as if none of them had ever seen it before, then Roger turned to Hugo. 'I wonder, Hugo, whether you'd trust me with your car, if you're not planning to use it yourself, that is.'

Hugo's face was expressionless. Paula stared at him. 'Don't let him,' she beamed the message with her eyes.

'I'm not really sure,' Hugo began dubiously. 'It's not the easiest car to handle if you're not familiar with it.'

It was the worst thing he could have said.

'I'd have thought it'd be just like any other car,' Roger muttered, piqued at Hugo's implication that his driving skills were not up to handling it. He recovered himself almost immediately. 'That's all right, Hugo, silly of me to ask. I can see it's a very expensive machine.'

The snipe was intentional, and, coming from Roger, unexpected. A harsh, dark red seared up Hugo's throat. His eyes flashed with dislike. 'You're most welcome to borrow it, of course,' he said stiffly and Paula could have kicked him—kicked both of them for being so childish.

Hugo avoided her eyes. 'I'd better explain a few things to you,' he said to Roger.

Roger threw her a blissful glance over his shoulder and sprang after Hugo at a gallop—an excited little boy dying to try out a new toy—somebody else's toy at that.

She would refuse to go. It was not that Paula particularly distrusted Roger's driving; he was a competent driver and his less than average eyesight made him an especially careful one. But in a car he had never driven before? Along the island's narrow, winding roads? Her nerves were not up to that sort of challenge, not this morning. Paula marched up to the car, ready to tell him so.

Roger was in the driver's seat with Hugo leaning in explaining the intricacies of his toy to him. Paula stood by, seething with annoyance. Hugo finally finished his lecture on the knobs and dials on the dashboard, and straightening up, looked her hostile face over carefully. 'You're looking rather pale, Paula,' he said casually in what must have been the understatement of the year. 'Perhaps you'd prefer to leave the outing for another day. Roger and I can go for a run in the car.'

Hugo was giving her the opportunity to plead headache—or something; making it easy for her, and she should have felt grateful and snatched up the cue instead of bristling with resentment. There was anxiety in Hugo's eyes—doubtless for his precious machine in Roger's inexperienced hands, and that was the last straw. 'Thank you for letting us borrow your car, Hugo,' Paula said with stony politeness and started moving towards the passenger side.

'Don't be an idiot,' Hugo hissed, gripping her arm and preventing her from getting into the car. He flicked a glance into the car where Roger sat examining the dashboard with a concentration that momentarily excluded everything, and everybody. 'I want to talk to you,' Hugo said urgently.

Paula tried to pick his fingers off her arm. 'You had your say last night,' she returned in an angry hiss. 'Wasn't that enough for you?'

Hugo winced. 'For God's sake, Paula, I didn't mean all those things I said last night. I had no right to talk to you like that. I'm sorry, believe me.'

Paula looked him fully in the face. 'You meant them,' she said coldly, and as Hugo dropped his hand, got into the car slamming the door behind her with a viciousness that made the car shake.

Roger set the car into motion with a jump out of the garage that had Hugo springing sideways for safety. Let him worry, Paula thought meanly, catching the final look of consternation on Hugo's face. They lurched for a bit but Roger seemed to be getting the hang of it as they followed the winding track through Sir Iain's estate. At the end of it, where it joined the main road, Roger stopped. 'What would you say if, instead of going into town, we drove to the little village on the Butt and had lunch at the pub there?'

Paula smiled tightly. The Butt was miles away across the island and would take ages to reach, especially if they went via the winding coastal road. She could see right through the ingenuous suggestion; the longer the drive, the more time in his borrowed plaything. Strange she had missed the streak of childishness in Roger. Paula shrugged. 'It's up to you, Roger,' and the token assent was all he needed. Roger swung the car left instead of right, happy as the proverbial sandboy, and Paula leaned back in her seat in sulky silence.

They went the coastal road—of course. It took forever and by the time the village finally came into sight at the bottom of the steep slope that ran towards the sea, Paula was tired, headachey and surprisingly hungry. Added to which, she was still very much annoyed with Roger for his unexpected display of childishness.

Roger parked the car outside the tiny pub and gave her a sheepish grin as he helped her out. 'I'm rather keen on cars, my secret passion.'

'I'd never have guessed,' Paula returned snappishly.

Roger coloured. 'You must think I'm an awful idiot. I know Hugo did, but it's not every day I get the chance to drive the car of my dreams,' he explained leading her into the tiny pub.

Paula had already learnt that time was not a precious commodity on the island; everyone had plenty of it and the proprietor's wife might never have heard of clocks. If someone wanted lunch at three o'clock in the afternoon that was fine by her, and when the accommodating lady eventually emerged from the kitchen, Paula was so hungry she could have eaten the leg of the chair instead of the rack of lamb presented to them with a self-conscious flourish.

By the end of the meal, hunger appeased, irritation washed away by several glasses of excellent claret, Paula felt a new woman and Roger was quick to sense the adjustment of her mood in his favour. 'I hope you've forgiven me for my childishness?' he asked, still a little diffident.

Paula laughed. 'Was I so obvious? I didn't mean to be so bad-tempered about it. It was a beautiful lunch, Roger. Thank you. I suppose we ought to make a start back,' she added, without enthusiasm, too relaxed and mellowed to want to move.

Roger examined his wrist. 'After four, but we've time for a walk down to the cove before heading back, if you'd like to, that is. I know a nice spot down there,' he suggested with a peculiar earnestness, and Paula felt her earlier nervousness stirring back to life.

'That sounds nice,' she agreed tentatively, on guard, but obliged to put herself out to make up for her previous display of bad temper.

CHAPTER EIGHT

THEY HAD not thought to bring a rug but some thoughtful person had long ago erected a seat of sorts out of smooth rounded stones, and they sat on that, watching the sea lapping into the delicately tinted sands of the small bay. The silence felt awkward already, or was that her imagination working overtime? Roger put an arm around her shoulder. 'There's something I wanted to talk to you about,' he started and Paula seized up inside. She shifted her position a little, intending to stand up, walk about, anything to put off what she was afraid was coming.

Roger's arm tightened around her. 'Don't get up yet.'

Paula looked at him uneasily and even prepared as she was, gave an involuntary start at the expression on his face; Roger had looked just like that a moment before he had kissed her the day before, that same unfamiliar intensity.

Paula swerved her face away and suddenly bent down to pick up a stone lying at her feet. She had to stop his next words, whatever they were, before he hurt himself by voicing them. She was too slow. As she straightened up, Roger said, 'I love you Paula. You must know that. I've loved you for years, ever since we met.' The words tumbled out in a desperate stream as if he couldn't get them out quickly enough. 'I meant to tell you then, only I'm such a slow-witted fool and Mark got in first. It was hell for me, then after the accident, I thought there might be hope for me again, only I couldn't bring myself to speak to you about it because you seemed all shut in on yourself, taking Mark's death so hard, and Stephen's. It's only now that you seem, well, more like you used to be—alive and glowing. And yesterday when I held you in my arms, I wanted to ask you then. Oh hell, Paula, I'm trying to ask you to marry me and I'm making my usual hash of it.'

Hugo had been right—half right anyway. That was Paula's first uncontrollable thought. Hugo had spotted Roger's intention with deadly accuracy, only he'd been a day premature. She had wanted to laugh then, but the joke was on her. Except that it wasn't a joke and the laugh now welling up dangerously inside her was hysteria; she would die of mortification if it came out, and so would Roger.

Paula could not look at him while she tried to get a grip on her crazy reaction. She fumbled around in her dazed mind for words that would sound less hurtful than a blunt 'no.' 'Roger dear,' she began gently, forcing herself to meet the expectant eyes that were fixed on her unblinkingly. 'Please don't think that I don't care for you, I do, very much. I'm very fond of you,' she struggled on. How to go on without that soul-destroying 'but'? 'It's just that...' Paula shook her head dumbly and saw the light flicker out behind the thick lenses.

'Then it was only happy relief yesterday?' Roger's lips twisted with faint bitterness. 'I should have realised. I should have realised it didn't mean anything to you.' He continued to stare at her, frowning at first, then nodding slowly, as if something was becoming clear to him. 'Of course,' he murmured softly under his breath. 'I'm too late again, aren't I?'

Paula looked back at him perplexed.

Roger gave a small, tight smile. 'Hugo Cameron,' he muttered, 'of course.'

The denial sprang to her lips but stayed unvoiced. Let him think that, Paula thought. Let him think she was in-terested in someone else if it made him feel any better, less hurt. It didn't matter whether he picked on Hugo or anybody else.

'I should have tried harder earlier,' Roger said, without rancour. 'There might have been hope for me then, even while Mark was alive.' He looked at her oddly and said suddenly. 'You never meant to marry Mark, did you?'

The unexpectedness, not to say accuracy of the question caught Paula off-balance. 'I...I don't know,' she said evasively.

Roger nodded, peculiarly satisfied. 'Mark always felt you wouldn't,' he said astonishingly and Paula felt her blood run cold.

'What?'

Roger flushed slightly. 'I shouldn't be talking to you like this, it's not my business. It's just that I gathered from something Mark said quite a long time before the accident, that he had the feeling you wouldn't go through with the marriage. I should have made my move then.' Roger's mind switched back to his own train of thought, his own regrets. He had no inkling of the implication of what he had just told her.

How could he? He didn't know she had been blaming herself for the accident, thinking it was the shock of her statement that had made Mark momentarily careless at the wheel. But if Mark had suspected all along that she wouldn't marry him, then he can't have been surprised when she came out with it. He certainly could not have been shocked. Paula's emotions came back to life. She turned on Roger, breathless, angry. 'Why didn't you tell me before? Why did you keep it back from me?'

Roger looked nonplussed. 'What? Keep what back?'

Paula shook her head in frustration. It was pointless railing at him for his silence, pointless to tell him he had unwittingly let her carry the awful guilt for a year. 'Let's go back now,' Paula said, feeling as if she had been kicked in the stomach. Was that relief? She had never felt more ill.

'Yes, very well.' Roger wasn't sure what to make of the change in her. 'It looks like rain,' he observed dismally.

About three miles out of the village the first drops fell. Large and heavy. Roger made an agitated attack on the knobs and dials in front of him and by the process of elimination, finally managed to hit the right one and sent the windscreen wipers swishing across the wide expanse of glass. In those few moments the rain had thickened into a dark mass and the wipers seemed to make very little difference to the visibility.

Paula gripped the edge of the seat tightly as they ploughed in lurches through the wall of water. She tried to quell the rising panic but as Roger missed the curve in the track and the car gave a sudden lunge to the left, a tiny scream jolted itself out of her before she could stop it. 'I'm sorry,' she mumbled.

Roger switched off the engine.

'I'm sorry,' Paula said again. 'I just got a little fright. We don't have to stop. I'm okay, really,' she tried to assure him.

'You might be, I'm not. I can't see, damn it,' Roger said through his teeth. 'I can't risk going on.'

'But if we go very slowly?'

Roger shook his head. 'Too dangerous. I don't know the road well enough to drive by instinct, and the wretched car has a mind of its own. Not my day, is it?' He smiled weakly and looked as if he wanted to howl—and just might.

Paula reached out a hand and gave him a small pat on the arm. 'It's not the end of the world, Roger.'

'No, but jolly inconvenient. We'll have to sit here and hope the rain eases enough for me to try and go on—or at least get us back to the village. And pray that that's before dark.' He gave an angry laugh. 'Because I wouldn't trust myself to handle this chariot in the dark, either. Can't win, can I?'

An hour later when they were still sitting there in dispirited silence, Paula forced herself to face a few un-pleasant facts: the rain was not going to stop; Roger had given up on the day and was resigned to sitting it out for as long as it took, and that looked like being all night; no one was going to come by and rescue them. The next move was up to her.

'I'm going to walk back to the village,' Paula said with sudden decision. 'Don't look so horrified, it's only a few miles.' She glossed over that bit lightly. 'When I get there I'll find a couple of men to drive me back here, then one of them can drive this car back to the village. We'll have to spend the night there.'

'I can't let you do that—not alone,' Roger protested in a whisper of sheer horror.

'It'll be much easier if I go alone Roger,' Paula stated the unkind truth briskly. 'I'll be perfectly all right. Yes, I'll get wet,' she anticipated his next protest irritably, 'but that can't be helped. Now, put the high-beam on and leave it on until I disappear from sight, then switch it off and just keep the parking lights on,' Paula instructed rapidly not letting him get a word in. 'I shouldn't be all that long.' She flung the door open and leapt out before Roger could stop her, and heard his final protest as a distorted wail against the pounding rain.

She was drenched to the skin in seconds and shocked to the bone by the ferocity of the wind which she hadn't taken into account when she left the car. It was shock that made Paula go on. The rain-dispersed light of the high-beam was blotted out within a few feet of the car, and while it couldn't yet have been anywhere near nightfall, she could barely see a step in front of her and tripped almost imme-diately she was out of range of the light.

Struggling to her feet, Paula kept on walking but knew she hadn't a hope of making it to the village, and that very soon she was going to have to do something, either sit down and stay down before the wind bowled her over again, or possibly try to retrace her steps to the car.

Roger would be relieved if she came back; he had been beside himself when she climbed out of the car and would be having a seizure by now. Poor Roger, Paula thought miserably, it certainly had not been his day, and she had not made it any easier for him with her unreasonable anger that he hadn't told her about Mark's suspicion. In that moment she had forgotten about his proposal entirely and hadn't given a thought to his feelings of hurt and rejection. Was it any wonder that Roger had thrown in the towel on the disastrous day and couldn't think of anything more constructive than waiting for the rain to stop.

It had not been her day either, and it was Hugo's fault, his fault that she was stumbling blindly through the rain, his fault that Roger sat distraught in that monster of a car.

The twisted logic brought a surge of anger that spurred Paula on, and the road seemed easier to see all of a sudden too. The rain must be easing, Paula thought, and in the same moment she could have sworn she heard her own name drifting through the wind. The sound, the voice, came again and this time seemed so clear and so close that Paula actually turned around—and saw everything all at once, only nothing registered, not the headlights, car, nor the figure almost on top of her. 'Roger,' she greeted in happy surprise, as if she'd just come across him unexpectedly at a cocktail party. 'You've managed it.' Paula laughed idiotically through the water streaming down her face.

Amazingly, Roger turned into Hugo and the next thing Paula knew she was scooped off her feet, rushed to the car and practically hurled into it. Too dazed for anything else, all her mind could take in was that Roger was not there. 'Where is he? What have you done with him?' she yelled in a burst of hysteria as Hugo threw himself into the driver's seat and slammed the door behind him. His face was murderous and any other time Paula might have been alarmed, only she was too terrified for Roger to worry about herself. When Hugo didn't answer she hit him wildly on the shoulder in a mindless panic. 'What have you done with him?'

Hugo swore savagely as he caught her hand and flung it back into her lap. 'For God's sake stop belting me and calm down.'

'Where is he?' Imagination running riot, she had a terrible vision of Roger lying helpless by the side of the road, tossed out by a furious Hugo. In the craze-induced picture, she even had his glasses broken.

'He's all right. I didn't throw him out,' Hugo shouted at her in an uncanny display of mind-reading. 'Though heaven knows I should have. The damn fool is with Neil in the other car.' He turned on the ignition with a grinding wrench and the car sprang forward.

Too angry to be relieved, Paula rose like a tigress in Roger's defence. 'He's not a fool and don't you dare call him one. It's all your fault. If you hadn't let him take the car...'

'You're damn right it's my fault, and I'm a bigger fool than the pair of you put together,' Hugo returned in a vicious mutter, manoeuvring the car around in a complicated U-turn. 'But if you hadn't been such an idiot and encouraged him, this would never have happened. I could have taken him for a drive and it would have been enough to get his fetish out of his system. Instead—' Hugo broke off, muttering.

'He was extra careful of your stupid car,' Paula screeched above the combined roar of the engine, swishing wipers, the rain, and whatever Hugo was muttering under his breath. 'It hasn't even got a scratch on it, as you'll find out when you go over it with your magnifying glass tomorrow.'

'You're unbelievable, do you know that?' Hugo hissed in mock amazement. 'Hasn't it penetrated your thick little skull that everyone was worried? How do you think I would have felt if anything had happened to you or your wretched fiancé? And if you couldn't care less about that, you might have considered my father. You're damn lucky you were spotted taking the turn for the Butt road or I wouldn't have known where to begin looking for you when the rain started. It would have served you idiots right if...' He cut off his tirade abruptly. 'Oh hell, I'm sorry,' he muttered tersely and fell silent.

It had not crossed Paula's mind to wonder how Hugo happened to turn up, nor, to her shame, had she given a thought to how worried Sir Iain might be—let alone Hugo. Chastened, she slumped miserably in the seat, water pouring down her back from her hair, streams of it trailing down behind her ears and down her neck, while the wet curls clung like red leeches to her forehead and cheeks. Paula stared bleakly down at her knees at the patches of mud, then at her grazed hands and remembered she had fallen. She sat up suddenly and shifted to the very edge of the seat so that she was almost overhanging the dashboard.

Hugo shot out an arm and pushed her roughly back into the seat. 'What now? Want to go through the windscreen?'

'I'm wet in case you haven't noticed, and dirty because I fell over. You wouldn't want me to mark your lovely suede, would you?' Paula replied, trying to sound sarcastic but succeeding only in sounding teary.

'I wouldn't—what?' Hugo quite yelped at her. He took his eyes off the road to stare at her.

Through the hair plastered over her forehead, Paula stared back belligerently. She was a sight and she knew it, but Hugo was looking at her as if she'd gone mad to boot. He shook his head, bewildered, then his eyes flickered with what seemed to be faint alarm and he said, 'That's all right, Paula. I can get the suede cleaned.' He said it very kindly, soothingly, and with no trace of anger—like humouring someone a bit odd who might possibly turn dangerous. 'Don't worry about anything. Just sit back and I'll have you home in no time.'

Paula's bottom lip was quivering uncontrollably. She thought at first that everything was catching up with her and she was going to start howling in front of him, then the next moment, she was quivering—shaking, more like, all over. Her whole body was racked by the great waves of shivering. The car was warm yet the shivering just went on and on; her teeth were chattering and when Paula opened her mouth to speak, her teeth nicked her tongue in a spiteful little bite. She clenched her mouth tightly, fighting to get some control over the shaking.

When she was sure she could get words out without biting off her tongue, she said in a small uneven voice, 'We didn't mean to cause you so much trouble.'

Hugo's reply to that was to give a frustrated click of his tongue and throw her a quick glance. Paula hunched herself up and shivered violently for the rest of the way and neither of them said another word until the car sped up the drive to the house. Hugo screeched it to a stop outside the front door. 'Come on, we've got to get you inside before you collapse.'

Paula shook her head frantically. 'No...n...not the house...please.' She felt wretched and looked worse and couldn't face the thought of parading herself in front of everyone in her miserable state.

Hugo's eyes sized up her agitation. 'The cottage then.' He restarted the car with a roar and eased it as far as he could along the drive around the side of the house to where the path to her cottage began.

'I can walk,' Paula told him hastily when Hugo helped her out of the car, thinking he was going to carry her again.

He let her stay on her feet—just; the arm around her waist was nearly lifting her off the ground as Hugo rushed her down the path through the driving rain that had him almost as wet as she was when they burst into the cottage.

Hugo flicked the switch by the door and flooded the cottage with reassuring light. In a moment he had turned on the electric heater.

'Th...thank you. I...I'll be fine now,' Paula chattered out the obligatory words of thanks.

Ignoring her, Hugo disappeared into the bathroom and Paula stood where he left her, inanely thinking that he must have been in a terrible hurry to get to the bathroom, when he came out almost immediately with a couple of towels in his hands. Then she wondered why he was going to bother drying himself when he'd get drenched again getting back to the house.

Hugo tossed the towels on to the table and swung around to her. 'Out of those clothes—quickly.'

'What are you...?' Paula began, puzzled. Her mind was not exactly functioning at full speed and Hugo's hands were on her, grabbing at the bottom of her sweater before Paula realised what he was about to do. 'No!' She hit out at him. 'Don't you dare.'

'You've got to get out of these wet things.' Hugo rasped at her.

'I...I'll do it. I'll do it.' Paula swatted at him ineffectually with hands that felt like they were encased in boxing gloves. 'I...I can do it.'

'When you're shivering so much you can't even land a decent swipe on me?' Hugo retorted with grim humour and the rest of her protest was lost in dank-smelling wool as the sweater came off over her head.

The spencer Paula wore underneath for warmth stuck wetly to her breasts in a parody of the wet tee-shirt sexiness favoured by girlie magazines. Hugo whipped it off without so much as a glance and snatching up a towel from the table, shoved it into her hands. 'Rub yourself down with this,' he ordered, his own hands already working at the fastening at her waist.

Outraged and humiliated, Paula stood helpless while the saturated, clinging jeans were dragged down over her hips and down her legs. She was shaking so much Hugo had to lift each foot up for her to get the shoes and jeans off while she made uncoordinated clutches at his wet pullover and hair to stop herself toppling over.

It was all done so quickly she was left in a daze but managed a final strangled wail of protest when he peeled off her skimpy pants. After that Paula fell silent, tears of misery running down her cheeks as Hugo attacked her with the towel, so roughly it hurt.

It only took seconds but her skin felt raw when he finished. Hugo plucked the towel out of her hand and wrapped it around her head. 'Don't just stand there, woman, dry your hair for heaven's sake.' He spun around and wrenched aside the curtain of the bedroom area. 'Where do you keep that damn bunny-rug?' he barked, then spotted the dressing-gown hanging from the hook on the wall beside the bed and snatched it up. He bundled her into it and took over on her hair.

'Ow...you're hurting me,' Paula whimpered, her ears on fire.

'Shut up.' Hugo gave her head one more vicious rub, flung the towel down and propelled her to the bed. Yanking back the bed-clothes, he pushed her down into it and whisked up the covers around her ears. 'Stay there,' he ordered, unnecessarily, since Paula was in no condition to go anywhere or do anything except shiver. The pillow-case felt like ice against the heat of her cheek and dampish where the tears were dripping on to it. She couldn't stop the crying any more than she could the shivering and after a moment, gave in to both of them and wallowed in sheer misery.

She missed hearing the click of the switch but knew the light had been turned off from the change of sensation behind her tightly-shut eyelids. Opening her eyes to darkness, Paula waited for the sound of the door closing, vaguely surprised that Hugo was leaving without saying anything. And what had she expected? An apology for humiliating her? Hugo had stripped her like a six-year-old about to be flung into the bath after playing in the rain. She had never experienced anything more galling, and no apology could make her forgive him for the indignity.

In between the racking shivers, Paula pricked up her ears. She couldn't see a thing but became conscious of some sort of movement beside the bed. The bolt of alarm was pure instinct, then as Hugo climbed into the bed, she went so rigid with panic that for an instant the shivering stopped dead—and her mind with it.

Making inarticulate squeaks in her throat, Paula came out of her shock and tried to rear up from the pillow. Hugo wrapped his arms around her.

'Warmth, you idiot, you need warmth. Don't you realise that? Trust me for once. I'm not going to touch you.' Hugo railed at her in angry frustration.

If he had held her any tighter her ribs would have been at risk; Hugo seemed to be naked—or half naked, and their bodies could not have been more intimately entwined in the narrow bed than if they had been making love. And he was telling her he was not going to touch her? In the far reaches of her mind, Paula understood what he was trying to tell her but it took long moments for it to work through to her consciousness, before the struggle went out of her and she lay quite still in his arms.

Aware of the slackening of her body, Hugo released his hold slightly but still kept her pressed against himself as if afraid she was only decoying him before trying to spring out of the bed. Paula could feel the warmth of his body seeping through the wool of the dressing-gown and against her bare breasts where the dressing-gown gaped open.

'I was so worried.'

The murmur came from a long way away. The shivers were coming less and less frequently and each one less racking. Paula felt warm. Safe.

'Why don't you sleep now?' Hugo suggested softly. The idea of sleep was lovely but there was something drifting in and out of the fog in her mind; something she wanted to tell him. Paula remembered and was pleased.

'Roger and I are not engaged,' she said, suddenly pulling her face away from his chest, and felt Hugo's surprise in the way his hands made an abrupt tightening movement around her. 'We never were. He did ask me to marry him—today, not yesterday, like you thought. And I said no because I don't love him.' The voice was hers; matter-of-fact; emotionless. Paula could hear it very clearly saying these amazing things but it seemed to have nothing to do with her. Hugo must have been holding his breath because she couldn't feel the rise and fall of his chest against her. 'I never loved Mark either,' she went on, lifting the lid off the Pandora's box that was lodged in her head. 'I didn't realise it at first, but that must be why I kept putting off the wedding. And he kept trying to change me…into…I don't know. In the end I didn't even like him.'

Things kept coming out; things so repressed that Paula hadn't even been aware she had felt or thought that way until the words surfaced. About Mark and her crazy, mixed-up feelings, about the accident, her guilt; about not being able to draw for so long. And all the time Hugo listened in that utter silence while she exorcised her ghosts.

'It wasn't my fault—the accident. Mark knew—suspected, I wouldn't marry him. Roger told me today.' For the first time emotion came through in her voice, the same bewildered anger she had fleetingly unleashed at Roger. Paula started crying soundlessly. 'Why didn't Roger tell me earlier? I've wasted so much time being miserable, mixed-up. I haven't slept properly, the nightmare...'

'Won't come again.' Hugo's voice cut in fiercely through the darkness.

No, it wouldn't. Paula knew that too. She burrowed closer into his chest, overcome with weariness and relief. There was still something else; something that seemed important but it kept eluding her. It came at last. 'I love you, Hugo,' she murmured, satisfied, and thought she heard him say softly, 'I know,' but wasn't sure.

When Paula woke she was alone. Disconcerted, she turned her head towards the room, half-expecting to see Hugo. The curtain was still drawn to the side and the first thing she saw was Anna's scrawny back. Paula stared at it in perplexed dismay until the housekeeper must have sensed the eyes on her because she spun around from the table and looked to the bed. She's got her po-face on, Paula thought, before she wondered what the housekeeper was doing in the cottage at all.

'I've made your breakfast,' Anna said without preliminaries.

Making her breakfast was not something Anna had ever done for her before. 'Why?' Paula asked mechanically.

'Because Mr Cameron told me to, that's why.' No 'Mr Hugo'; it was 'Mr Cameron,' and very tart at that.

So Hugo had ordered Anna to the cottage and the housekeeper was none too pleased about it. That explained Anna's presence and the bad temper. It explained something else too; Hugo couldn't disappear fast enough. The previous night was a half-remembered blur, but one thing stood out in embarrassing clarity; she had told Hugo she loved him and he hadn't even risked staying around to give her a chance to explain she hadn't meant it—that it had been shock or something. It must have been. In the cold light of morning the whole thing seemed preposterous; she did not love Hugo Cameron, Paula told herself angrily; she'd run a mile if she thought there was any danger of falling in love with him. Hugo was another man with a child, and she had been through all that before, thank you very much. Then why was she feeling so hurt, let down, by Hugo's absence—very pointed absence?

'That was very kind of him—and of you, but quite unnecessary,' Paula said with a weak smile that cost her a lot of effort.

Anna gave a huffy sniff. 'I'm sure I don't mind since Mr Cameron thought it so necessary,' she replied and looked as if she was sucking on a lemon.

An ache was starting behind Paula's forehead; she felt drained and jaded and not in the mood for one of Anna's standard huffs. She sat up, remembered her state of undress and hastily drew the fronts of the dressing-gown together. 'There's no need for you to stay, Anna. I'm perfectly all right.'

'So I see,' Anna observed sourly, 'but it would seem Mr Cameron thought otherwise, and that being the case he should have brought you into the house last night instead of...' She broke off, lips pinched up into a little furrowed circle of disapproval.

'Yes, Anna? Do go on. Instead of what?' Paula inquired icily, her face flaring by angry contrast. Anna glowered back.

'Here on this island, Miss, we observe proprieties—old-fashioned as that might seem to some folk.'

Paula climbed out of bed very calmly, not quite sure whether she was actually going to hit the old lady when she reached her or bundle her out of the cottage by the scruff of her skinny neck. 'And what has your hyper-active imagination worked out happened here last night, Anna?' Paula asked with a dangerous pleasantness that made the housekeeper edge away from the table.

'That's not for me to say, and I wasn't saying anything happened,' Anna muttered defensively, doing a kind of sideways swirl towards the kitchen as Paula advanced on her. Then in an abrupt change of mind Anna pulled up short and stood her ground defiantly. 'It's not proper for a young lady to be put to bed by a gentleman, that's what I say.' She came out with it in a burst of belligerent self-righteousness.

And that was just the half of it. The other half would have stood the grey hair on its moralistic end, and for a moment Paula was sorely tempted to give the old lady the complete picture—and a likely heart attack; only the brief moment of malicious satisfaction would not have been worth the humiliation of Anna knowing what had really happened.

'How is Roger?' Paula changed the subject pointedly and felt a vague guilt that she had only just remembered to ask.

Anna came off her high-horse grudgingly. 'He's all right,' she answered gruffly. 'Subdued, but I don't think it was your caper in the car that's responsible for that. He's leaving today, I gather, but he'll probably come by to tell you that himself.'

'Poor Roger,' Paula murmured softly—to herself, she thought, without allowing for the sharpness of Anna's ears.

'Yes, he's that right enough,' Anna agreed, shrewd old eyes fixed on Paula's face. Paula stared back blandly.

'Young Jamie was at the door earlier wanting to see you. I shooed him away but he's bound to be back, and Sir Iain will be along later too, I dare say, to check you out. Quite a busy morning you'll be having with all your visitors, won't you?' The tartness sprang back.

'For heaven's sake, Anna, stop it!' Paula snapped in irritation. 'I'm sorry you've been put to so much bother. Thank you for making my breakfast but I'm sure you're needed back at the house, so don't let me detain you any longer,' Paula sniped heatedly. 'And you needn't worry that I'll be offending your island's morals and good name for much longer because I intend to leave today too.'

Anna's wrinkled features took on a sudden pinkness. 'There's no need to carry on so. I'm sure I didn't mean...'

'I know exactly what you meant.' Paula didn't let her finish. 'And if it's any satisfaction to you, it offended my senses of propriety too, to be put to bed by a gentleman as you call him.'

'Well!' Anna sucked in her breath through her teeth.

'Go away, Anna. Please.' Paula appealed wearily, sick of the sight of the old lady and her innuendos.

'Now don't take on so, lass. I didn't mean to upset you,' Anna urged placatingly. 'I'm an old woman and you mustn't mind what I say. I'll stay and run your bath for you while you have some breakfast. Mr Hugo said...' She hesitated. 'Come and eat,' she coaxed, placing a hand on Paula's arm.

Paula shook it off. 'Mr Hugo said—what?' she demanded sharply. What tactful little message had Hugo left, she wondered, bitterly.

'Nothing lass. Only that he'll be back soon. He had to go into town to make a telephone call because our wires came down in the storm last night and he wanted to get in touch with Miss...' She caught back the name—not quickly enough. 'With somebody,' she finished rather lamely.

Paula smiled wincingly. 'Why so discreet, Anna? I presume the somebody is Miss Hunt, and Mr Cameron is welcome to get in touch with her where and when and as often as he chooses. That's his prerogative and I couldn't care less.'

That was not the way she was sounding. And not the way she was feeling either, which was hurt, resentful, and downright jealous.

The bath was ready when Paula finished picking at her toast. In the corner by the tub, her clothes of the previous evening were stacked up into an incongruously neat soggy little pile. Paula eyed them with distaste, mortified that Hugo had lavished such housewifely concern over them instead of kicking them into the nearest corner.

CHAPTER NINE

AFTER THE bath her body felt better but the quick hot soak had not done anything much for the mess inside her head and the only thing half-way clear was that she had to get herself off the island and away from Hugo. She had made too much of a fool of herself last night, and practically every other time they'd been together if it came to that. No more.

Paula threw on her dressing-gown and after a rummage in the kitchen, found a plastic bag large enough to accommodate the offending damp clothes of the night before. Anna was gone and she flew about unhindered gathering her bits and pieces and throwing them unceremoniously into the case. She was on her knees, muttering to herself in irritation as she pushed the heaps of clothes this way and that to make room for the plastic bag, when for no particular reason, Paula suddenly glanced up to find Hugo watching her from the doorway and nearly jumped out of her skin. With all her concentration on what she was doing she hadn't heard the door open and had no idea how long he had been there.

Flushing guiltily, Paula scrambled to her feet clutching the lapels of the dressing-gown—again, and wishing she'd taken the precaution of dressing before she started the packing. 'I'm packing,' she said in a tone of voice used to reply to a question even though Hugo had not asked one.

Hugo's eyes hadn't left her face. 'So I see,' he said expressionlessly as he came into the room. There was nothing in his manner that was overtly threatening yet Paula instinctively made a dart past him so that they in fact reversed places—she at the kitchen end by the door, and Hugo near the suitcase by the bedroom area.

Dressed as she was she had nowhere to go and the room had never seemed so small. It was claustrophobic. Paula remained at her end aware that Hugo was watching her every move and taking care to avoid eye contact with him while she hurriedly tried out opening lines in her head. 'Look, about last night... I hope you didn't take me seriously.' Laugh. 'I'm not sure what I said last night, but...'

'What's all this about, Paula?' Hugo broke into her mental rehearsal with controlled testiness.

Paula flicked him a nervous glance. 'I'm leaving.'

Hugo crossed the room in a couple of strides. Paula was standing with her back against the kitchen counter. He placed both hands on the counter, hemming her in between them. 'That much I've gathered. I want to know why,' he said, very patiently. Paula stared into his face without answering. 'After last night,' Hugo began.

'You'll have to forgive me,' Paula interrupted with a scratchy laugh, 'but I'm afraid I don't remember anything about last night,' she said, looking him straight in the eye. 'Anna mentioned that I was in a bit of a state and that you were very kind to me. I'm very grateful. Thank you,' she added primly. Her eyes were starting to feel very stary. 'I know you're a busy man and it's most kind of you to look in on me. I really do appreciate it.' The words spilled out in a positively gracious stream but Paula didn't have much clue what she was saying. Hugo's expression unnerved her. 'I hope I wasn't too much trouble,' she prattled on.

Hugo was breathing hard, each intake of breath flaring his nostrils with rhythmic evenness. 'Keep this up and I shall slap you, Paula,' he threatened without raising his voice.

Judging from his eyes there was a strong probability he would do just that.

'What do you want?' Paula muttered sullenly.

'I want to talk about last night,' Hugo replied quietly.

'And I told you I don't remember anything.' Paula took a chance and persisted with her lie, moving her body slightly against his arm to gauge whether she could push it aside and get away from him. The arm felt like an iron rod.

'A very convenient attack of amnesia. I don't happen to believe you.' Hugo shook his head. 'You can't take them back, Paula, all the things you told me last night . . .'

'Shock,' she retorted. 'Haven't you ever heard of it? Perfect strangers spill out secrets to each other when they're sitting in a plane they think is going to crash. I believe it's quite a common phenomenon.'

'True,' Hugo agreed reasonably. 'Only we weren't about to take a nose-dive in a plane. You might remember you were safe in my arms and that you trusted me, and wanted me to comfort you.'

The laugh that came out of her mouth was horrible. 'Under the circumstances I would have been just as comforted by the Hunchback of Notre Dame, so don't flatter yourself that it meant anything.'

The hurt was in his eyes one moment, gone the next. 'And told him you loved him?' Hugo asked with soft anger.

His body was too close. The counter dug painfully into the back of her waist as Paula pulled further away from him. 'Probably,' she returned, indifferently, wrenching her neck back as far as it would go as Hugo brought his face closer.

Hugo laughed angrily. 'A real little expert at paring egos down to size, aren't you?'

'Maybe that's because I've picked up a few tricks from the real expert. Isn't it enough for you that you reduced me to the level of a helpless kid, stripped me, put me to bed and then had the satisfaction of hearing me blurt things you had no right to hear? Why do you have to come and rub my nose in it? Don't you think I feel humiliated enough already?' Paula's voice shook. She felt alarmingly like howling.

Hugo drew back suddenly, taking his hands off the counter. His eyes were wide with surprise—genuine surprise. 'Good grief, is that what's bothering you? The fact that I had to undress you and put you to bed?' He seemed to find it difficult to believe. 'Come off it, Paula, we've got more important things to discuss than that.'

'Like what? Jamie?' The child's name popped out to Paula's own surprise.

'Jamie?' Hugo looked at her blankly. 'What the hell has the child got to do with this?'

Everything, Paula wanted to scream at him. Everything. If she had blurted out the truth last night when she told Hugo she loved him—and she was half-afraid that she had—then where did that leave her? Tangled up with another man with another kid, never sure where she stood; never sure she was loved or needed for herself. Loved? That was a laugh. Hugo had never mentioned the word to her. 'Well, if it's not Jamie, we haven't anything to discuss,' Paula said dismissively.

'What about us, Paula? There's something between us whether you want to admit it or not, and we have to discuss where we go from here,' Hugo pointed out, almost gently.

Paula twisted out a smile. 'Oh that. I can tell you that, no trouble. From here I go back to London a.s.a.p. It's of no interest to me where you go, but I'm sure Miss Whatsit will be only too happy to organise an itinerary for you—

both of you that is. You should have asked her for it when you telephoned her this morning.'

Hugo stared, taken aback, then grimaced. 'Drat that interfering old crone,' he muttered.

'Goodness, was it supposed to be a secret?' Paula jeered blithely. 'Don't worry, Anna was very discreet. She didn't tell me anything I didn't know—or guessed.'

Hugo made a peculiar sound like a strangled groan and suddenly grabbed her away from the counter. He held her arms pinned hard to her sides, hurting her in the grip. 'Now you listen to me. Yes, I did go into town early this morning to ring Louise Hunt—about business, and if that's what's made you seize up with fury, not to say jealousy, then I'm flattered, or would be if it wasn't for the fact that you're hell-bent on bolting back behind that no-speaks barrier of yours. And I'm not having that. We're going to have this out.'

'Spare me another of your psychological analyses. I'm sick of them,' Paula hissed at him.

'And I'm sick to death of you jumping to your twisted conclusions. I did not hop out of this bed and go racing off to tell Louise that I'd been in it, or whatever your feverish little mind has concluded I couldn't wait to tell her. That's the trouble with you, Paula, you latch on to something and hang on like a dog with a bone. When you're wrong you simply close your mind off and won't admit it. That's how you could have a relationship with someone like Mark Naughton—some relationship when he couldn't bed you once in fourteen months . . . or didn't he get a chance to try?' Hugo sneered with a nasty softness.

She hadn't told him that. That part of her relationship with Mark was so humiliating, nothing could have dragged it out of her—not even delirium. Hugo was making wild stabs in the dark—and hitting raw nerves with horrible precision. If her hands had been free she would have hit him. They weren't free and Paula felt helpless with fury. Her eyelids prickled. 'I wondered how long it would take you to start throwing Mark in my face,' she choked out scornfully and turned away from him before the tears could spill out.

Hugo released her arms. 'And I'm going to throw a lot more in your face before I'm finished,' he muttered. 'About me, for instance. You decided I was a heartless monster, a womaniser, and God only knows what else, before you'd even met me. Damn it, Paula, when you burst into the hall that day with Jamie, I thought you were the most beautiful woman I'd seen and you looked at me as if I was something that had just slithered out from under a rock. But the attraction was there, Paula, and it didn't take you long to realise it, only then of course, you had to camouflage it, use Jamie.'

'What?' Paula spun back to him.

Hugo contemplated her shocked face with malicious satisfaction. 'You were going to use Jamie when you changed your mind and offered to look after him as I'd asked.'

She stared so hard her eyes felt on stalks. 'Are you implying I did that so I could be around you?'

'Yes, I am,' Hugo replied infuriatingly calm.

'You're mad,' Paula spluttered, shaken, because the repressed suspicion about her own motives sprang forward in her mind and she remembered the peculiar disappointment she had felt when Hugo told her he didn't want her for the job after all. She remembered, too, how easy it had been for him to persuade her to stay when she had said she was leaving. She had already questioned herself about that, but not about offering to look after Jamie. What if what Hugo said was true, really true? What sort of hypocrite did that make her? Paula could not stand the scrutiny of the dark eyes boring into hers. She moved past Hugo abruptly and went to the table and sat down.

Hugo followed her to the table. 'It's me you want, Paula. When you told me last night that you loved me, you meant it. It had nothing to do with shock, deny it all you like.

'I do,' Paula shot back, not meeting his eyes.

'Of course you do,' Hugo agreed with a sneer in his voice. 'But you can lie until you're blue in the face and it won't change a thing because actions speak louder than words, and you gave me enough evidence before last night of how you really feel about me.'

Paula lifted her face to him angrily. 'I was drunk,' she burst out as the uncontrollable images and sensations rushed the red up her cheeks and right into her scalp.

'Not so drunk you didn't enjoy everything I did to you,' Hugo said coolly. 'And you weren't drunk the night I came back, when you wanted me to make love to you, nor the night we came back from the pub.' He looked down at her, taunting her with a smile, and the shiver of humiliated fury that shot through her made Paula want to kill him.

'Then you should have taken the opportunity while you had it,' she shouted.

Hugo laughed. 'And have you yell "rape" two minutes later? You're so uptight about your own sexuality you'd have had to foist the blame on me, and I wasn't going to have you that way, certainly not your first time.'

Oh God, had she told him that too? Paula gaped at him, her face on fire. How much more had she burbled out last night?

'When we make love it's going to be because we both want to, Paula, not because your frustrations get the better of you and you can't help yourself.'

'Don't hold your breath,' she bit out with all the venom she could muster. 'You've missed your chance to get me to bed, and missed the chance to get a nanny for Jamie at the same time. It's too late now. I told you before I'm not interested in playing mummies and daddies with you. You'll just have to work harder on one of your other girlfriends now, won't you? I'm leaving.'

She thought he would hit her and realised it took a lot for him not to. Hugo was clenching and unclenching his fists as they stared at each other in the long angry silence. He studied her hostile face intently as if searching for something in it, then frowned and shook his head as if he couldn't find whatever it was he was looking for.

'You win, Paula. I give up,' Hugo said with a sudden bitter weariness. 'I thought I understood you; it seems I don't.' He shrugged dispiritedly. 'God knows I've tried, but I haven't got a clue what's going on inside your head.' He bent over her, angry again. 'I'm me, Paula, not Mark Naughton in disguise. And yes, I do have responsibility for a child. I can't change that—and wouldn't even if I could. Jamie's part of my life now, and if you can't accept that, well then, yes, I think you're right.'

Paula lifted her brows questioningly at him, not certain what Hugo was talking about, what she was supposed to be right about.

'You're right, Paula,' he repeated for her. 'I think you should leave. Only don't think I'll be coming looking for you—I won't. The next move is up to you. If you ever sort yourself out, let me know.'

She watched him walk to the door and had the awful sense of watching him walk out of her life, and would have given anything to stop him but couldn't. Pride, the old distrust, the old insecurity all mingled together; the barrier was well and truly up. When Hugo turned from the door to look at her, Paula presented a hard frozen mask, which was how she felt inside. Cold and hard, but brittle too, as if she was going to crack into a million tiny pieces.

'I'll tell Neil he'll have another passenger for the airport, shall I?' Hugo said with toneless politeness. His face, Paula guessed, looked like her own.

'Thank you, yes,' she enunciated frigidly, still not believing that he was doing this to her, expecting, hoping, that before the door closed he would stride back across the room and take her in his arms and everything would be all right—somehow; that he would sweep all her doubts away from her, somehow.

Paula sat at the table for a long time after Hugo had gone, not thinking about anything, her mind quite soothingly blank until the sight of the open suitcase on the floor penetrated her consciousness at last. And then she whirled about at a great pace, getting dressed, tidying up and finishing the packing moments before Neil turned up to take her suitcase and folders to the house.

She left with Roger on the midday flight. Sir Iain was the only one to see them off from the house and it was a subdued, embarrassing, no-questions-asked leave-taking. Paula murmured her thanks and something about keeping in touch and couldn't leave quickly enough. Only later did she remember that there had been no sign of Hugo's car, which meant Hugo had gone off in it, and presumably taken Jamie with him since there had been no sign of the child either. That had been a relief. She did not know how she would have coped with saying goodbye to Jamie or explaining her sudden departure because she hadn't worked out what there was to explain, let alone how, to the child who in some illogical way she felt stood between herself and Hugo.

She would come up with something and explain it in a letter, Paula decided, and three weeks later still hadn't written. All she had managed to do was send the briefest of thank-you notes to Sir Iain and it took her a couple of days after she'd sent it to realise the ulterior motive behind that little bit of courtesy. She was staying with her parents at the farm and wanted Sir Iain to know that—or rather, wanted Hugo to know, just in case. Just in case what?

Rationally, she did not expect to hear from Hugo; told herself she did not want to hear from him; that she had to put Hugo and the island behind her and get on with her life, her work.

Work was a godsend and Paula worked like someone possessed, driving herself almost to the point of exhaustion every day so that when she fell into bed there was no gap to fill with thoughts before she lapsed into heavy dreamless sleep, and in the morning was at the drawing-board again with a frenzied energy. It was as if nothing else in the world mattered except the illustrations.

'You're working too hard, Paula.' Her mother had slipped into Paula's studio unnoticed and Paula started jerkily at the sound of her voice.

Mrs Halstead frowned at the nervous movement. 'Sorry, I didn't mean to startle you.'

'You didn't,' Paula lied, embarrassed and angry for the uncontrollable reaction. Her nerves were like guitar strings about to snap and lately every unexpected sound made her jump. 'I was just concentrating.'

'Can't you take it a little easier, darling? Surely Roger can wait another week or two.' Karen Halstead's smile couldn't cover up the anxiety in her eyes.

Paula's work had nothing to do with Roger any more. Roger had disappeared from her mind so completely that she had to make a conscious effort to connect him with the illustrations at all. 'I want to get the last few finished, a couple more days should do it.' Paula gave her mother what she hoped passed for a reassuring smile.

'And then?' The older woman did not smile back. 'What then, Paula?'

Paula was afraid to think about that. More work? There would always be more work. She would ask Roger for something else when she took in the finished artwork to him. 'I think Roger has something else for me—now that I've got my touch back, so to speak,' Paula said lightly but faint bitterness showed through in her voice willy-nilly. She could draw again; her stay on the island had achieved that much at least.

Mrs Halstead arranged her long, jean-clad legs under her, settling into the studio's one armchair with the air of someone about to stay a while. Paula tried not to show her annoyance. Her mother had been great—asked no questions when she must have been dying to do so. It was too good to last and the questions had to come sooner or later.

'You know, Paula.' Karen Halstead studied her daughter carefully. 'When you came home you looked marvellous, and I thought, well, I thought everything was all right again. You looked so much like your old self.'

This was familiar territory. Roger had said something to the same effect too. The only trouble was Paula didn't know any more what that 'old self' had been like—or if she wanted to be that self again.

Her mother was twirling a strand of the gorgeous red hair absent-mindedly, eyes still on Paula's face.

'But something is still wrong, something else, isn't it? It's not Mark or Stephen any more, I can sense that.' A whimsical little smile flitted over her face. 'I'm not that scatty you know, dear, that I can't see how things are.'

'I never assumed you were,' Paula replied crossly. She had long ago seen through her mother's endearingly vague façade. It was just that—façade; behind it was a very astute lady whose beautiful green eyes didn't miss much.

'Don't be cross with me, Paula. I don't want to pry; I'm just concerned.'

'I know,' Paula mumbled miserably, and just for a moment wished she could pour out her misery into a sympathetic ear. Paula got up from the drawing board and, moving to her mother's side, kissed the porcelain-white skin of the cheek under the vibrant hair. 'Please don't worry about me.'

'If you ever do want to tell me...' Her mother's voice trailed away. The elongated green eyes stayed troubled.

'I will,' Paula murmured hastily, and knew she wouldn't, and guessed by the sigh that her mother knew that too.

And what was there to tell? That she was miserable because she had run away from a man and regretted it, and now, contrarily, wanted him to come searching her out even though he had told her he wouldn't, even though she wasn't really sure how she felt about him. Not deep down. There were still so many doubts. Yes, she found him immensely attractive; yes, she did want to go to bed with him. But all that was purely a physical reaction. Her mind, the rational part of it, kept trotting out the warnings to leave well alone.

Her mother uncurled herself from the armchair and drifted aimlessly around the studio, pausing to cast a professional eye over Paula's work as she passed. Nothing Karen Halstead did was ever really without purpose. Paula watched her expectantly. At the door her mother turned, as if something had only just occurred to her.

'When you've handed the work in to Roger, will you come to Italy with me?' she asked, casually. 'There's a new exhibition of Firelli sculptures on in Rome and your father is too busy to come,' she rushed on breathlessly. 'I'd love the company, we could do some shopping.'

Italy. Paula might have guessed; her mother's panacea for anything and everything. And yet, facile as it was, it could solve a lot of problems. Paula was dreading the

blank that would come after the commission was finished. There was always a let-down phase to get through
after any commission and it would be worse this time.
Italy. Paula turned the idea over in her mind. Exhibitions,
trailing around the galleries, churches; shopping till their
feet were ready to drop off; long, lazy evenings in cafés and
artists' studios. Paula gave her mother a sudden smile.
'Yes, I'd like that,' she said brightly on a wave of relief that
a ready-made solution for keeping Hugo Cameron out of
her mind had presented itself so easily.

Only it didn't quite work out that way. Somehow the
distance made it worse because a new note crept into Paula's thoughts of Hugo and she found herself worrying incessantly—about how Hugo was coping with Jamie,
whether he'd found someone yet to look after the child;
whether he'd managed to sort out all the business problems, and small, silly things like whether Hugo was getting enough rest, eating properly.

It was those unexpected small concerns that finally
brought it home: sexual attraction doesn't make anyone
worry about a man, not the way she was doing. She cared
about Hugo Cameron—desperately—and was very
frightened that she'd lost him through her own stupidity
and immaturity.

It was her hopeless insecurity about herself that had
made her act as if she hated him and resort to denying her
true feelings—to herself as much as Hugo. She hadn't been
able to believe Hugo could return those feelings, that he
could be interested in her for herself. Mark had seen her
primarily in terms of a stepmother, not a wife, but Hugo
was not Mark. He had told her that—or tried to, at their
last angry meeting. Yes, he was another man with a child,
but half a dozen children hanging around his neck couldn't
make the slightest difference to how she felt about him.

They had come to Italy for six weeks; at the end of the second week Paula flew back to England. She went straight to her own flat in London, and leaving the suitcase where the cab driver had left it in the hall, sprang to the telephone to ring her father at the farm. Lingering at the back of her mind was the unbearable hope that there would be some word from Hugo. There wasn't and she felt shattered. The hasty decision to cut short the holiday no longer seemed the good idea it had been at the time. The doubts came thick and fast. What if she had left it too late and Hugo didn't care any more? What if she had never been anything more than a passing attraction anyway, just someone to bed for a night or two?'

But Hugo hadn't bedded her, Paula reminded herself with a small surge of hope. He could have, but hadn't taken advantage of her inexperience and frustrations. Surely that meant something. What? That he had cared, or not cared enough? Paula pushed the last thought out of her mind. There was only one way to find out, to settle things between them once and for all and it terrified her. 'The next move is up to you,' Hugo had told her. Well, she was about to make that move.

It was early evening with the shadows only beginning to lengthen. The air was still full of warmth but without the engulfing heaviness of the Italian summer evenings she had just left behind. After a hurried bath Paula dressed carefully. She had bought new clothes in Rome—her mother had seen to that, but there was a difference this time: they were all Paula's choice—her own style, not her mother's flamboyant purchases in which Paula felt overwhelmed, nor Mark's dreary notions of good taste which left her feeling reduced to a drab shadow. The clothes seemed to say, I'm Paula Halstead—at last; take me or leave me.

Paula put on an olive green textured linen skirt and a loose-fitting cream silk shirt. Her hair had been trimmed—

ecstatically, by a frenziedly artistic young man in one of Rome's top salons, and her skin glowed with soft golden colour. Paula knew she looked great but felt terrible, and the only way she could even think of acting on her decision was to keep telling herself that Hugo was on the island or somewhere in New York and it was only an old housekeeper she was going to see.

Even then she took the coward's way out. She had bought a present for Jamie—a box of construction blocks, a sort of Italian version of Lego, and intended to use that as the excuse for the call. She would leave the present with the housekeeper and Hugo would know she had made the move. Of sorts. It was a roundabout way of doing it but just the fact that she had turned up on his doorstep should be enough to tell him she was sorry. It had to be, because Paula simply didn't have the courage to tell him any other way.

She knew the address; Sir Iain had given it to her when he had gone to London with Hugo, but when the cab dropped her off, Paula's nerve momentarily failed her and instead of going to the door, she went across the road to the square's garden. There was a bench almost directly opposite Hugo's house and she sat on that, playing with the box on her lap and telling herself she was an idiot for being so nervous. The housekeeper was hardly going to spring questions on her or put her through the third-degree before accepting a present for the child; that sort of thing was Anna's speciality, and mercifully that curiosity-riddled little crone was hundreds of miles away on a remote island.

Rehearsing her lines, Paula recrossed the road at last. She was going to be super-casual—breezy, was the word. '...just passing by and...'

She had barely touched the brass knocker when the door was flung open by Hugo.

CHAPTER TEN

'I WAS just passing by.' The rehearsed lie came automatically. Unaware she'd even spoken, Paula's eyes were on Hugo's face, taking in the difference made by the six weeks or so that she hadn't seen him. Hugo looked older and almost drawn. His hair needed a trim and under the T-shirt tucked carelessly into his jeans, he seemed to be thinner. She had been right: Hugo hadn't been getting enough rest or eating properly. Her mind registered every detail of him like an instamatic camera, then Paula realised she was staring and that Hugo was staring back at her in pretty much the same way, with the same sort of fixed intensity. And yet there was something else about his expression too—or possibly something missing from it that Paula couldn't quite put her finger on.

'I didn't think you'd...I wasn't expecting you to be home,' she mumbled in a fluster and jerkily thrust the colourfully-wrapped box at him. 'For Jamie. I was just passing by and...'

'So you said.' Hugo took the parcel with one hand, her elbow with the other. 'Come in, won't you?' The tone of the voice did away with any connotation of the words being a polite invitation, and his grip was too firm to be the casual gesture of the polite host about to shepherd his guest inside.

'No, oh no,' Paula returned hastily. 'I was just passing.' She snapped off the phrase that was starting to sound like a track with the needle stuck in it and allowed herself to be drawn into the hall then stayed silent as Hugo led the way up the stairs and into a large sitting-room on the next floor.

The first thing that caught and held her eyes when Paula came into the room was the enormous window that took up most of one wall. Its heavy drapes to the sides, it gave anyone standing near it a bird's-eye view of the gardens across the road—and the bench where she had sat gathering up her courage. The perplexing feeling about Hugo's reaction at the sight of her on his doorstep clarified itself in an instant. Hugo had shown no surprise at seeing her when he should have been surprised. Paula tossed him a quick glance. Hugo's face gave nothing away; his eyes carefully avoided the window and she knew immediately that he had been watching her from that very window for at least some of the time. The realisation didn't do much for what was left of her self-possession.

'Won't you sit down,' Hugo suggested, courteously.

Paula looked about uncertainly, picked on a straight-backed chair which was furthest away from the window and sat down on the edge of it.

'Drink?' Hugo offered and she nodded a jerky assent and dropped her eyes to her lap.

This was wrong, all wrong, Paula thought despairingly. She had made the move and whatever fib she had produced to account for it, Hugo must know what that move meant. And he was acting like a stranger—polite to his back teeth. Their last emotion-charged encounter with its intimate anger seemed like a figment of her imagination, as unreal as her expectation that the next time they met Hugo would simply gather her into his arms and... She must have been crazy.

Paula looked up to take the proffered drink and watched bleakly as Hugo returned to the drinks cabinet. What was she supposed to say or do, now?

With his own drink in hand, Hugo turned around to face her. Paula hurriedly averted her eyes and as she did so her glance flicked off Jamie's present on the coffee-table where Hugo had put it. 'How is Jamie?' she asked, pouncing on the subject of the child with a desperate brightness.

'Fine.'

'Where is he?'

'In bed.'

'Here?' Paula was surprised enough to momentarily meet Hugo's eyes.

'Yes. I brought him down with me a couple of weeks ago when I got back from the States. He's settled in quite well and I shouldn't need to return to America for a good while yet, if at all,' Hugo volunteered casually.

'That's nice,' Paula murmured mechanically. Part of her mind noted the fact that Hugo must have ironed out his business problems and she was quite genuinely glad for him. Under different circumstances she would have liked to tell him so; under present circumstances she didn't know how.

In the drawn-out silence Paula studied the room; a masculine room but with warmth. The furnishings were a mixture of antique and modern; a comfortable blend and she liked it.

'Did you finish the illustrations?' Hugo asked conversationally, and to Paula the question sounded like a conversation gap-filler; just something to fill the silence with no real interest behind it. More fool her for expecting some.

Cutting off her inspection of the room, Paula glanced at him briefly. 'Yes, I did,' she replied shortly and looked down at her lap. She held her drink tightly with both hands and felt sick inside. Her worst fears were true. If Hugo had ever been interested in her he certainly wasn't any more. She had one consolation though, albeit a very small one, and that was that she hadn't flung herself into his arms on the doorstep and blurted out everything, that she loved him; that she was sorry she had hurt him. That would have been the final humiliation; just sitting here and being treated to a dose of Hugo's detached politeness was bad enough. Paula put down the barely-tasted drink on the small wine-table by the chair and sprang to her feet.

'You're looking very well,' Hugo said, ignoring her sudden move. 'Italy must have suited you.'

Hardly listening, Paula muttered a distracted, 'Thank you. Yes,' and headed for the door. 'I must go. I was just passing by.' It came out again before she could catch it and she could have kicked herself for doing herself out of a cool dignified exit. 'Thank you for the drink,' she added in a mumble, desperate to get out of the room.

She had reached the door before Hugo's words penetrated; one word, rather: Italy. Paula stopped. Italy. How did Hugo know she had been to Italy? She hadn't written to Sir Iain from Rome—not even sent a postcard. Roger knew she had gone there, and her family of course, but the only way Hugo could have found out was to have got in touch with one of them during the last two weeks. And that meant... Paula's thinking process was tortuous and slow and she almost had to spell out each word to herself. It meant Hugo had tried to reach her; that he had come after her without waiting for her to make the next move. Paula turned around slowly.

'You said you wouldn't be coming to look for me,' she accused. 'You said...'

'In which case I make almost as good a liar as you do, don't I?' Hugo's voice was gently mocking but there was an uncertain note in it just beneath the surface. The smile was uncertain too, as if Hugo wasn't at all sure what her reaction was going to be.

Paula wasn't sure either. Everything became a momentary jumble in her head. She was confused, piercingly happy, and unaccountably angry in lightning turn, and then she was across the room and in Hugo's arms without knowing how she got there.

Their mouths came together in a kiss that was an explosion of emotional violence and seemed to have nothing to do with love. There was anger in both of them and it surged out, demanding physical release. Hugo's mouth probed deeply and bruisingly, his hands hurt her back, and Paula responded with the same mindless intensity. Her mouth returned Hugo's fierceness; her fingers gripped and dug into his shoulders as if she wanted desperately to hurt him back, but underneath it all she recognised the love, hers, Hugo's; the tenderness would have to come later.

Passion exhausted at last, their hands stilled around each other while their lips stayed locked and motionless until Paula pulled her mouth away with abruptness.

'Why did you do that to me? Why did you make me sit through all that terrible politeness, deliberately let me think you didn't care any more?' she cried out reproachfully.

Hugo pressed his eyes shut and grimaced. He opened them and stared at her in confusion. 'I don't know. I didn't mean . . . I'm sorry,' he mumbled, reddening.

Paula gazed at him steadily and realised that deep down she understood, perhaps better than he did, what had made him act that way. Hugo was as vulnerable to hurt and uncertainty as anybody else and he had simply been protecting himself—and his bruised pride with that façade of stony politeness; behind it he had been as scared as she was.

'It's all right,' she said softly. 'I understand.'

'Then tell me you love me,' Hugo pleaded raggedly.

'I love you,' Paula obeyed in a husky little whisper and felt a tremor run through Hugo's body as the deep sigh of relief drained itself out of him and he dropped his head to bury his face in her shoulder. Very gently, Paula curved a hand around the back of his head and pressed him to her in the long sweet moment of silence.

Hugo lifted his head. 'I thought you'd never come,' he said wearily. 'I was going mad with the waiting and had to ring Harris last week to find out where you were because I couldn't stand it any longer, not knowing.' Hugo smiled shakily. 'And all the time you were just calling my bluff.'

Paula frowned into his face. 'Bluff?' she repeated incredulously.

Hugo gave a raspy laugh. 'You can't have believed I'd let you walk out of my life just like that? I'd have gone looking for you to the ends of the earth. I love you, Paula—loved you from the moment I set eyes on you, don't you understand that?'

'But you sent me away—let me leave the island,' Paula amended, but it was all one and the same in her mind. Frustration flickered sharply. 'Why did you do that?' she demanded plaintively. 'We could have sorted this out six weeks ago without—everything.' Without the doubts and the torment, she meant. They could have been together weeks ago instead of being miserably apart.

'Could we? Have sorted it out? I don't think so, Paula.' Sensing her agitation, Hugo was serious. 'I realised that morning I had to give you space, time, to work things through for yourself—to see things clearly.'

'But if you had only told me you loved me then,' Paula persisted heatedly. 'Really told me. You never did that. If you had...'

Hugo intervened with sudden sharpness. 'And would you have believed me? Wouldn't you have concluded it was some sort of ploy on my part to snare a nanny for Jamie, or that I was angling for a stepmother for the child?'

Paula couldn't answer immediately. She forced her mind back six weeks and made herself look at the irrational woman she had been. 'I don't know,' she mumbled at last. 'I honestly don't know what I would have thought, then.'

'But I do,' Hugo said firmly. 'You were so mixed-up, my darling, you drove me to despair. I thought I'd never get through to you. My main mistake was asking you to look after Jamie in the first place.' Hugo laughed, a little bitterly. 'At the time it seemed like a heaven-sent opportunity of ensuring that I kept you near me, but I didn't know then about your past involvement with Naughton and his child. Believe me, I would never have asked you if I'd known about them,' Hugo assured her earnestly. 'And then when you suddenly changed your mind I couldn't risk accepting your offer. I couldn't be sure of your reasons— whether it was me or simply Jamie you were interested in, although that became pretty clear soon enough—when you turned against both of us.' Hugo smiled, but what he was saying was not the least bit amusing. Paula winced.

'About Jamie, I didn't mean to,' she started, abashed.

'Jamie is part of my life, Paula.'

He had told her that before.

'I know. And I'm glad,' Paula replied softly. 'I love Jamie too.' A smile teased her lips. 'One child or six, it couldn't change the way I feel about you.'

Hugo grinned suddenly. 'Six? I hadn't planned on quite that many, but if you...'

She reached around his neck with her hands and brought his mouth down to hers. There was no shattering violence left in either of them. The kiss was lingering and unbearably tender. Paula wanted it to go on forever.

Hugo drew away from her. 'Marry me.'

'Yes,' Paula said simply, then added with a tiny laugh, 'I thought you'd never ask.'

The comment was meant to be light-hearted but Hugo
didn't take it that way. 'I wanted to ask you that morning—our last morning together, after you'd finally told me
about yourself...about your feelings for me,' he explained anxiously. 'Only I didn't get the chance because all
your distrust of me was back—with a vengeance. What in
heaven's name did that man do to you to make you
so...so...' The word Hugo was searching for eluded him.

'Twisted?' Paula prompted matter-of-factly. Like it or
not, that was the right word. She had been 'twisted';
twisted up in knots with distrust and guilt; her perception
of herself and everybody around her had been twisted too.
'It wasn't Mark's fault—not entirely,' she admitted honestly. 'I was just confused about things, myself mainly; not
knowing who I was or what I wanted.' Paula shrugged and
said determinedly, 'I don't want to talk about Mark.'
Mark's memory was no longer threatening but Mark was
the past and she didn't want to look back any more. She
had spent a fruitless year doing just that but now she was
ready for the present—and the future with Hugo.

'Good.' Hugo's happy laugh made him sound and look
years younger. 'Neither do I.' He gathered her to himself
closely, running his hands caressingly down the curve of
her back. 'And we're never going to talk about that misunderstanding of mine about Harris either. Agree?'

'Agree,' Paula murmured into his chest, then yanked
herself away from him with a jerk. 'I want to know about
Louise Hunt,' she said, because at this moment it seemed
very important to know. Louise, she realised, was still a
block in her mind, big and black—or was it green for jealousy?

The unexpected mention of Louise's name brought momentary surprise to Hugo's face, then he grinned hugely
with satisfaction. 'I love it when you're jealous; your eyes
go a deep, deep green—very fetching,' he teased, and when

Paula refused to return a smile Hugo's grin vanished. 'Listen Paula, I'm thirty-six years old and I can't—won't pretend that I've led a monastic life to date. I haven't,' Hugo said frankly, and wasn't telling her anything that Paula hadn't been able to work out for herself. Only Hugo's other women were shadows in his past and didn't count. Louise Hunt was uncomfortably real and for some inexplicable reason did count, surprisingly a lot.

'But,' Hugo continued with emphasis, 'Louise Hunt has never been part of my private life. She's been my personal assistant for seven years and in all that time I have never made love to her,' Hugo told her, patiently, as if he was carefully explaining something to someone who might have difficulty understanding. 'I have never made love to Louise because I've never wanted to. In fact,' he added on an afterthought, 'I doubt if any man has bedded her for years. Louise is strictly a career lady and a very fine one at that. I couldn't have done without her these last few months since James's death and I've already nominated her for James's seat on the Board. Later, she'll be taking over the directorship of the American side of the business, and a jolly good job she'll make of it too. Does that set your little mind at rest?' The teasing note edged back.

'But Louise hated me,' Paula burst out, puzzled and not fully reassured; Hugo might not have been interested in Louise, but what about the reverse?

'Don't be so melodramatic,' Hugo laughed outright. 'Louise merely disliked you. Nothing personal; she disliked Jamie—and my father too, I dare say, because they take up my time; time which in Louise's book should be devoted exclusively to business. Louise is nothing if not single-minded. And she's very perceptive too. She knew the moment she saw you that you'd be taking up a lot of my time. And she was right—she usually is,' Hugo added, frankly impressed.

'Yes, but I still don't understand why.' Paula couldn't let go of the bone.

'Hush, that's enough.' Hugo placed a finger over her lips and cut her off, and whatever Paula was about to say vanished from her mind. So did Louise. There was only Hugo and herself and Paula knew what was coming next; Hugo's eyes were telling her as they combed her face. She was aware her breathing had changed rhythm and her excitement was mounting under the promise and desire in Hugo's gaze.

'It's been a long wait, Paula,' Hugo said huskily.

Shy and all at once a little frightened, Paula moistened her dry lips with the tip of her tongue. She had never made love before and needed to tell him that, needed to explain things.

'Trust me, Paula.' It was a plea, question, command all rolled into one.

Hugo understood. The last barrier in her mind melted away without a trace. 'Yes,' Paula answered in a firm clear voice and closed her eyes with a contented sigh as she lifted her face for his kiss.

THE AUTHOR

EDWINA SHORE spent thirteen years working in Australia's publishing community, editing mainly academic work, with a few brief forays into general trade or "bestseller" publishing. Now, when she isn't immersed in her own writing, she tries to work on her other interests, which include travel to Great Britain, Europe and throughout Australia, learning Scottish Gaelic, sculpting and painting. She is single and lives in Victoria.